There's Always Room for a Little *Taste of Home!*

Whatever the occasion, you'll set family favorites on the table with this incredible collection.

50

153

S erving hearty meals is a snap with *Taste of Home* at your fingertips. From weekday dinners to holiday menus, *Taste of Home* magazine delivers family-favorite dishes shared by home cooks from coast to coast. Now you can find hundreds of these comforting classics inside *Taste of Home Annual Recipes.*

This exciting cookbook features an entire year's worth of tasty recipes—a total of 509! With so many specialties to choose from, it's easy to find the perfect bite for every occasion. Just consider these chapters:

- **Quick Fixes**
  When the kitchen clock is ticking, turn here for no-fuss staples that are sure to satisfy.
- **Holiday & Seasonal Celebrations**
  From Easter eye-openers to Christmas cookies, these impressive ideas will become new traditions.
- **Family Best**
  Enjoy complete menus, as well as the stories behind them, in this heartwarming section.

Four icons make it a snap to pick the right dish:
FAST FIX = Recipes finished in 30 minutes or less
EAT SMART = Recipes lower in calories, fat and sodium
SLOW COOKER = Recipes made in a slow cooker
(5) INGREDIENTS = Recipes made with 5 or fewer ingredients (excluding water, salt, pepper and canola/olive oil)

Simply page through *Taste of Home Annual Recipes* and find the perfect meal today...and every day!

11

BEST-LOVED RECIPES

No matter what you're craving, you'll find a winner in *Taste of Home Annual Recipes.* Want a flame-broiled masterpiece? Give Grilled Veggies with Mustard Vinaigrette (top) a try, and if you're a baker, don't miss Ricotta-Raisin Coffee Cake (center). Need to stay cool this summer or want to surprise the kids with a special treat? Whip up Coconut Lover's Frappe (bottom).

Taste of Home

Annual Recipes 2016

40

127

88

159

EDITORIAL

Editor-in-Chief **Catherine Cassidy**
Creative Director **Howard Greenberg**
Editorial Operations Director **Kerri Balliet**

Managing Editor/Print & Digital Books **Mark Hagen**
Associate Creative Director **Edwin Robles Jr.**

Editor **Michelle Rozumalski**
Art Director **Maggie Conners**
Layout Designers **Catherine Fletcher, Nancy Novak, Courtney Lovetere**
Editorial Production Manager **Dena Ahlers**
Copy Chief **Deb Warlaumont Mulvey**
Copy Editors **Mary-Liz Shaw, Dulcie Shoener, Joanne Weintraub**
Editorial Intern **Michael Welch**

Food Editors **James Schend; Peggy Woodward, RD**
Recipe Editors **Mary King; Jenni Sharp, RD; Irene Yeh**
Business Analyst, Content Tools **Amanda Harmatys**
Content Operations Assistant **Shannon Stroud**
Editorial Services Administrator **Marie Brannon**

Test Kitchen & Food Styling Manager **Sarah Thompson**
Test Cooks **Nicholas Iverson (lead), Matthew Hass, Lauren Knoelke**
Food Stylists **Kathryn Conrad (lead), Shannon Roum, Leah Rekau**
Prep Cooks **Bethany Van Jacobson (lead), Megumi Garcia, Melissa Hansen**

Photography Director **Stephanie Marchese**
Photographers **Dan Roberts, Jim Wieland**
Photographer/Set Stylist **Grace Natoli Sheldon**
Set Stylists **Melissa Franco, Stacey Genaw, Dee Dee Jacq**
Photo Studio Assistant **Ester Robards**

Editorial Business Manager **Kristy Martin**
Editorial Business Associate **Samantha Lea Stoeger**

Editor, *Taste of Home* **Jeanne Ambrose**
Associate Creative Director, *Taste of Home* **Erin Burns**
Art Director, *Taste of Home* **Kristin Bowker**

BUSINESS

Vice President, Group Publisher **Kristen Marchioli**
Publisher, *Taste of Home* **Donna Lindskog**
General Manager, Taste of Home Cooking School
Erin Puariea
Executive Producer, Taste of Home Online Cooking School
Karen Berner

THE READER'S DIGEST ASSOCIATION, INC.

President & Chief Executive Officer
Bonnie Kintzer
Chief Financial Officer **Tom Callahan**
Vice President, Chief Operating Officer, North America
Howard Halligan
Chief Revenue Officer **Richard Sutton**
Chief Marketing Officer **Leslie Dukker Doty**
Senior Vice President, Global HR & Communications
Phyllis E. Gebhardt, SPHR
Vice President, Content Marketing & Operations
Diane Dragan
Vice President, Brand Marketing **Beth Gorry**
Vice President, Financial Planning & Analysis
William Houston
Publishing Director, Books **Debra Polansky**
Chief Technology Officer **Aneel Tejwaney**
Vice President, Consumer Marketing Planning **Jim Woods**

COVER PHOTOGRAPHY

Photographer **Dan Roberts**
Food Stylist **Diane Armstrong**
Set Stylist **Melissa Franco**

© 2015 RDA Enthusiast Brands, LLC
1610 N. 2nd St., Suite 102, Milwaukee WI 53212-3906

International Standard Book Number: 978-1-61765-390-2

International Standard Serial Number: 1094-3463

Component Number: 117400052H00

Printed in China
1 3 5 7 9 10 8 6 4 2

Contents

PICTURED ON THE COVER
Cheesecake with Berry Sauce (p. 173), Mixed Greens with Orange-Ginger Vinaigrette (p. 23), Citrus-Molasses Glazed Ham (p. 190) and Oven-Roasted Spiced Carrots (p. 50).

FOR OTHER INCREDIBLE TASTE OF HOME BOOKS AND PRODUCTS, VISIT
ShopTasteofHome.com

**LORI STEFANISHION'S
CURRY & MANGO CHUTNEY
CHICKEN WINGS** *PAGE 7*

Appetizers & Beverages

Whether you have **holiday guests** or children clamoring for **after-school snacks,** rely on this chapter. You'll find page after page packed with **satisfying munchies and more!**

**TARA CRUZ'S
BLUE CHEESE & BACON
STUFFED PEPPERS** *PAGE 8*

**CAROLE RESNICK'S
HOT DOG SLIDERS WITH
MANGO-PINEAPPLE SALSA** *PAGE 14*

**LISA VARNER'S
SAUCY ASIAN MEATBALLS**
PAGE 16

ROASTED GRAPE CROSTINI

Fruity Smoothies

When this is the way you eat your fruit, you just might forget that it's good for you! Strawberry or blueberry yogurt would be just as yummy as raspberry.

—**JULIE PUDERBAUGH** BERWICK, PA

START TO FINISH: 10 MIN.
MAKES: 3 SERVINGS

- 2 **tablespoons orange juice**
- 2 **tablespoons cherry juice blend**
- 1 **cup fresh strawberries, hulled**
- 1 **cup seedless red grapes**
- ¾ **cup (6 ounces) raspberry yogurt**
- ½ **cup fresh or frozen blueberries**
  Red grapes and fresh strawberries, optional

In a blender, combine all ingredients; cover and process for 20-30 seconds or until blended. Pour into chilled glasses; garnish smoothies with red grapes and strawberries if desired. Serve immediately.

PER SERVING *¾ cup (calculated without garnishes) equals 137 cal., 1 g fat (1 g sat. fat), 3 mg chol., 35 mg sodium, 30 g carb., 2 g fiber, 3 g pro. Diabetic Exchanges: 1 fruit, ½ reduced-fat milk.*

FRUITY SMOOTHIES

Roasted Grape Crostini

A vacation in Spain introduced me to many of that country's culinary treasures, including Manchego cheese. Now I like to sprinkle it over little appetizer toasts topped with warm roasted grapes.

—**JANICE ELDER** CHARLOTTE, NC

PREP: 25 MIN. • **BAKE:** 30 MIN.
MAKES: 2 DOZEN

- 3 **cups seedless red or green grapes, halved lengthwise**
- 2 **tablespoons sherry vinegar or rice vinegar**
- 2 **tablespoons olive oil**
- ½ **teaspoon salt**
- ¼ **teaspoon freshly ground pepper**
- 1 **teaspoon grated orange peel**
- 24 **slices French bread baguette (diagonally cut ½ inch thick)**
- ½ **cup shaved Manchego or Romano cheese**
  Thinly sliced fresh basil leaves

1. Preheat oven to 400°. In a bowl, toss the grapes with the sherry vinegar, olive oil, salt and pepper. Transfer to a greased 15x10x1-in. baking pan. Roast 30-35 minutes or until softened and lightly browned. Transfer to a small bowl; stir in orange peel.

2. Change the oven setting to broil. Place the French bread baguette slices on an ungreased baking sheet. Broil 3-4 in. from the heat 1-2 minutes on each side or until light brown.

3. To serve, spoon the warm grape mixture over the toasts; top with the cheese and basil.

PER SERVING *1 appetizer equals 52 cal., 2 g fat (1 g sat. fat), 2 mg chol., 110 mg sodium, 8 g carb., trace fiber, 1 g pro. Diabetic Exchanges: ½ starch, ½ fat.*

SANTA FE SPINACH DIP

Curry & Mango Chutney Chicken Wings

PREP: 15 MIN. + MARINATING
BAKE: 45 MIN.
MAKES: 1 DOZEN (1 CUP SAUCE)

- ¼ cup plain Greek yogurt
- ¼ cup mango chutney
- 2 tablespoons curry paste
- 2 tablespoons lemon juice
- 2 garlic cloves, minced
- 12 chicken wings (about 3 pounds), wing tips removed if desired

SAUCE

- ¾ cup plain Greek yogurt
- ½ cup finely chopped peeled English cucumber
- 3 tablespoons minced fresh cilantro
- 1 teaspoon lemon juice
- 1 garlic clove, minced
- ¼ teaspoon salt

1. In a large resealable plastic bag, combine the first five ingredients. Place chicken wings in bag; seal bag and turn to coat. Refrigerate 4 hours or overnight.
2. In a small bowl, mix the sauce ingredients until blended. Refrigerate, covered, at least 1 hour.
3. Preheat oven to 400°. Drain the chicken wings, discarding marinade. Place the chicken wings on a rack in a foil-lined 15x10x1-in. baking pan. Bake 45-50 minutes or until the juices run clear, turning every 15 minutes. Serve with sauce.
PER SERVING *1 chicken wing with 4 teaspoons sauce equals 170 cal., 10 g fat (4 g sat. fat), 42 mg chol., 207 mg sodium, 6 g carb., trace fiber, 12 g pro.*

Santa Fe Spinach Dip

A Southwestern food fan asked our staff of cooking pros to bring home a taste of her favorite restaurant snack, a cheesy baked spinach dip. Here it is!
—*TASTE OF HOME* **TEST KITCHEN**

PREP: 30 MIN. • **BAKE:** 25 MIN.
MAKES: 5 CUPS

- 1 medium onion, chopped
- 1 can (14½ ounces) diced tomatoes with mild green chilies, drained
- 2 garlic cloves, minced
- 1 package (8 ounces) cream cheese, cubed
- 1 cup (4 ounces) shredded white cheddar cheese
- 1 cup (4 ounces) shredded part-skim mozzarella cheese
- 1 cup (4 ounces) shredded Monterey Jack cheese
- 1 cup refrigerated Alfredo sauce
- 1 package (10 ounces) frozen leaf spinach, thawed and squeezed dry
- 1 tablespoon lime juice
- ½ teaspoon Cajun seasoning
- 2 tablespoons sour cream
  Tortilla chips

1. In a large nonstick skillet coated with cooking spray, saute onion until tender. Add tomatoes and garlic; cook 2 minutes longer. Remove from the heat and set aside.
2. In a large saucepan, combine the cheeses and Alfredo sauce. Cook and stir over medium-low heat until cheese is melted, about 10 minutes. Add the tomato mixture, spinach, lime juice and Cajun seasoning. Transfer to a greased 1½-qt. round baking dish.
3. Bake dip, uncovered, at 350° for 25-30 minutes or until bubbly. Dollop with sour cream. Serve with chips.
PER SERVING *¼ cup (calculated without chips) equals 149 cal., 12 g fat (7 g sat. fat), 33 mg chol., 358 mg sodium, 4 g carb., 1 g fiber, 6 g pro.*

BLUE CHEESE &
BACON STUFFED PEPPERS

Grilling is one of summer's highlights for my family. Whenever I'm cooking Blue Cheese & Bacon Stuffed Peppers, people always gather with their plates at the ready.

—TARA CRUZ KERSEY, CO

(5) INGREDIENTS | FAST FIX

Blue Cheese & Bacon Stuffed Peppers

START TO FINISH: 20 MIN.
MAKES: 1 DOZEN

- 3 medium sweet yellow, orange or red peppers
- 4 ounces cream cheese, softened
- ½ cup crumbled blue cheese
- 3 bacon strips, cooked and crumbled
- 1 green onion, thinly sliced

1. Cut peppers into quarters. Remove and discard stems and seeds. In a small bowl, mix cream cheese, blue cheese, bacon and green onion until blended.

2. Grill the peppers, covered, over medium-high heat or broil 4 in. from heat 2-3 minutes on each side or until slightly charred.

3. Remove the peppers from grill; fill each with about 1 tablespoon cheese mixture. Grill 2-3 minutes longer or until cheese is melted.

PER SERVING 1 appetizer equals 73 cal., 6 g fat (3 g sat. fat), 17 mg chol., 136 mg sodium, 3 g carb., trace fiber, 3 g pro.

FAST FIX

Candy Cane Hot Cocoa Mix

We whip up this malted milk-flavored mix to give as gifts during the holiday season. Be prepared—your friends may return the empty containers for refills!

—SARA TATHAM PLYMOUTH, NH

PREP TIME: 30 MIN.
MAKES: 20 SERVINGS (6⅔ CUPS HOT COCOA MIX)

- 1⅓ cups instant chocolate drink mix
- 1⅓ cups chocolate malted milk powder
- ⅓ cup baking cocoa
- 1 cup confectioners' sugar
- 6 tablespoons powdered nondairy creamer
- 3 cups nonfat dry milk powder
- 1½ cups miniature semisweet chocolate chips
- 1 cup crushed candy canes (about 40 mini candy canes)

EACH SERVING
- ¾ cup hot water

1. In a large bowl, mix the chocolate drink mix, malted milk powder and baking cocoa. In another bowl, mix confectioners' sugar and creamer.

2. In each of four 1-pint canning jars, layer ¾ cup dry milk powder, ¾ cup chocolate mixture, 3 tablespoons mini chocolate chips, ⅓ cup confectioners' sugar mixture, 3 tablespoons mini chocolate chips and ¼ cup crushed candy canes, pouring the ingredients through a large funnel or waxed-paper cone. Press the crushed candy canes down to fit if needed.

3. Cover and store in a cool dry place up to 2 months (mixture will settle). To use, transfer the contents of jar to a covered container or large resealable plastic bag; mix well.

TO PREPARE HOT COCOA Place ⅓ cup combined mix in a mug; stir in ¾ cup hot water until blended.

PER SERVING 1 serving prepared hot cocoa equals 315 cal., 6 g fat (3 g sat. fat), 2 mg chol., 155 mg sodium, 63 g carb., 3 g fiber, 6 g pro.

CANDY CANE
HOT COCOA MIX

BAKED CRANBERRY MEATBALLS

Baked Cranberry Meatballs

Bored with the same old meatball recipe? Jazz up lean ground beef with chili sauce, sauerkraut, cranberries and a few other ingredients. Everyone loves the tangy taste and mouthwatering aroma.

—LISA POTTER CAMP DOUGLAS, WI

PREP: 30 MIN. • **BAKE:** 1 HOUR 20 MIN.
MAKES: 4½ DOZEN

- 1 cup dry bread crumbs
- 1 envelope onion soup mix
- 2 pounds lean ground beef (90% lean)
- 2 large eggs, lightly beaten

SAUCE

- 1 can (14 ounces) sauerkraut, rinsed and well drained
- 1 can (14 ounces) whole-berry cranberry sauce
- 1 bottle (12 ounces) chili sauce
- 1¼ cups water
- 1 cup packed brown sugar

1. Preheat oven to 350°. In a large bowl, mix the dry bread crumbs and onion soup mix. Add beef and eggs; mix lightly but thoroughly. Shape into 1-in. balls. Arrange in a greased 13x9-in. baking dish.
2. In a large saucepan, combine sauce ingredients; bring just to a boil over medium heat, stirring to dissolve the sugar. Pour over uncooked meatballs.
3. Bake, covered, 1 hour. Uncover; bake 20-30 minutes longer or until meatballs are cooked through and sauce is thickened.

PER SERVING *1 meatball equals 72 cal., 2 g fat (1 g sat. fat), 17 mg chol., 225 mg sodium, 11 g carb., trace fiber, 4 g pro.*

EAT SMART **FAST FIX**
Crab Wonton Cups

Making appetizers with wonton wrappers couldn't be quicker or easier. I just press them into miniature muffin cups, bake, add a creamy seafood mixture and pop them in the oven one more time for a batch of hot and crispy finger food.

—CONNIE MCDOWELL GREENWOOD, DE

START TO FINISH: 30 MIN.
MAKES: 32 APPETIZERS

- 32 wonton wrappers
  Cooking spray
- 1 package (8 ounces) cream cheese, softened
- ½ cup heavy whipping cream
- 1 egg
- 1 tablespoon Dijon mustard
- 1 teaspoon Worcestershire sauce
- 5 drops hot pepper sauce
- 1 cup lump crabmeat, drained
- ¼ cup thinly sliced green onions
- ¼ cup finely chopped sweet red pepper
- 1 cup grated Parmesan cheese

1. Press wonton wrappers into mini muffin cups coated with cooking spray. Spritz wrappers with cooking spray. Bake at 350° for 8-9 minutes or until lightly browned.
2. Meanwhile, in a small bowl, beat cream cheese, cream, egg, mustard, Worcestershire sauce and pepper sauce until smooth. Stir in crab, onions and red pepper; spoon into wonton cups. Sprinkle with Parmesan cheese.
3. Bake for 10-12 minutes or until the filling is heated through. Serve warm. Refrigerate leftovers.

PER SERVING *1 appetizer equals 77 cal., 5 g fat (3 g sat. fat), 26 mg chol., 153 mg sodium, 5 g carb., trace fiber, 3 g pro.* **Diabetic Exchanges:** *1 fat, ½ starch.*

CRAB WONTON CUPS

3-in-1 Cheese Ball

At Christmastime, decorate these cheese balls to resemble tree ornaments.
—*TASTE OF HOME* TEST KITCHEN

PREP: 30 MIN. + CHILLING
MAKES: 3 LARGE CHEESE BALLS
(ABOUT 1 CUP EACH)

- 2 packages (8 ounces each) cream cheese, softened
- 1 cup grated Parmesan cheese
- 2 garlic cloves, minced

PESTO BALL
- 2 tablespoons prepared pesto
- 2 tablespoons minced fresh basil

HORSERADISH-BACON BALL
- 2 tablespoons prepared horseradish
- ½ cup crumbled cooked bacon
- 1 green onion, finely chopped

GORGONZOLA-CRANBERRY BALL
- ⅓ cup crumbled Gorgonzola cheese
- ⅓ cup dried cranberries
- ½ cup chopped walnuts, toasted

FOR SERVING
   Miniature pretzels, cooked bacon, dried cranberries, basil leaves and green onion, optional
   Assorted crackers

1. In a large bowl, beat cream cheese, Parmesan cheese and garlic until blended. Divide into three portions; place each in a small bowl.
PESTO BALL Beat the pesto into one portion cheese mixture. Stir in basil. Shape into a ball.
HORSERADISH-BACON BALL Beat horseradish into a second portion of cheese mixture. Stir in bacon and onion. Shape into one large or three mini balls.

3-IN-1 CHEESE BALL

GORGONZOLA-CRANBERRY BALL
Beat Gorgonzola cheese into remaining cheese mixture. Stir in the cranberries. Shape into a ball; roll in walnuts to coat.
2. Wrap cheese balls in plastic wrap; refrigerate at least 1 hour or until firm. Unwrap and decorate as desired. Serve with crackers.
NOTE *To toast nuts, bake in a shallow pan in a 350° oven for 5-10 minutes or cook in a skillet over low heat until lightly browned, stirring occasionally.*
PER SERVING *Pesto Ball: 2 tablespoons (calculated without crackers and decorations) equals 94 cal., 9 g fat (4 g sat. fat), 24 mg chol., 157 mg sodium, 1 g carb., trace fiber, 3 g pro. Horseradish-Bacon Ball: 2 tablespoons (calculated without crackers and decorations) equals 109 cal., 9 g fat (5 g sat. fat), 29 mg chol., 226 mg sodium, 1 g carb., trace fiber, 4 g pro. Gorgonzola-Cranberry Ball: 3 tablespoons (calculated without crackers and decorations) equals 159 cal., 14 g fat (6 g sat. fat), 28 mg chol., 175 mg sodium, 6 g carb., 1 g fiber, 5 g pro.*

Layered Mexican Dips

These personal-size layered dips are perfectly portioned for Cinco de Mayo parties. Grab small clear jars, then layer in your favorite Tex-Mex ingredients—think guacamole, sour cream, pico de gallo, etc. Or let your guests load up their own jars to their liking—then just point the way to the margarita station!
—*TASTE OF HOME* TEST KITCHEN

LAYERED MEXICAN DIPS

Pesto Swirled Cheesecake

This spread was such a hit at our last party, it was gone before my husband got a bite!
—**ELIZABETH JACKSON** PORTLAND, OR

PREP: 30 MIN. • **BAKE:** 35 MIN. + CHILLING
MAKES: 24 SERVINGS

- ⅔ **cup dry bread crumbs**
- 5 **tablespoons finely chopped pine nuts, toasted**
- 2 **tablespoons butter, melted**

FILLING
- 1 **carton (15 ounces) ricotta cheese**
- ½ **cup half-and-half cream**
- 2 **tablespoons grated Parmesan cheese**
- 2 **tablespoons all-purpose flour**
- ½ **teaspoon salt**
- ¼ **teaspoon garlic salt**
- 2 **large eggs, lightly beaten**

PESTO TOPPING
- ½ **cup loosely packed basil leaves**
- 2 **tablespoons grated Parmesan cheese**
- 1 **tablespoon pine nuts, toasted**
- 2 **garlic cloves, peeled**
- 2 **tablespoons olive oil**
  Assorted crackers

1. In a small bowl, combine the bread crumbs, pine nuts and butter. Press onto the bottom of a greased 9-in. springform pan; set aside.
2. In a small bowl, beat ricotta, cream, Parmesan, flour, salt and garlic salt until smooth. Add eggs; beat on low speed just until combined. Pour into crust.
3. For topping, combine the basil, Parmesan, nuts and garlic in a food processor; cover and process until finely chopped. While processing, gradually add oil in a steady stream. Drop by teaspoonfuls over filling; cut through with a knife to swirl.
4. Place pan on a baking sheet. Bake at 350° for 35-40 minutes or until center is almost set. Cool on a wire rack for 10 minutes. Carefully run a knife around edge of pan to loosen; cool 1 hour longer. Refrigerate overnight.
5. Serve with crackers. Refrigerate leftovers.
PER SERVING *1 slice (calculated without crackers) equals 87 cal., 6 g fat (2 g sat. fat), 28 mg chol., 144 mg sodium, 4 g carb., trace fiber, 4 g pro.*

Coconut Lover's Frappe

FAST FIX ▶

A fan of frozen beverages, I wanted to come up with one similar to those I've sampled in coffeehouses—but without the coffee. When I sip my creamy coconut frappe, I think it tastes just as good as the drinks sold in pricey cafes.
—**EMILY SEMMELROCK** JEWETT CITY, CT

START TO FINISH: 10 MIN.
MAKES: 3 SERVINGS

- ½ **cup white baking chips**
- ½ **cup flaked coconut**
- 2 **cups 2% milk**
- 2 **snack-size cups (3½ ounces each) vanilla pudding, frozen**
- ⅓ **cup refrigerated Almond Joy nondairy creamer**
- ¼ **teaspoon vanilla extract**
- 10 **ice cubes**

Place white baking chips and coconut in a blender; cover and process until chopped. Add remaining ingredients; cover and process until blended. Serve immediately.
PER SERVING *1 cup equals 468 cal., 23 g fat (15 g sat. fat), 19 mg chol., 242 mg sodium, 57 g carb., 1 g fiber, 9 g pro.*

COCONUT LOVER'S FRAPPE

Sweet Sriracha Wings

Prefer a little less sweetness in your wings? Add the honey slowly and taste as you go.

—LOGAN HOLSER CLARKSTON, MI

PREP: 20 MIN. + MARINATING
GRILL: 15 MIN.
MAKES: 1 DOZEN

- 12 chicken wings (about 3 pounds)
- 1 tablespoon canola oil
- 2 teaspoons ground coriander
- ½ teaspoon garlic salt
- ¼ teaspoon pepper

SAUCE

- ¼ cup butter, cubed
- ½ cup orange juice
- ⅓ cup Sriracha Asian hot chili sauce
- 3 tablespoons honey
- 2 tablespoons lime juice
- ¼ cup chopped fresh cilantro

1. Place the chicken wings in a large bowl. Mix the oil, coriander, garlic salt and pepper; add to the wings and toss to coat. Refrigerate, covered, 2 hours or overnight.

2. For sauce, in a small saucepan, melt butter. Stir in orange juice, chili sauce, honey and lime juice until blended.

3. Grill wings, covered, over medium heat 15-18 minutes or until the juices run clear, turning occasionally; brush with some of the sauce during the last 5 minutes of grilling.

4. Transfer chicken to a large bowl; add remaining sauce and toss to coat. Sprinkle with cilantro.

PER SERVING *1 chicken wing equals 201 cal., 13 g fat (5 g sat. fat), 46 mg chol., 321 mg sodium, 8 g carb., trace fiber, 12 g pro.*

THIN MINT MILK SHAKE

SWEET SRIRACHA WINGS

⑤ INGREDIENTS | FAST FIX ▶

Thin Mint Milk Shake

Save a sleeve of those yummy chocolate-mint Girl Scout cookies to use for creamy milk shakes. They go over big with kids and adults alike.

—SHAUNA SEVER SAN FRANCISCO, CA

START TO FINISH: 5 MIN.
MAKES: 2 SERVINGS

- 3 tablespoons creme de menthe or 2% milk plus a dash of peppermint extract
- 1¼ to 1½ cups vanilla ice cream
- 7 Girl Scout Thin Mint cookies
  Green food coloring, optional

Place all ingredients in a blender in order listed; cover and process until blended. Serve immediately.

PER SERVING *⅔ cup equals 363 cal., 12 g fat (7 g sat. fat), 36 mg chol., 70 mg sodium, 49 g carb., 1 g fiber, 3 g pro.*

DID YOU KNOW?

The Girl Scouts of America first sold commercially baked cookies to raise money in the 1930s. Originally called Chocolate Mints, their beloved Thin Mints are now the organization's best-selling variety.

PARTY POPCORN

SNACK CHAMPIONS

These *Taste of Home* fans shared their favorite **comfort-food bites** for munching during the big game. **Get ready to cheer!**

Cinnamon Sugar Chips

Cut large flour tortillas into triangles. Heat canola oil in a large frying pan; fry the tortilla triangles in batches until golden. Drain on paper towels. In a large container, mix sugar and cinnamon. Gently coat the chips in the mixture.

—**SHELLI CORRELL**
QUEEN CREEK, AZ

BLT Cucumbers

Peel and slice cucumbers; set aside. Chop seeded tomatoes and lettuce (or spinach), mix with bacon bits and mayo, and spoon on each cucumber slice.

—**VANESSA FULLER**
SEQUIM, WA

Super Salsa

A tomato, cilantro, lemon and onion salsa is our quick-fix appetizer. We always have the ingredients on hand.

—**KAREN PRATT**
POPLAR BLUFF, MO

Lemony Shrimp

Add the juice of a lemon, 1 tsp. salt and a head of roasted garlic to a generous cup of mayo. Dip grilled shrimp in the mayo and enjoy.

—**JEANNIE HUTCHINS**
NEWPORT, WA

Sugar-Roasted Garbanzo Beans

Rinse canned garbanzo beans and pat them dry. Place on a parchment paper-lined baking pan and toss with a drizzle of oil. Sprinkle cinnamon sugar over the beans, then add kosher salt. Roast for 35 minutes at 350°, stirring every 15 minutes. If you like, spice 'em up a little with a shake of cayenne—my husband's favorite way to eat them.

—**DOREEN PASQUARELLA**
STANFORDVILLE, NY

Orange Sticks

Spread butter over both sides of very thin party bread slices. Then add sugar and grated orange peel. Cut the slices into thirds and bake at 250° for 1 hour. Addictive!

—**JOAN HALLFORD**
LUBBOCK, TX

Bacon-Wrapped Chicken Bites

We love these snacks rolled in chili powder and brown sugar, then grilled. (Cook them over indirect heat until the chicken is no longer pink.) They disappear very quickly.

—**CINDY GREENTREE**
VANCOUVER, BC

Ham Roll-Ups

Spread slices of ham with chive cream cheese. Roll up a green onion in the ham. Refrigerate, then cut into ¾-in. pieces.

—**WENDY PRUCHA PESTER**
LINCOLN, NE

Party Popcorn

Melt 1½ cups white chocolate chips with ¼ cup canola oil, then mix in one 3.4-oz. pkg. French vanilla instant pudding mix. Toss with 6 cups popped popcorn. Let cool, then break up into large chunks. Add a little rah-rah spirit by sprinkling on team-color jimmies or M&M's.

—**RACHEL SEIS**
TASTE OF HOME
ASSOCIATE EDITOR

Pickle Dip

It's four ingredients: 1½ cups plain Greek yogurt, a packet of Hidden Valley Original ranch salad dressing mix, a block of cream cheese and plenty of chopped pickles. Mix and chill. Serve with tortilla chips or as a creamy relish on bratwurst.

—**DANA BLAIS**
ROYALTON, MN

SUPER SALSA

SLOW COOKER SPICED MIXED NUTS

SLOW COOKER 🍲

Slow Cooker Spiced Mixed Nuts

What slow cookers do for soups and stews, they can do for mixed nuts, too. You're sure to love the sweetness, spice and crunch.

—STEPHANIE LOAIZA LAYTON, UT

PREP: 15 MIN.
COOK: 1 HOUR 50 MIN. + COOLING
MAKES: 6 CUPS

- 1 **large egg white**
- 2 **teaspoons vanilla extract**
- 1 **cup unblanched almonds**
- 1 **cup pecan halves**
- 1 **cup shelled walnuts**
- 1 **cup unsalted cashews**
- 1 **cup sugar**
- 1 **cup packed brown sugar**
- 4 **teaspoons ground cinnamon**
- 2 **teaspoons ground ginger**
- 1 **teaspoon ground nutmeg**
- ½ **teaspoon ground cloves**
- ⅛ **teaspoon salt**
- 2 **tablespoons water**

1. In a large bowl, whisk egg white and vanilla until blended; stir in nuts. In a small bowl, mix sugars, spices and salt. Add to nut mixture and toss to coat.
2. Transfer mixture to a greased 3-qt. slow cooker. Cook, covered, on high 1½ hours, stirring every 15 minutes. Gradually stir in water. Cook, covered, on low 20 minutes.
3. Spread nuts onto waxed paper; cool completely. Store in airtight containers up to 1 week.
PER SERVING *⅓ cup equals 261 cal., 15 g fat (2 g sat. fat), 0 chol., 26 mg sodium, 30 g carb., 2 g fiber, 5 g pro.*

FAST FIX ▶

Hot Dog Sliders with Mango-Pineapple Salsa

START TO FINISH: 30 MIN.
MAKES: 2 DOZEN (2 CUPS SALSA)

- 3 **tablespoons lime juice**
- 2 **tablespoons honey**
- ¼ **teaspoon salt**
- 1 **cup cubed fresh pineapple (½ inch)**
- 1 **cup cubed peeled mango (½ inch)**
- ¼ **cup finely chopped red onion**
- 2 **tablespoons finely chopped sweet red pepper**
- 12 **hot dogs**
- 12 **hot dog buns, split**

1. For the fruit salsa, in a small bowl, whisk the lime juice, honey and salt until blended. Add the fresh pineapple, mango, onion and sweet red pepper; toss to coat.
2. Grill the hot dogs, covered, over medium heat or broil 4 in. from heat 7-9 minutes or until heated through, turning occasionally.
3. Place the hot dogs in the buns; cut each crosswise in half. Serve sliders with fruit salsa.
PER SERVING *1 slider with 1 tablespoon salsa equals 146 cal., 8 g fat (3 g sat. fat), 13 mg chol., 361 mg sodium, 15 g carb., 1 g fiber, 5 g pro.*

When I need party snacks, I shrink down our favorite foods to create smaller bites. Hot Dog Sliders with Mango-Pineapple Salsa are a popular choice.
—CAROLE RESNICK CLEVELAND, OH

HOT DOG SLIDERS WITH MANGO-PINEAPPLE SALSA

PASTRAMI ROLL-UPS

Pastrami Roll-Ups

For a book club event, I tried wrapping deli pastrami around a blend of two soft cheeses and a dill pickle spear, then cutting the roll-ups into slices. They disappeared in a flash!

—**MERRITT HEINRICH** OSWEGO, IL

START TO FINISH: 15 MIN.
MAKES: 4 DOZEN

- ¾ **cup spreadable cream cheese**
- ½ **cup crumbled blue cheese**
- 12 **slices lean deli pastrami**
- 12 **dill pickle spears**

1. In a small bowl, mix the cream cheese and blue cheese until blended. If necessary, pat pastrami and pickles dry with paper towels.
2. Spread about 1 tablespoon cheese mixture over each slice of pastrami; top with a dill pickle spear. Roll up tightly. Cut each roll into four slices. Refrigerate leftovers.

PER SERVING *1 appetizer equals 25 cal., 2 g fat (1 g sat. fat), 8 mg chol., 158 mg sodium, trace carb., 0 fiber, 2 g pro.*

Citrus Tea with Tarragon

This citrusy tea accented with tarragon is the perfect way to warm up on a chilly afternoon. To make it extra special, add a pretty sugared rim to each mug.

—**MARY JANE WALTERS** WESTERVILLE, OH

PREP: 15 MIN. • **COOK:** 10 MIN. + STANDING
MAKES: 8 SERVINGS (2 QUARTS)

- ½ **cup sugar**
- ½ **cup orange juice**
- ¼ **cup plus 8 cups water, divided**
- ¼ **cup honey**
- 3 **tablespoons lemon juice**
- 2 **tablespoons lime juice**
- ½ **cup fresh tarragaon leaves**
- 4 **individual Earl Grey tea bags**

OPTIONAL SUGARED RIM

- ½ **cup coarse sugar**
- 1 **teaspoon minced fresh tarragon**
- 1 **teaspoon grated orange peel**
  Orange wedges

1. In a small saucepan, combine the sugar, orange juice, ¼ cup water, honey, lemon juice and lime juice. Bring to a boil over medium-high heat, stirring constantly. Remove from the heat. Let stand for 15 minutes.
2. Transfer the mixture to a blender. Add tarragon leaves; cover and process for 30 seconds or until blended. Strain and set aside.
3. In a large saucepan, bring remaining water to a boil. Remove from the heat; add the tea bags. Cover and steep for 3-5 minutes. Discard tea bags. Stir in citrus mixture.
4. For optional sugared rims, sprinkle the coarse sugar, 1 tsp. tarragon and orange peel on a plate. Using orange wedges, moisten the rims of eight mugs; hold the mugs upside down and dip each rim into the sugar mixture. Serve hot tea in mugs.

PER SERVING *1 cup (calculated without the sugared rim) equals 93 cal., trace fat (0 sat. fat), 0 chol., 1 mg sodium, 24 g carb., trace fiber, trace pro.*

CAJUN SHRIMP SPREAD

SAUCY ASIAN MEATBALLS

Saucy Asian Meatballs

Garlic, soy sauce, ginger and hot sauce give these meatballs amazing flavor. Made with lean ground turkey, they're on the lighter side but don't taste like it.

—**LISA VARNER** EL PASO, TX

PREP: 20 MIN. • **BAKE:** 20 MIN.
MAKES: ABOUT 3 DOZEN

- 1 **pound lean ground turkey**
- 2 **garlic cloves, minced**
- 1 **teaspoon plus ¼ cup reduced-sodium soy sauce, divided**
- ½ **teaspoon ground ginger**
- ¼ **cup rice vinegar**
- ¼ **cup tomato paste**
- 2 **tablespoons molasses**
- 1 **teaspoon hot pepper sauce**

1. Preheat oven to 350°. Place ground turkey in a large bowl. Sprinkle with garlic, 1 teaspoon soy sauce and ginger; mix lightly but thoroughly. Shape into 1-in. balls; place in a 15x10x1-in. baking pan. Bake 20-25 minutes or until cooked through.

2. In a large saucepan, combine the rice vinegar, tomato paste, molasses, hot pepper sauce and remaining soy sauce; cook and stir over medium heat 3-5 minutes. Add the meatballs; heat through, stirring gently to coat.

PER SERVING *1 meatball equals 26 cal., 1 g fat (trace sat. fat), 10 mg chol., 87 mg sodium, 2 g carb., trace fiber, 2 g pro.*

Cajun Shrimp Spread

I tried mixing my favorite spinach dip with shrimp. My family couldn't get enough of the spicy, creamy combination.

—**LISA HUFF** WILTON, CT

START TO FINISH: 15 MIN.
MAKES: 4½ CUPS

- 1 **package (8 ounces) cream cheese, softened**
- ⅔ **cup sour cream**
- ⅔ **cup mayonnaise**
- 2 **garlic cloves, minced**
- 1½ **teaspoons Cajun seasoning**
    Dash hot pepper sauce
- 2 **cups chopped cooked peeled shrimp**
- 1 **package (10 ounces) frozen chopped spinach, thawed and squeezed dry**
- 2 **tablespoons chopped sweet red pepper**
- 2 **tablespoons chopped green onion Assorted crackers**

In a large bowl, whisk the first six ingredients until blended. Stir in the shrimp, spinach and sweet red pepper. Chill until serving. Sprinkle with green onion. Serve with crackers.

PER SERVING *2 tablespoons spread (calculated without crackers) equals 76 cal., 6 g fat (2 g sat. fat), 31 mg chol., 89 mg sodium, 1 g carb., trace fiber, 3 g pro.*

APPETIZERS & BEVERAGES

BRUSCHETTA MELTS

Bruschetta Melts

When I served these at my daughter's baby shower, we ran out almost immediately!

—COLEEN KATZ
HAVERTOWN, PA

PREP: 25 MIN. • **BAKE:** 10 MIN.
MAKES: 2 DOZEN

- ¼ cup olive oil
- 1 teaspoon lemon juice
- ½ teaspoon seasoned salt
- ½ teaspoon pepper
- ¼ teaspoon garlic powder
- 4 plum tomatoes, seeded and finely chopped
- ½ cup finely chopped sweet onion
- 2 tablespoons minced fresh basil
- 1 carton (8 ounces) spreadable chive and onion cream cheese
- 24 slices French bread (¼ inch thick)
- 2 cups (8 ounces) shredded part-skim mozzarella cheese
  Additional minced fresh basil

1. Preheat oven to 425°. In a small bowl, whisk the first five ingredients until blended; stir in tomatoes, onion and 2 tablespoons basil.

2. Spread cream cheese over bread slices; place slices on greased baking sheets. Top with the tomato mixture; sprinkle with the mozzarella cheese.

3. Bake 7-9 minutes or until cheese is melted. Sprinkle with additional basil.

PER SERVING *1 appetizer equals 127 cal., 9 g fat (4 g sat. fat), 18 mg chol., 214 mg sodium, 5 g carb., trace fiber, 6 g pro.*

FAST FIX

Layered Greek Dip

It's easy to fix a tasty Greek-style snack using convenient store-bought hummus.

—PATTERSON WATKINS
PHILADELPHIA, PA

START TO FINISH: 15 MIN.
MAKES: 20 SERVINGS

- 2½ cups roasted garlic hummus
- ¾ cup chopped roasted sweet red peppers
- 1 cup fresh baby spinach, coarsely chopped
- 3 tablespoons lemon juice
- 2 tablespoons olive oil
- 2 tablespoons coarsely chopped fresh basil
- 1 tablespoon coarsely chopped fresh mint
- ½ cup crumbled feta cheese
- ½ cup Greek olives, sliced
- ¼ cup chopped red onion
  Assorted fresh vegetables or baked pita chips

1. Spread roasted garlic hummus onto a 12-in. round serving platter; top with roasted red peppers.

2. In a small bowl, combine spinach, lemon juice, olive oil, basil and mint. Using a slotted spoon, spoon spinach mixture over peppers. Top with the feta cheese, Greek olives and onion. Serve with vegetables or pita chips.

PER SERVING *¼ cup (calculated without vegetables or chips) equals 83 cal., 6 g fat (1 g sat. fat), 2 mg chol., 347 mg sodium, 6 g carb., 1 g fiber, 2 g pro.*

LAYERED GREEK DIP

**SHELLY GRAMER'S
GINGER-CASHEW CHICKEN SALAD**
PAGE 23

Salads & Dressings

Potluck favorites, holiday classics, weekday sides—they're all here in this **refreshing selection.** Which recipe will you want to make for your family first? **It's sure to be a toss-up!**

**JOY ZACHARIA'S
MIXED GREENS WITH ORANGE-
GINGER VINAIGRETTE** *PAGE 23*

**MELISSA MCCABE'S
STRAWBERRY, CUCUMBER
& HONEYDEW SALAD** *PAGE 26*

**CARLY CURTIN'S
SUMMER MACARONI SALAD**
PAGE 28

Antipasto Salad with Basil Dressing

Enjoy this fresh-tasting Italian medley as an appetizer, side or light dinner.

—**HUNTER MARLO** BLACKSBURG, VA

START TO FINISH: 30 MIN.
MAKES: 8 SERVINGS

- 1 package (6 ounces) torn mixed salad greens
- 6 thin slices hard salami, quartered
- 1 jar (7½ ounces) marinated quartered artichoke hearts, drained
- 1 large sweet red pepper, sliced
- ½ cup pitted Greek olives
- 1 small red onion, thinly sliced
- 1½ cups (6 ounces) crumbled feta cheese
- 15 cherry tomatoes, halved
- ½ cup chopped walnuts
- 1 cup salad croutons

BASIL SALAD DRESSING
- ½ cup olive oil
- ¼ cup balsamic vinegar
- 5 fresh basil leaves, thinly sliced
- ½ teaspoon sugar
- ½ teaspoon garlic powder
- ¼ teaspoon salt
- ¼ teaspoon pepper

1. In a 3½-qt. glass bowl, layer the first 10 ingredients in order listed. Cover and chill until serving.
2. In a small bowl, whisk the dressing ingredients. Just before serving, pour over salad; toss to coat.

PER SERVING *1¼ cups equals 332 cal., 29 g fat (6 g sat. fat), 13 mg chol., 579 mg sodium, 13 g carb., 3 g fiber, 8 g pro.*

ANTIPASTO SALAD WITH BASIL DRESSING

Green Bean & Potato Salad

My mom was always the one who brought everybody's favorite salad to our family reunions. Now I carry on her tradition.

—**CONNIE DICAVOLI** SHAWNEE, KS

PREP: 15 MIN. • **COOK:** 20 MIN. + CHILLING
MAKES: 10 SERVINGS

- 2 pounds red potatoes (about 6 medium), cubed
- 1 pound fresh green beans, trimmed and halved
- 1 small red onion, halved and thinly sliced
- ¼ cup chopped fresh mint, optional

DRESSING
- ½ cup canola oil
- ¼ cup white vinegar
- 2 tablespoons lemon juice
- 1 teaspoon salt
- ½ teaspoon garlic powder
- ¼ teaspoon pepper

1. Place the red potatoes in a 6-qt. stockpot; add water to cover. Bring to a boil. Reduce heat; cook, uncovered, 10-15 minutes or until tender, adding green beans during the last 4 minutes of cooking. Drain.
2. Transfer the potatoes and green beans to a large bowl; add onion and, if desired, mint. In a small bowl, whisk dressing ingredients until blended. Pour over potato mixture; toss gently to coat. Refrigerate, covered, at least 2 hours before serving.

PER SERVING *¾ cup equals 183 cal., 11 g fat (1 g sat. fat), 0 chol., 245 mg sodium, 19 g carb., 3 g fiber, 3 g pro.*
Diabetic Exchanges: 2½ fat, 1 starch.

Cranberry-Pineapple Gelatin Mold

This tangy gelatin has become one of the mainstays on our Christmas menu.

—**BETHANY BEERS** FAIRVIEW, PA

PREP: 15 MIN. • **COOK:** 5 MIN. + CHILLING
MAKES: 10 SERVINGS

- 1 can (20 ounces) unsweetened crushed pineapple
- 2 envelopes unflavored gelatin
- 1 package (12 ounces) fresh or frozen cranberries

CRANBERRY-PINEAPPLE GELATIN MOLD

- 3 medium navel oranges, peeled and cut into segments
- ½ cup honey
  Whipped cream, optional

1. Drain pineapple, reserving juice; set pineapple aside. Place reserved juice in a small saucepan. Sprinkle with gelatin; let stand for 1 minute or until softened. Heat over low heat, stirring until gelatin is completely dissolved. Remove from the heat.
2. In a food processor, combine the cranberries and oranges; cover and pulse until chunky. Add honey and pineapple; cover and pulse just until blended. Stir in juice mixture. Transfer to a 6-cup mold coated with cooking spray. Refrigerate until firm.
3. Unmold onto a serving platter. Serve with whipped cream if desired.

PER SERVING *1 slice (calculated without whipped cream) equals 126 cal., trace fat (trace sat. fat), 0 chol., 5 mg sodium, 32 g carb., 3 g fiber, 2 g pro.*

TOP TIP

Having trouble unmolding gelatin? Loosen it from the top edge of the mold by gently pulling the gelatin away from the edge with a moistened finger. Dip the mold up to its rim in warm water for a few seconds or until the edges begin to release from the mold. Then place a plate over it, invert and lift the mold from the gelatin.

Roasted Sweet Potato Salad with Honey-Maple Vinaigrette

Here's a wonderful choice for a special meal. The cranberries and sweet potatoes are perfect for the holiday season.
—SUSAN BICKTA KUTZTOWN, PA

PREP: 20 MIN. • **BAKE:** 35 MIN.
MAKES: 8 SERVINGS

- 2 pounds sweet potatoes, peeled and cut into ¾-inch pieces (about 7 cups)
- 5 tablespoons canola oil, divided
- 3 tablespoons cider vinegar
- 2 tablespoons honey
- 2 tablespoons maple syrup
- 1 small garlic clove, minced
- ½ teaspoon Dijon mustard
- ⅛ teaspoon salt
- ⅛ teaspoon pepper
- 1 package (6 ounces) fresh baby spinach
- 1 medium apple, chopped
- ½ cup dried cranberries
- ½ cup chopped pecans, toasted
- ½ cup crumbled blue cheese

1. Preheat oven to 400°. Place the sweet potatoes in a greased 15x10x1-in. baking pan; toss with 2 tablespoons oil. Roast 35-40 minutes or until tender. Transfer to a large bowl; cool slightly.
2. In a small bowl, whisk the cider vinegar, honey, maple syrup, garlic, mustard, salt, pepper and remaining oil until blended. Add the spinach, apple, dried cranberries and pecans to the sweet potatoes. Drizzle with vinaigrette and toss to coat. Top with cheese. Serve immediately.
NOTE *To toast nuts, bake in a shallow pan in a 350° oven for 5-10 minutes or cook in a skillet over low heat until lightly browned, stirring occasionally.*
PER SERVING *1 cup equals 340 cal., 16 g fat (3 g sat. fat), 6 mg chol., 192 mg sodium, 46 g carb., 5 g fiber, 5 g pro.*

EAT SMART FAST FIX
Spring Greek Pasta Salad

START TO FINISH: 30 MIN.
MAKES: 16 SERVINGS

- 4 cups veggie rotini or other spiral pasta (about 12 ounces)

SPRING GREEK PASTA SALAD

With plenty of rotini, vegetables and feta cheese, Spring Greek Pasta Salad is a satisfying meatless entree. For an even heartier dish, add grilled chicken.
—CHRISTINE SCHENHER EXETER, CA

VINAIGRETTE
- ¼ cup olive oil
- 3 tablespoons lemon juice
- 2 tablespoons balsamic vinegar
- 1 tablespoon water
- 3 garlic cloves, minced
- 1 teaspoon salt
- ¼ teaspoon pepper
- 3 tablespoons minced fresh oregano or 1 tablespoon dried oregano

SALAD
- 3 large tomatoes, seeded and chopped
- 1 medium sweet red pepper, chopped
- 1 small cucumber, seeded and chopped
- 1 small zucchini, chopped
- 1 small red onion, halved and thinly sliced
- ⅓ cup sliced pitted Greek olives, optional
- 1 cup (4 ounces) crumbled feta cheese

1. Cook the pasta according to the package directions. Drain; rinse with cold water and drain well.
2. In a small bowl, whisk oil, lemon juice, vinegar, water, garlic, salt and pepper until blended. Stir in oregano.
3. In a large bowl, combine the pasta, vegetables and, if desired, olives. Add vinaigrette and cheese; toss to combine. Refrigerate, covered, until serving.
PER SERVING *¾ cup (calculated without olives) equals 142 cal., 5 g fat (1 g sat. fat), 4 mg chol., 219 mg sodium, 20 g carb., 2 g fiber, 5 g pro.* **Diabetic Exchanges:** *1 starch, 1 fat.*

CHIPOTLE LIME AVOCADO SALAD

I try to use my music to promote a healthy lifestyle, which includes eating nutritious food. Chipotle Lime Avocado Salad fits into that plan and has a little heat, too.
—DJ CAVEM DENVER, CO

FAST FIX ▸
Mom's Chopped Coleslaw

For our Friday fish dinners, my mother treated us to her homemade coleslaw on the side. That creamy, tangy favorite is still a family tradition.
—CYNTHIA MCDOWELL BANNING, CA

START TO FINISH: 20 MIN.
MAKES: 6 SERVINGS

- ½ medium head cabbage (about 1¼ pounds)
- ½ cup finely chopped celery
- ½ cup finely chopped sweet red or green pepper
- ⅓ cup finely chopped sweet onion

DRESSING
- ½ cup mayonnaise
- ¼ cup sugar
- ¼ cup 2% milk
- ¼ cup buttermilk
- 2 teaspoons white vinegar
- ¼ teaspoon hot pepper sauce
  Dash pepper

1. Cut the cabbage into 1½- to 2-in. pieces. Place half of the cabbage in a food processor; pulse until chopped. Transfer to a large bowl; repeat with remaining cabbage.

2. Add the remaining vegetables to the cabbage. In a small bowl, whisk dressing ingredients until blended. Pour over coleslaw and toss to coat. Refrigerate until serving.

PER SERVING *¾ cup equals 203 cal., 15 g fat (2 g sat. fat), 8 mg chol., 147 mg sodium, 16 g carb., 2 g fiber, 2 g pro.*

MOM'S CHOPPED COLESLAW

EAT SMART **FAST FIX** ▸
Chipotle Lime Avocado Salad

START TO FINISH: 15 MIN.
MAKES: 4 SERVINGS

- ¼ cup lime juice
- ¼ cup maple syrup
- ½ teaspoon ground chipotle pepper
- ¼ teaspoon cayenne pepper, optional
- 2 medium ripe avocados, peeled and cubed
- ½ medium cucumber, peeled and chopped

- 1 tablespoon minced fresh chives
- 2 large tomatoes, cut into ½-inch slices

In a small bowl, whisk the lime juice, maple syrup, chipotle pepper and, if desired, cayenne until blended. In another bowl, combine avocados, cucumber and chives. Drizzle with the dressing; toss gently to coat. Serve over tomato slices.

PER SERVING *1 serving equals 191 cal., 11 g fat (1 g sat. fat), 0 chol., 26 mg sodium, 25 g carb., 6 g fiber, 3 g pro.*

Ginger-Cashew Chicken Salad

While trying to revamp a similar Asian-style recipe, I came up with this crunchy entree. It always proves popular at luncheons.

—SHELLY GRAMER LONG BEACH, CA

PREP: 20 MIN. + MARINATING
BROIL: 10 MIN. • **MAKES:** 8 SERVINGS

- ½ cup cider vinegar
- ½ cup molasses
- ⅓ cup canola oil
- 2 tablespoons minced fresh gingerroot
- 2 teaspoons reduced-sodium soy sauce
- 1 teaspoon salt
- ⅛ teaspoon cayenne pepper
- 4 boneless skinless chicken breast halves (6 ounces each)

SALAD
- 8 ounces fresh baby spinach (about 10 cups)
- 1 can (11 ounces) mandarin oranges, drained
- 1 cup shredded red cabbage
- 2 medium carrots, shredded
- 3 green onions, thinly sliced
- 2 cups chow mein noodles
- ¾ cup salted cashews, toasted
- 2 tablespoons sesame seeds, toasted

1. In a small bowl, whisk the first seven ingredients until blended. Pour ¾ cup marinade into a large resealable plastic bag. Add the chicken; seal the bag and turn to coat. Refrigerate at least 3 hours. Cover and refrigerate remaining marinade.

2. Preheat broiler. Drain the chicken, discarding the marinade in bag. Place chicken in a 15x10x1-in. baking pan. Broil 4-6 in. from heat 4-6 minutes on each side or until a thermometer reads 165°. Cut chicken into strips.

3. Place spinach on a serving platter. Arrange chicken, oranges, cabbage, carrots and green onions. Sprinkle with chow mein noodles, cashews and sesame seeds. Stir reserved molasses mixture; drizzle over salad and toss to coat. Serve immediately.

NOTE *To toast nuts, bake in a shallow pan in a 350° oven for 5-10 minutes or cook in a skillet over low heat until lightly browned, stirring occasionally.*

MIXED GREENS WITH ORANGE-GINGER VINAIGRETTE

PER SERVING *1½ cups equals 379 cal., 18 g fat (3 g sat. fat), 47 mg chol., 533 mg sodium, 33 g carb., 3 g fiber, 23 g pro.* **Diabetic Exchanges:** *2½ fat, 2 lean meat, 1½ starch, 1 vegetable.*

Mixed Greens with Orange-Ginger Vinaigrette

Plain greens go from ordinary to amazing when you drizzle on a zingy vinaigrette featuring orange juice and grated ginger.

—JOY ZACHARIA CLEARWATER, FL

START TO FINISH: 20 MIN.
MAKES: 8 SERVINGS

- ¼ cup orange juice
- ¼ cup canola oil
- 2 tablespoons white vinegar
- 2 tablespoons honey
- 2 teaspoons grated fresh gingerroot
- ½ teaspoon salt
- ¼ teaspoon cayenne pepper

SALAD
- 12 cups torn mixed salad greens
- 2 medium navel oranges, peeled and sliced crosswise
- 1 cup thinly sliced red onion

In a small bowl, whisk the first seven ingredients until blended. In a large bowl, toss the greens with ¼ cup vinaigrette; transfer to a serving dish. Top with the oranges and red onion. Serve immediately with remaining vinaigrette.

PER SERVING *1½ cups equals 119 cal., 7 g fat (1 g sat. fat), 0 chol., 202 mg sodium, 15 g carb., 3 g fiber, 2 g pro.* **Diabetic Exchanges:** *1½ fat, 1 vegetable, ½ starch.*

EAT SMART FAST FIX
Shrimp & Nectarine Salad

For a substantial side or light main course on a hot summer day, toss mixed greens with seasoned shrimp, nectarines and vegetables. We prefer this dish chilled, but it's delicious warm, too.

—MARY ANN LEE CLIFTON PARK, NY

START TO FINISH: 30 MIN.
MAKES: 4 SERVINGS

- ⅓ cup orange juice
- 3 tablespoons cider vinegar
- 1½ teaspoons Dijon mustard
- 1½ teaspoons honey
- 1 tablespoon minced fresh tarragon

SALAD

- 4 teaspoons canola oil, divided
- 1 cup fresh or frozen corn
- 1 pound uncooked shrimp (26-30 per pound), peeled and deveined
- ½ teaspoon lemon-pepper seasoning
- ¼ teaspoon salt
- 8 cups torn mixed salad greens
- 2 medium nectarines, cut into 1-inch pieces
- 1 cup grape tomatoes, halved
- ½ cup finely chopped red onion

1. In a small bowl, whisk orange juice, cider vinegar, mustard and honey until blended. Stir in tarragon.

2. In a large skillet, heat 1 teaspoon oil over medium-high heat. Add the corn; cook and stir for 1-2 minutes or until crisp-tender. Remove from pan.

3. Sprinkle shrimp with the lemon pepper and salt. In same skillet, heat remaining oil over medium-high heat. Add shrimp; cook and stir 3-4 minutes or until shrimp turn pink. Stir in corn.

4. In a large bowl, combine remaining ingredients. Drizzle with ⅓ cup salad dressing; toss to coat. Divide mixture among four plates. Top with shrimp mixture; drizzle with the remaining dressing. Serve immediately.

PER SERVING *1 serving equals 252 cal., 7 g fat (1 g sat. fat), 138 mg chol., 448 mg sodium, 27 g carb., 5 g fiber, 23 g pro.* **Diabetic Exchanges:** *3 lean meat, 2 vegetable, 1 fat, ½ starch, ½ fruit.*

FAST FIX
Fresh Pear & Romaine Salad

A family member gave me a great tip—when making salad dressing, use whatever fruit is in the salad. That idea works like a charm here, thanks to the mellow fresh pears.

—JENNIFER GREILING FAIRVIEW, OR

START TO FINISH: 30 MIN.
MAKES: 6 SERVINGS

- 1 tablespoon lemon juice
- 1 tablespoon rice vinegar
- 1 tablespoon white balsamic vinegar
- 1 tablespoon honey
- ½ teaspoon salt
- ½ teaspoon Dijon mustard
- ¼ teaspoon coarsely ground pepper
- ⅔ cup coarsely chopped peeled fresh pear
- ⅓ cup olive oil

SALAD

- 1 large pear, thinly sliced
- 1 tablespoon lemon juice
- 8 cups torn romaine
  Salt and pepper to taste
- 1 cup glazed pecans
- 1 cup (4 ounces) crumbled Gorgonzola cheese
- ½ cup dried cherries

1. Place the first eight ingredients in a blender; cover and process until smooth. While processing, gradually add oil in a steady stream.

2. For the salad, toss the sliced pear with the lemon juice. In a large bowl, toss the romaine with ½ cup dressing; season with salt and pepper to taste. Top with the pear, glazed pecans, Gorgonzola cheese and dried cherries. Serve immediately with remaining dressing on the side.

PER SERVING *1½ cups equals 360 cal., 25 g fat (6 g sat. fat), 17 mg chol., 541 mg sodium, 30 g carb., 5 g fiber, 6 g pro.*

SHRIMP & NECTARINE SALAD

1 cup masa harina
¼ cup all-purpose flour

CHIPOTLE RANCH DRESSING
¼ cup buttermilk
¼ cup mayonnaise
1 teaspoon buttermilk ranch salad dressing mix
1 teaspoon minced chipotle peppers in adobo sauce

SALAD
6 cans (7 ounces each) white or shoepeg corn, drained
2 cups grape tomatoes, chopped
1 can (10 ounces) diced tomatoes and green chilies, well drained
1 small red onion, chopped
½ cup chopped peeled jicama
¼ cup minced fresh cilantro
¼ cup lime juice
1 jalapeno pepper, seeded and minced
4 medium ripe avocados, peeled and cubed
¾ cup shredded Mexican cheese blend

TANGY BLUE CHEESE DRESSING

1. Place 2 cups corn in food processor; cover and process until finely chopped. Add the butter, sugar and salt; cover and process until blended. Stir in the masa harina and flour until a soft dough forms; fold in the remaining corn. Using wet hands, press dough into a greased 15x10x1-in. baking pan.
2. Bake at 400° for 20 minutes. Score the dough into 1-in. squares. Bake 4-6 minutes longer or until golden brown. Immediately cut along the scored lines; cool croutons in the pan on a wire rack.
3. In a small bowl, combine the salad dressing ingredients. In a large bowl, combine the corn, tomatoes, red onion, jicama, cilantro, lime juice and jalapeno pepper. Pour the dressing over the salad and toss to coat; gently stir in the avocados. Sprinkle with Mexican cheese blend and croutons. Serve immediately.
NOTE *Wear disposable gloves when cutting hot peppers; the oils can burn skin. Avoid touching your face.*
PER SERVING *¾ cup with ⅓ cup croutons and 1 tablespoon cheese equals 449 cal., 26 g fat (10 g sat. fat), 35 mg chol., 638 mg sodium, 53 g carb., 9 g fiber, 8 g pro.*

EAT SMART
Tangy Blue Cheese Dressing

Caramelized onions lend a depth of flavor you won't find in a store-bought bottle. Keep this blend on hand to add some zip to everything from sandwich spreads to dips.
—**ALISHA GOINS** SABIN, MN

PREP: 10 MIN. • **COOK:** 35 MIN.
MAKES: 2½ CUPS

1 cup chopped sweet onion
2 teaspoons canola oil
1 cup reduced-fat mayonnaise
½ cup reduced-fat sour cream
½ cup buttermilk
1 teaspoon hot pepper sauce
¼ teaspoon Worcestershire sauce
½ cup crumbled blue cheese

1. In a large skillet, saute the onion in oil until softened. Reduce the heat to medium-low; cook, uncovered, for 30-35 minutes or until deep golden brown, stirring occasionally. Set onion aside to cool.

2. In a small bowl, whisk mayonnaise, sour cream, buttermilk, hot pepper sauce and Worcestershire sauce. Stir in crumbled blue cheese and onion. Store in an airtight container in the refrigerator for up to 2 weeks.
PER SERVING *2 tablespoons equals 70 cal., 6 g fat (2 g sat. fat), 9 mg chol., 156 mg sodium, 3 g carb., trace fiber, 1 g pro.* **Diabetic Exchange: 1 fat.**

Fiesta Corn Salad

I took the recipe for a delectable but complicated appetizer and transformed it into something completely different. Feel free to adjust the heat level from the peppers to suit your taste.
—**RICHI REYNOLDS** SCOTTSBORO, AL

PREP: 30 MIN. • **BAKE:** 25 MIN.
MAKES: 12 SERVINGS

TAMALE CROUTONS
3 cups frozen corn, divided
⅔ cup butter, softened
⅓ cup sugar
¼ teaspoon salt

Grilled Southwestern Potato Salad

Like food that has some heat? You'll enjoy triple the peppery goodness in this medley, thanks to the poblanos, jalapenos and cayenne.

—JOHNNA JOHNSON SCOTTSDALE, AZ

PREP: 30 MIN. • **GRILL:** 20 MIN. + STANDING
MAKES: 6 SERVINGS

- 1½ pounds large red potatoes, quartered lengthwise
- 3 tablespoons olive oil
- 2 poblano peppers
- 2 medium ears sweet corn, husks removed
- ½ cup buttermilk
- ½ cup sour cream
- 1 tablespoon lime juice
- 1 jalapeno pepper, seeded and minced
- 1 tablespoon minced fresh cilantro
- 1½ teaspoons garlic salt
- 1 teaspoon ground cumin
- ¼ to ½ teaspoon cayenne pepper
  Lime wedges

1. Place the red potatoes in a large saucepan; add water to cover. Bring to a boil. Reduce heat; cook, uncovered, 5 minutes. Drain the potatoes; toss with oil.

2. Grill the poblanos, covered, over high heat 8-10 minutes or until skins are blistered and blackened on all sides, turning occasionally. Immediately place poblanos in a small bowl; let stand, covered, 20 minutes. Reduce grill temperature to medium heat.

3. Grill corn and potatoes, covered, over medium heat 12-15 minutes or until tender and lightly browned, turning occasionally. Cool slightly.

4. Peel off and discard charred skin from poblanos; remove the stems and seeds. Cut poblanos into ½-in. pieces and place in a large bowl. Cut corn from cobs and cut the potatoes into ¾-in. pieces; add to poblanos.

5. In a small bowl, whisk buttermilk, sour cream and juice until blended; stir in the jalapeno pepper, cilantro, garlic salt, cumin and cayenne pepper. Add to the potato mixture, stirring in as much salad dressing to coat as

STRAWBERRY, CUCUMBER & HONEYDEW SALAD

desired. Serve with the lime wedges. Refrigerate leftovers.
PER SERVING ¾ cup equals 229 cal., 11 g fat (4 g sat. fat), 14 mg chol., 301 mg sodium, 28 g carb., 3 g fiber, 5 g pro.

EAT SMART **FAST FIX**
Strawberry, Cucumber & Honeydew Salad

When I was a girl in upstate New York, we used to visit fruit and veggie stands to get cucumbers, honeydew melons and strawberries for this salad.
—MELISSA MCCABE LONG BEACH, CA

START TO FINISH: 20 MIN.
MAKES: 8 SERVINGS

- 1 container (16 ounces) fresh strawberries, halved
- 1 English cucumber, halved lengthwise and cut into ¼-inch slices
- 1 cup cubed honeydew (½ inch)
- 3 tablespoons honey
- 2 tablespoons lime juice
- 1 teaspoon grated lime peel

1. In a large bowl, combine the berries, cucumber and honeydew. Chill until serving.

2. In a small bowl, whisk remaining ingredients. Just before serving, drizzle over the strawberry mixture; toss gently to coat.
PER SERVING ¾ cup equals 56 cal., trace fat (trace sat. fat), 0 chol., 6 mg sodium, 15 g carb., 2 g fiber, 1 g pro.
Diabetic Exchange: 1 fruit.

FAST FIX ▶

Cranberry-Sesame Spinach Salad

For a special autumn dinner or anytime, toss together a simple mix of toasted almonds, dried cranberries and spinach coated with a sesame dressing.

—STEPHANIE SMOLEY ROCHESTER, MN

START TO FINISH: 25 MIN
MAKES: 4 SERVINGS

- 1 teaspoon butter
- 2 tablespoons slivered almonds
- 2½ cups fresh baby spinach
- 2 tablespoons dried cranberries

DRESSING

- 2 tablespoons canola oil
- 1 tablespoon sugar
- 1 tablespoon cider vinegar
- 2 teaspoons toasted sesame seeds
- ½ teaspoon dried minced onion
- ½ teaspoon poppy seeds
- ⅛ teaspoon salt
  Dash paprika

1. In a small skillet, heat butter over medium heat. Add almonds; cook and stir until lightly browned. Remove from heat.

2. Place the spinach and cranberries in a bowl. In a small bowl, whisk the dressing ingredients until blended. Add to the salad and toss to coat. Sprinkle with the toasted almonds. Serve immediately.

PER SERVING 1¼ cups salad equals 257 cal., 21 g fat (3 g sat. fat), 5 mg chol., 207 mg sodium, 16 g carb., 3 g fiber, 3 g pro.

EAT SMART ⑤ INGREDIENTS FAST FIX ▶

Pina Colada Carrot Salad

Taste buds travel to a tropical paradise when carrots and grapes combine with pina colada yogurt and macadamia nuts.

—EMILY TYRA MILWAUKEE, WI

START TO FINISH: 10 MIN.
MAKES: 4 SERVINGS

- 1 package (10 ounces) julienned carrot
- 1 cup green grapes, halved
- ¾ cup (6 ounces) pina colada yogurt
- ⅓ cup salted dry roasted macadamia nuts, chopped
  Lemon wedges

In a large bowl, combine the carrots, green grapes, pina colada yogurt and chopped macadamia nuts; toss to coat. Squeeze lemon wedges over the salad before serving.

PER SERVING ¾ cup equals 184 cal., 9 g fat (2 g sat. fat), 2 mg chol., 157 mg sodium, 24 g carb., 3 g fiber, 3 g pro. *Diabetic Exchanges: 1½ fat, 1 starch, 1 vegetable.*

FAST FIX ▶

Creamy Egg Salad

Whenever I make this lunchtime favorite, I think of my mom. We came up with this recipe for a 4-H demonstration when I was 11. We called our version "eggceptional!" I loved cooking so much that I became a family consumer sciences teacher.

—CYNTHIA KOHLBERG SYRACUSE, IN

START TO FINISH: 10 MIN.
MAKES: 3 CUPS

- 3 ounces cream cheese, softened
- ¼ cup mayonnaise
- ½ teaspoon salt
- ⅛ teaspoon pepper
- ¼ cup finely chopped green or sweet red pepper
- ¼ cup finely chopped celery
- ¼ cup sweet pickle relish
- 2 tablespoons minced fresh parsley
- 8 hard-cooked eggs, chopped

In a bowl, mix the cream cheese, mayonnaise, salt and pepper until smooth. Stir in the green pepper, celery, sweet pickle relish and parsley. Fold in the eggs. Refrigerate, covered, until serving.

PER SERVING ½ cup equals 234 cal., 19 g fat (6 g sat. fat), 268 mg chol., 466 mg sodium, 5 g carb., trace fiber, 9 g pro.

CREAMY EGG SALAD

Summer Macaroni Salad

When we have a family cookout, my mother asks me to fix our traditional macaroni dish. For extra creaminess, I keep a small amount of dressing separate and stir it in just before serving.

—**CARLY CURTIN** ELLICOTT CITY, MD

PREP: 20 MIN. + CHILLING • **COOK:** 15 MIN.
MAKES: 16 SERVINGS

- 1 **package (16 ounces) elbow macaroni**
- 1 **cup reduced-fat mayonnaise**
- 3 **to 4 tablespoons water or 2% milk**
- 2 **tablespoons red wine vinegar**
- 1 **tablespoon sugar**
- 1½ **teaspoons salt**
- ¼ **teaspoon garlic powder**
- ¼ **teaspoon pepper**
- 1 **small sweet yellow, orange or red pepper, finely chopped**
- 1 **small green pepper, finely chopped**
- 1 **small onion, finely chopped**
- 1 **celery rib, finely chopped**
- 2 **tablespoons minced fresh parsley**

1. Cook the macaroni according to the package directions. Drain; rinse with cold water and drain again.

2. In a small bowl, mix mayonnaise, water, vinegar, sugar and seasonings until blended. In a large bowl, combine macaroni, peppers, onion and celery. Add 1 cup dressing; toss gently to coat. Refrigerate, covered, 2 hours or until cold. Cover and refrigerate remaining dressing to add just before serving.

3. To serve, stir in reserved dressing. Sprinkle with parsley.

PER SERVING *¾ cup equals 160 cal., 6 g fat (1 g sat. fat), 5 mg chol., 320 mg sodium, 24 g carb., 1 g fiber, 4 g pro.* **Diabetic Exchanges:** *1½ starch, 1 fat.*

MODERN WALDORF SALAD

Modern Waldorf Salad

Here's my updated take on the classic Waldorf. Feel free to experiment with rotisserie chicken or other fruits in place of the deli smoked turkey, strawberries and apples.

—**SONYA LABBE** WEST HOLLYWOOD, CA

START TO FINISH: 30 MIN. • **MAKES:** 4 SERVINGS

- 2 **cups uncooked orecchiette or small tube pasta (about 6 ounces)**
- ¼ **cup reduced-fat plain yogurt**
- 2 **tablespoons mayonnaise**
- 2 **tablespoons 2% milk**
- 4 **teaspoons Dijon mustard**
- ½ **teaspoon dried thyme, optional**
- 1 **medium apple, chopped**
- 1 **tablespoon lemon juice**
- ½ **pound thick-sliced deli smoked turkey, cut into bite-size pieces**
- 1 **cup quartered fresh strawberries**
- 1 **celery rib, sliced**
- ¼ **cup toasted chopped walnuts, optional**

1. Cook the pasta according to the package directions. Drain; rinse with cold water and drain well.

2. Meanwhile, in a small bowl, mix yogurt, mayonnaise, milk, Dijon mustard and, if desired, thyme until blended. Toss apple with lemon juice.

3. In a large bowl, combine the pasta, apple, deli turkey, strawberries and celery. Add dressing; toss gently to coat. If desired, sprinkle with walnuts. Refrigerate until serving.

PER SERVING *1½ cups (calculated without walnuts) equals 313 cal., 8 g fat (1 g sat. fat), 24 mg chol., 606 mg sodium, 42 g carb., 3 g fiber, 19 g pro.* **Diabetic Exchanges:** *2 starch, 2 lean meat, 1 fat, ½ fruit.*

SUMMER MACARONI SALAD

Wendy's Apple Pomegranate Salad

My grandparents grew pomegranates, pecans and walnuts. Some of my best memories are the days I spent with my grandmother learning how to cook. Whenever I make this recipe, it's like having lunch with her all over again.
—**WENDY BALL** BATTLE CREEK, MI

START TO FINISH: 20 MIN. • **MAKES:** 8 SERVINGS

- 1 **bunch romaine, torn (about 8 cups)**
- ½ **cup pomegranate seeds**
- ½ **cup chopped pecans or walnuts, toasted**
- ½ **cup shredded Parmesan cheese**
- 1 **large Granny Smith apple, chopped**
- 1 **tablespoon lemon juice**
- ¼ **cup olive oil**
- ¼ **cup white wine vinegar**
- 2 **tablespoons sugar**
- ¼ **teaspoon salt**

1. In a large bowl, combine romaine, pomegranate seeds, pecans and Parmesan cheese. Toss apple with lemon juice and add to salad.

2. In a small bowl, whisk the remaining ingredients until blended. Drizzle the dressing over the salad; toss to coat. Serve immediately.

NOTE *To toast nuts, bake in a shallow pan in a 350° oven for 5-10 minutes or cook in a skillet over low heat until lightly browned, stirring occasionally.*

PER SERVING *1 cup equals 165 cal., 13 g fat (2 g sat. fat), 4 mg chol., 163 mg sodium, 10 g carb., 2 g fiber, 3 g pro.*
Diabetic Exchanges: *2½ fat, 1 vegetable.*

WENDY'S APPLE POMEGRANATE SALAD

VEGGIE LOVERS COMBO SALAD

Top your Veggie Lovers Combo Salad with nuts, sesame seeds or bacon.
—**MARIANNE TAYLOR** SOUTH HADLEY, MA

Veggie Lovers Combo Salad

START TO FINISH: 25 MIN. • **MAKES:** 10 SERVINGS

- 2 **cups cut fresh green beans or wax beans (1 inch)**
- 2 **cups fresh or frozen peas, thawed**
- 2 **medium sweet red or yellow peppers, chopped**
- 2 **plum tomatoes, chopped**
- ½ **cup finely chopped red onion**
- 1 **cup mayonnaise**
- ¾ **cup loosely packed fresh basil or Italian parsley leaves**
- 2 **tablespoons red wine vinegar**
- 1 **garlic clove, quartered**
  Optional toppings: chopped cashews, chopped pecans, toasted sesame seeds and cooked and crumbled bacon

1. In a saucepan, bring 4 cups water to a boil. Add beans; cook, uncovered, 2-3 minutes or just until crisp-tender. Remove the beans and immediately drop into ice water. Drain beans and pat dry; place in a large bowl. Add the remaining vegetables.

2. Place mayonnaise, basil, vinegar and garlic in a food processor; process until blended. Add to vegetables; toss to coat. Refrigerate, covered, at least 1 hour before serving. Just before serving, sprinkle with toppings as desired.

PER SERVING *¾ cup equals 204 cal., 18 g fat (2 g sat. fat), 8 mg chol., 125 mg sodium, 9 g carb., 3 g fiber, 2 g pro.*

VEGGIE CHOPPED SALAD

Watermelon & Spinach Salad

Celebrate the delights of summer with a combo of melons, spinach and more.

—**MARJORIE AU** HONOLULU, HI

START TO FINISH: 30 MIN.
MAKES: 8 SERVINGS

- ¼ cup rice vinegar or white wine vinegar
- 1 tablespoon grated lime peel
- 2 tablespoons lime juice
- 2 tablespoons canola oil
- 4 teaspoons minced fresh gingerroot
- 2 garlic cloves, minced
- ½ teaspoon salt
- ¼ teaspoon sugar
- ¼ teaspoon pepper

SALAD

- 4 cups fresh baby spinach or arugula
- 3 cups cubed seedless watermelon
- 2 cups cubed cantaloupe
- 2 cups cubed English cucumber
- ½ cup chopped fresh cilantro
- 2 green onions, chopped

In a small bowl, whisk the first nine ingredients. In a large bowl, combine the salad ingredients. Drizzle with the salad dressing and toss to coat; serve immediately.

PER SERVING *1 cup equals 84 cal., 4 g fat (trace sat. fat), 0 chol., 288 mg sodium, 13 g carb., 1 g fiber, 1 g pro.* **Diabetic Exchanges:** *1 vegetable, 1 fat, ½ fruit.*

Veggie Chopped Salad

My husband's aunt gave me this recipe 30 years ago, and it's been a staple at our house ever since. I like to do the prep work a day in advance because a little time in the fridge makes the flavor even better.

—**MADELINE ETZKORN** BURIEN, WA

START TO FINISH: 25 MIN.
MAKES: 12 SERVINGS

- 3 cups finely chopped fresh broccoli
- 3 cups finely chopped cauliflower
- 3 cups finely chopped celery
- 2 cups frozen peas (about 8 ounces), thawed
- 6 bacon strips, cooked and crumbled
- 1⅓ cups mayonnaise
- ¼ cup sugar
- 2 tablespoons grated Parmesan cheese
- 1 tablespoon cider vinegar
- ¼ teaspoon salt
- ¾ cup salted peanuts

1. In a large bowl, combine the first five ingredients. In a small bowl, mix mayonnaise, sugar, Parmesan cheese, cider vinegar and salt until blended. Add to the salad and toss to coat.

2. Just before serving, stir in peanuts. Refrigerate leftovers.

PER SERVING *¾ cup equals 308 cal., 26 g fat (4 g sat. fat), 14 mg chol., 357 mg sodium, 12 g carb., 3 g fiber, 7 g pro.*

Low-Fat Tangy Tomato Dressing

This zesty blend is delicious over greens, pasta or fresh garden vegetables. I love that it's a healthier alternative to the oil-heavy versions sold in stores.

—**SARAH EIDEN** ENID, OK

START TO FINISH: 5 MIN.
MAKES: 2 CUPS

- 1 can (14½ ounces) no-salt-added diced tomatoes, undrained
- 1 envelope Italian salad dressing mix
- 1 tablespoon cider vinegar
- 1 tablespoon olive oil

Place all ingredients in a blender; cover and process until blended.

PER SERVING *2 tablespoons equals 15 cal., 1 g fat (trace sat. fat), 0 chol., 170 mg sodium, 2 g carb., trace fiber, trace pro.* **Diabetic Exchange:** *Free food.*

WATERMELON & SPINACH SALAD

Orange-Wild Rice Salad with Smoked Turkey

For picnics and potlucks, we toss together turkey, rice, celery and fruit. Everyone says the cold salad tastes refreshing and light.
—**SHARON TIPTON** CASSELBERRY, FL

PREP: 5 MIN. + COOLING • **COOK:** 50 MIN.
MAKES: 4 SERVINGS

- 1 **cup uncooked wild rice**
- ½ **pound deli smoked turkey, cubed (about 1¾ cups)**
- 1 **cup orange sections**
- 1 **celery rib, chopped**
- ⅓ **cup dried cherries**

DRESSING

- 6 **tablespoons orange juice**
- 2 **tablespoons lemon juice**
- 1 **tablespoon Dijon mustard**
- 1½ **teaspoons olive oil**
- ¼ **teaspoon salt**
- ¼ **teaspoon freshly ground pepper**

1. Cook the wild rice according to the package directions. Transfer to a large bowl; cool completely.

2. Add the turkey, oranges, celery and cherries to cooled rice. In a small bowl, whisk dressing ingredients. Pour over the salad; toss to coat. Refrigerate, covered, until cold.
PER SERVING *1¼ cups equals 303 cal., 3 g fat (trace sat. fat), 20 mg chol., 678 mg sodium, 50 g carb., 4 g fiber, 19 g pro.*

Wedge Salad with Blue Cheese Dressing

Here's a special treatment for wedges of iceburg lettuce. The dressing also makes a great dip for Buffalo wings.
—**JENN SMITH** RUMFORD, RI

START TO FINISH: 20 MIN.
MAKES: 6 SERVINGS

- ⅔ **cup crumbled blue cheese**
- ⅔ **cup mayonnaise**
- ⅓ **cup reduced-fat sour cream**
- 2 **teaspoons water**
- 1½ **teaspoons red wine vinegar**
- ⅛ **teaspoon Worcestershire sauce**
  Dash cayenne pepper
- 1 **large head iceberg lettuce**
- 2 **cups chopped assorted tomatoes**
- 6 **bacon strips, cooked and crumbled**

In a small bowl, mix the first seven ingredients. Cut the lettuce into six wedges. To serve, top wedges with dressing, tomatoes and bacon.
PER SERVING *1 serving equals 313 cal., 28 g fat (7 g sat. fat), 33 mg chol., 473 mg sodium, 6 g carb., 2 g fiber, 8 g pro.*

DID YOU KNOW?

You can store wild rice in an airtight container indefinitely. Always rinse it before cooking. Wild rice may become tender without absorbing all the cooking liquid. If necessary, drain it before serving or combining with other ingredients. Leftover wild rice freezes well; defrost and reheat it in the microwave for use in recipes or as a fuss-free side dish.

PAULA HOMER'S
BBQ BACON BURGER *PAGE 43*

Soups & Sandwiches

What a **comforting combination**—a piping hot bowl of homemade soup and a stacked-high sandwich. Page through this cozy chapter to enjoy plenty of **classic recipes and new favorites, too.**

MARION ST. JEAN'S HAM & CORN CHOWDER PAGE 41

MACEY ALLEN'S CREAMY EGGPLANT & MUSHROOM MONTE CRISTO PAGE 42

RENÉE GREENE MURPHY'S HEARTY BEEF & SWEET POTATO STEW PAGE 45

FAST FIX ▶

Chicken Tortellini Soup

Here's a hearty soup that takes advantage of cheese tortellini and rotisserie chicken.

—CHARLENE CHAMBERS
ORMOND BEACH, FL

START TO FINISH: 25 MIN.
MAKES: 8 SERVINGS (2 QUARTS)

- 1½ cups sliced fresh mushrooms
- 2 tablespoons butter
- 2 garlic cloves, minced
- 4 cans (14½ ounces each) reduced-sodium chicken broth
- 1 package (9 ounces) refrigerated cheese tortellini
- 4 cups shredded rotisserie chicken
- 1 package (6 ounces) fresh baby spinach, coarsely chopped
- ½ teaspoon pepper
- 8 teaspoons grated Parmesan cheese

1. In a Dutch oven, saute mushrooms in butter until tender. Add garlic; cook 1 minute longer.

2. Add the broth and bring to a boil. Stir in tortellini; return to a boil. Cook for 7-9 minutes or until tender, stirring occasionally. Add chicken, spinach and pepper; cook until spinach is wilted. Sprinkle each serving with 1 teaspoon Parmesan cheese.

PER SERVING *1 cup equals 287 cal., 12 g fat (5 g sat. fat), 90 mg chol., 1,130 mg sodium, 17 g carb., 1 g fiber, 27 g pro.*

Sausage & Pepper Sandwiches

We use a dark, malty lager for simmering these Italian sausages. Grill 'em, split 'em and load 'em on toasted buns with garlicky peppers and onions. Delicious!

—JEANNE HORN DULUTH, MN

PREP: 30 MIN. • **GRILL:** 5 MIN.
MAKES: 8 SERVINGS

- 2 bottles (12 ounces each) beer or nonalcoholic beer
- 2 tablespoons prepared mustard
- 1 tablespoon ketchup
- 8 fresh Italian sausage, bratwurst or Polish sausage links
- 1 large onion, thinly sliced

SAUSAGE & PEPPER SANDWICHES

- 1 tablespoon olive oil
- 1 medium sweet red pepper, coarsely chopped
- 1 medium green pepper, coarsely chopped
- 1 medium onion, chopped
- 1 garlic clove, minced
- 1 teaspoon Italian seasoning
- ½ teaspoon salt
- ¼ teaspoon pepper
- 8 hot dog buns, split
  Spicy brown mustard

1. In a 6-qt. stockpot, combine the beer, prepared mustard and ketchup. Add the sausages, sliced onion and, if necessary, water to cover. Bring to simmer and cook, uncovered, 10-12 minutes or until a thermometer inserted in sausage reads 160°.

2. Meanwhile, in a large skillet, heat the olive oil over medium heat. Add the peppers and chopped onion; cook and stir 6-8 minutes or until tender. Stir in the garlic and seasonings; cook 30 seconds longer. Remove from heat.

3. Remove the sausages from beer mixture. Grill the sausages, covered, over medium heat or broil 4 in. from heat 1-2 minutes on each side or until lightly browned. Cut each sausage lengthwise in half. Serve in hot dog buns with the pepper mixture and brown mustard.

PER SERVING *1 sandwich with ¼ cup pepper mixture (calculated without brown mustard) equals 442 cal., 26 g fat (10 g sat. fat), 60 mg chol., 1,137 mg sodium, 31 g carb., 2 g fiber, 20 g pro.*

Mini Rosemary-Roast Beef Sandwiches

PREP: 25 MIN. + CHILLING
BAKE: 50 MIN. + CHILLING
MAKES: 2 DOZEN

- 1 beef top round roast (3 pounds)
- 3 teaspoons kosher salt
- 2 teaspoons crushed dried rosemary
- 2 tablespoons olive oil, divided
- 2 teaspoons pepper
- 2 cups mild giardiniera, drained
- 1 cup reduced-fat mayonnaise
- 2 tablespoons stone-ground mustard
- 1 to 2 tablespoons prepared horseradish
- 24 Hawaiian sweet rolls, split

1. Sprinkle the beef roast with salt and rosemary; wrap tightly in plastic wrap. Refrigerate at least 8 hours or up to 24 hours.

2. Preheat oven to 325°. Unwrap beef roast and pat dry. Rub the roast with 1 tablespoon oil; sprinkle with pepper. In a large ovenproof skillet, heat the remaining oil over medium-high heat. Brown roast on both sides.

3. Transfer the beef roast to the oven; roast 50-60 minutes or until a thermometer reads 135° for medium-rare. (The temperature of the roast will continue to rise about 10° upon standing.) Remove roast from skillet; let stand 1 hour. Refrigerate, covered, at least 2 hours or until cold.

4. Place the drained giardiniera in a food processor; pulse until finely chopped. In a small bowl, mix the mayonnaise, stone-ground mustard and horseradish.

5. To serve, thinly slice cold beef. Serve on rolls with the mayonnaise mixture and giardiniera.
PER SERVING *1 mini sandwich equals 220 cal., 9 g fat (3 g sat. fat), 50 mg chol., 466 mg sodium, 18 g carb., 1 g fiber, 17 g pro.*

Tomato-Orange Soup

Who knew orange and tomato were such a good pair? Whenever I serve this to new people, I keep copies of the recipe handy.
—**BARBARA WOOD** ST. JOHN'S, NL

PREP: 30 MIN. • **COOK:** 1 HOUR
MAKES: 6 SERVINGS

- 3 pounds medium tomatoes (about 12), halved
- 2 tablespoons canola oil, divided
- 2 medium onions, chopped
- 2 garlic cloves, minced
- 3 cups reduced-sodium chicken broth
- 1 cup orange juice
- 2 tablespoons tomato paste
- 4 teaspoons grated orange peel
- 1 tablespoon butter
- 1 tablespoon minced fresh cilantro
- 1 tablespoon honey
- ¼ teaspoon salt

1. Preheat oven to 450°. Place the tomatoes in a 15x10x1-in. baking pan, cut side down; brush tops with 1 tablespoon oil. Roast 20-25 minutes or until the skins are blistered and charred. Remove and discard skins.

2. In a 6-qt. stockpot, heat remaining oil over medium-high heat. Add the onions; cook and stir until tender. Add the garlic; cook 1 minute longer. Stir in the chicken broth, orange juice, tomato paste and roasted tomatoes; bring to a boil. Reduce heat; simmer, uncovered, 45 minutes.

3. Stir in orange peel, butter, cilantro, honey and salt. Remove from the heat; cool slightly. Process soup in batches in a blender until smooth. Return to the pot; heat through.
PER SERVING *1 cup equals 160 cal., 7 g fat (2 g sat. fat), 5 mg chol., 419 mg sodium, 22 g carb., 4 g fiber, 5 g pro. Diabetic Exchanges: 2 vegetable, 1½ fat, ½ starch.*

TOMATO-ORANGE SOUP

MUSHROOM-BEAN BOURGUIGNON

EAT SMART

Mushroom-Bean Bourguignon

Classic boeuf bourguignon is a tradition in our family. Here's my meatless version.
—**SONYA LABBE** WEST HOLLYWOOD, CA

PREP: 15 MIN. • **COOK:** 1¼ HOURS
MAKES: 10 SERVINGS (2½ QUARTS)

- **4 tablespoons olive oil, divided**
- **5 medium carrots, cut into 1-inch pieces**
- **2 medium onions, halved and sliced**
- **2 garlic cloves, minced**
- **8 large portobello mushrooms, cut into 1-inch pieces**
- **1 tablespoon tomato paste**
- **1 bottle (750 milliliters) dry red wine**
- **2 cups mushroom broth or vegetable broth, divided**
- **1 teaspoon salt**
- **1 teaspoon minced fresh thyme or ½ teaspoon dried thyme**
- **½ teaspoon pepper**
- **2 cans (15½ ounces each) navy beans, rinsed and drained**
- **1 package (14.4 ounces) frozen pearl onions**
- **3 tablespoons all-purpose flour**

1. In a Dutch oven, heat 2 tablespoons olive oil over medium-high heat. Add the carrots and onions; cook and stir 8-10 minutes or until the onions are tender. Add the garlic; cook 1 minute longer. Remove from pan.

2. In the same pan, heat 1 tablespoon oil over medium-high heat. Add half of the portobello mushrooms; cook and stir until lightly browned. Remove from pan; repeat with remaining oil and mushrooms.

3. Return the mushrooms to the pan. Add the tomato paste; cook and stir 1 minute. Stir in the wine, 1½ cups broth, salt, thyme, pepper and carrot mixture; bring to a boil. Reduce heat; simmer, covered, 25 minutes.

4. Add beans and pearl onions; cook 30 minutes longer. In a small bowl, whisk flour and remaining broth until smooth; stir into pan. Bring to a boil; cook and stir for 2 minutes or until slightly thickened.

PER SERVING *1 cup equals 234 cal., 6 g fat (1 g sat. fat), 0 chol., 613 mg sodium, 33 g carb., 7 g fiber, 9 g pro.* **Diabetic Exchanges:** *2 starch, 2 vegetable, 1 lean meat, 1 fat.*

New Orleans-Style Subs

The chopped olive spread makes this muffuletta-style sub, loaded with deli meat and cheese, a New Orleans classic.
—**SHANNON LEE DENNEY** MILWAUKEE, WI

PREP: 30 MIN. • **BROIL:** 5 MIN.
MAKES: 12 SERVINGS

- **1⅓ cups giardiniera**
- **⅔ cup chopped pitted green olives**
- **⅔ cup pitted ripe olives**
- **2 loaves (1 pound each) unsliced French bread**
- **¼ cup fat-free Italian salad dressing**
- **½ pound thinly sliced deli ham**
- **½ pound thinly sliced deli turkey**
- **½ pound sliced reduced-fat provolone cheese**
- **½ pound thinly sliced deli roast beef**
- **½ pound sliced reduced-fat Colby-Monterey Jack cheese**
- **2 medium tomatoes, sliced**
- **2 cups shredded lettuce**
- **1 large red onion, thinly sliced and separated into rings**

1. Place the giardiniera and olives in a food processor; cover and process until coarsely chopped. Set aside.

2. Cut the bread in half lengthwise; carefully hollow out top and bottom of loaves, leaving ½-in. shells (discard the removed bread or save for another use). Place on two large baking sheets. Broil 4-6 in. from heat for 3-4 minutes or until toasted.

3. Brush bottom halves with dressing; layer with ham, turkey and provolone cheese. Spread top halves with olive mixture; layer with roast beef and Colby-Monterey Jack cheese.

4. Broil 2-3 minutes longer or until the cheese is melted. Layer bottom halves with the tomatoes, lettuce and onion; replace the tops. Cut each loaf into six slices.

PER SERVING *1 slice equals 336 cal., 11 g fat (5 g sat. fat), 46 mg chol., 1,368 mg sodium, 32 g carb., 2 g fiber, 27 g pro.*

Comforting Beef Barley Soup

When the weather gets chilly in fall and winter, we find ourselves craving a bowl of soup full of beef, barley and vegetables. It's a delicious way to warm up!

—SUE JURACK MEQUON, WI

PREP: 10 MIN. • **COOK:** 35 MIN.
MAKES: 8 SERVINGS (3 QUARTS)

- 1 tablespoon butter
- ½ cup each chopped carrot, celery and onion
- 4 cups beef broth
- 4 cups water
- 1 can (14½ ounces) diced tomatoes, undrained
- 1 cup quick-cooking barley
- ½ teaspoon dried basil
- ½ teaspoon dried oregano
- ½ teaspoon pepper
- ¼ teaspoon salt
- 2 cups chopped cooked roast beef
- ½ cup frozen peas

1. In a 6-qt. stockpot, heat butter over medium-high heat. Add carrot, celery and onion; cook and stir 4-5 minutes or until tender.

2. Add broth, water, tomatoes, barley and seasonings; bring to a boil. Reduce heat; simmer, covered, 20 minutes, stirring occasionally. Add roast beef and peas; cook 5-7 minutes longer or until heated through.

PER SERVING 1½ cups equals 198 cal., 4 g fat (2 g sat. fat), 36 mg chol., 652 mg sodium, 23 g carb., 6 g fiber, 18 g pro. **Diabetic Exchanges:** 2 lean meat, 1½ starch, ½ fat.

COMFORTING BEEF BARLEY SOUP

GRILLED ITALIAN TURKEY BURGERS

Grilled Italian Turkey Burgers

These turkey patties are awesome at a cookout, especially if you're trying to eat healthier. For an extra flavor boost, top the burgers with marinara or steak sauce.

—DARLA ANDREWS LEWISVILLE, TX

START TO FINISH: 30 MIN.
MAKES: 4 SERVINGS

- ½ pound sliced baby portobello mushrooms
- 2 cups chopped fresh spinach

BURGERS

- 2 egg whites, lightly beaten
- ½ cup panko (Japanese) bread crumbs
- 2 tablespoons minced fresh parsley
- 2 tablespoons ketchup
- 1 tablespoon brown sugar
- 1 tablespoon Worcestershire sauce
- 2 teaspoons paprika
- 2 teaspoons prepared pesto
- ½ teaspoon garlic powder
- 1 pound lean ground turkey

- 4 slices reduced-fat provolone cheese
- 4 whole wheat hamburger buns, split

1. Place a large nonstick skillet coated with cooking spray over medium-high heat. Add portobello mushrooms; cook and stir 3-4 minutes or until tender. Add the spinach; cook and stir just until wilted.

2. In a large bowl, combine the first nine burger ingredients. Add ground turkey; mix lightly but thoroughly. Shape into four ½-in.-thick patties.

3. Moisten a paper towel with cooking oil; using long-handled tongs, rub on the grill rack to coat lightly. Grill the burgers, covered, over medium heat 4-6 minutes on each side or until a thermometer reads 165°.

4. Top with provolone cheese; grill, covered, 1-2 minutes longer or until cheese is melted. Serve on buns with mushroom mixture.

PER SERVING 1 burger equals 423 cal., 16 g fat (5 g sat. fat), 88 mg chol., 663 mg sodium, 37 g carb., 5 g fiber, 36 g pro. **Diabetic Exchanges:** 4 lean meat, 2 starch, 1 vegetable, 1 fat.

Chili Cook-Off

Let the competition begin! See how these chili recipes rate against ones you've tried. You may just discover a **new favorite for your family.**

MARTY'S BEAN BURGER CHILI

White Turkey Chili

Cut the fat and calories while savoring all the comfort, heartiness and flavor you love. This recipe makes it easy!

—TINA BARRETT HOUSTON, TX

PREP: 10 MIN. • **COOK:** 35 MIN. • **MAKES:** 6 SERVINGS

- 2 cans (15 ounces each) **white kidney or cannellini beans, rinsed and drained**
- 1 can (10¾ ounces) **reduced-fat reduced-sodium condensed cream of chicken soup, undiluted**
- 2 cups **cubed cooked turkey breast**
- 1⅓ cups **fat-free milk**
- 1 can (4 ounces) **chopped green chilies, drained**
- 1 tablespoon **minced fresh cilantro**
- 1 tablespoon **dried minced onion**
- 1 teaspoon **garlic powder**
- 1 teaspoon **ground cumin**
- 1 teaspoon **dried oregano**
- 6 tablespoons **fat-free sour cream**

In a large saucepan, combine the first 10 ingredients; bring to a boil, stirring occasionally. Reduce heat; simmer, covered, 25-30 minutes or until heated through. Top servings with sour cream.

PER SERVING *1 cup with 1 tablespoon sour cream equals 250 cal., 2 g fat (1 g sat. fat), 47 mg chol., 510 mg sodium, 31 g carb., 6 g fiber, 23 g pro.* **Diabetic Exchanges:** *3 lean meat, 2 starch.*

WHITE TURKEY CHILI

Marty's Bean Burger Chili

I met my husband while working the dinner shift at a homeless shelter, where his zesty meal-in-a-bowl was often on the menu.

—MRS. MARTY NICKERSON ELLINGTON, CT

PREP: 15 MIN. • **COOK:** 7 HOURS • **MAKES:** 6 SERVINGS

- 2 cans (14½ ounces each) **no-salt-added diced tomatoes, drained**
- 1 can (16 ounces) **kidney beans, undrained**
- 1 can (15 ounces) **black beans, undrained**
- 1 can (15 ounces) **garbanzo beans or chickpeas, rinsed and drained**
- 1 can (14½ ounces) **diced tomatoes, drained**
- 4 **frozen spicy black bean veggie burgers, thawed and coarsely chopped**
- 1 **large onion, finely chopped**
- 1 **large sweet red or green pepper, chopped**
- 2 tablespoons **chili powder**
- 1 tablespoon **Worcestershire sauce**
- 3 teaspoons **dried basil**
- 3 teaspoons **dried oregano**
- 2 teaspoons **hot pepper sauce**
- 2 **garlic cloves, minced**

Place all ingredients in a 5- or 6-qt. slow cooker; stir to combine. Cook, covered, on low 7-9 hours to allow the flavors to blend.

PER SERVING *1½ cups equals 348 cal., 6 g fat (trace sat. fat), 0 chol., 1,151 mg sodium, 58 g carb., 19 g fiber, 21 g pro.*

Black Bean-Tomato Chili

PREP: 10 MIN. • **COOK:** 35 MIN. • **MAKES:** 6 SERVINGS (2¼ QUARTS)

- 2 tablespoons olive oil
- 1 large onion, chopped
- 1 medium green pepper, chopped
- 3 garlic cloves, minced
- 1 teaspoon ground cinnamon
- 1 teaspoon ground cumin
- 1 teaspoon chili powder
- ¼ teaspoon pepper
- 3 cans (14½ ounces each) diced tomatoes, undrained
- 2 cans (15 ounces each) black beans, rinsed and drained
- 1 cup orange juice or juice from 3 medium oranges

1. In a Dutch oven, heat oil over medium-high heat. Add the onion and green pepper; cook and stir 8-10 minutes or until tender. Add the garlic, cinnamon, cumin, chili powder and pepper; cook 1 minute longer.

2. Stir in the remaining ingredients; bring to a boil. Reduce heat; simmer, covered, 20-25 minutes to allow the flavors to blend, stirring occasionally.

PER SERVING *1½ cups equals 232 cal., 5 g fat (1 g sat. fat), 0 chol., 608 mg sodium, 39 g carb., 10 g fiber, 9 g pro.* **Diabetic** *Exchanges: 2 vegetable, 1½ starch, 1 lean meat, 1 fat.*

My daughter called me about an idea she saw on a cooking show. We had fun experimenting in the kitchen and came up with Black Bean-Tomato Chili.

—LISA BELCASTRO VINEYARD HAVEN, MA

BLACK BEAN-TOMATO CHILI

GREEN CHILI GRILLED CHEESE MELT

If you like a bit more heat, just substitute 4 ounces of jalapenos for the chilies in Green Chili Grilled Cheese Melt. Either way, my daughter and I think it's a masterpiece!

—**JULIA HUNTINGTON** CHEYENNE, WY

FAST FIX ▸

Green Chili Grilled Cheese Melt

START TO FINISH: 25 MIN.
MAKES: 6 SERVINGS

- 4 **ounces cream cheese, softened**
- 1 **cup (4 ounces) shredded Colby-Monterey Jack cheese**
- 1 **cup (4 ounces) shredded part-skim mozzarella cheese**
- 1 **can (4 ounces) chopped green chilies, drained**
- 2 **tablespoons mayonnaise**
- ¼ **teaspoon garlic powder**
  Dash seasoned salt
- 12 **slices white bread**
- 6 **slices tomato**
- ¼ **cup butter, melted**

1. In a small bowl, mix the first seven ingredients until blended. Spread over half of the bread slices. Top with the tomato and remaining bread.
2. Brush the outsides of sandwiches with the melted butter. In a large skillet, toast the sandwiches in batches over medium-low heat 3-4 minutes on each side or until golden brown and heated through.
PER SERVING *1 sandwich equals 431 cal., 29 g fat (15 g sat. fat), 70 mg chol., 730 mg sodium, 29 g carb., 2 g fiber, 15 g pro.*

FAST FIX ▸

Golden Gouda Mushroom Soup

Here's a wonderful choice as a formal first course for a holiday dinner. With smoked Gouda, sherry and spices, every spoonful seems to taste better than the last.
—**CHARLOTTE ROGERS** VIRGINIA BEACH, VA

START TO FINISH: 30 MIN.
MAKES: 6 SERVINGS

- ½ **cup butter, cubed**
- ½ **cup all-purpose flour**
- ½ **teaspoon pepper**
- ½ **teaspoon ground allspice**
- 1 **carton (32 ounces) chicken broth**
- ½ **cup sherry or additional chicken broth**
- ½ **cup heavy whipping cream**
- ½ **pound sliced fresh mushrooms**
- 4 **garlic cloves, minced**
- 2 **cups (8 ounces) shredded smoked Gouda cheese**
  Chives and smoked paprika

1. In a large saucepan, melt butter. Stir in the flour, pepper and allspice until smooth; gradually add the broth, sherry and cream. Bring to a boil. Add mushrooms and garlic. Reduce heat; cover and simmer for 5-6 minutes or until mushrooms are tender.
2. Add the cheese; cook and stir until melted. Garnish servings with chives and paprika.
PER SERVING *1 cup equals 412 cal., 33 g fat (21 g sat. fat), 114 mg chol., 1,082 mg sodium, 13 g carb., 1 g fiber, 13 g pro.*

FAST FIX ▸

Blue Plate Open-Faced Turkey Sandwich

This comforting turkey sandwich reminds me of old-time diners on the East Coast. Instead of using jarred gravy, I prepare my own as an extra treat.
—**CHRISTINE SCHWESTER** DIVIDE, CO

START TO FINISH: 25 MIN.
MAKES: 6 SERVINGS

- ⅓ **cup butter, cubed**
- 1 **small onion, chopped**
- ⅓ **cup all-purpose flour**
- 2 **teaspoons minced fresh parsley**
- ¼ **teaspoon pepper**
- ⅛ **teaspoon garlic powder**
- ⅛ **teaspoon dried thyme**
- 3 **cups reduced-sodium chicken broth**
- 1¼ **pounds sliced deli turkey**
- 12 **slices white bread**

1. In a large saucepan, heat butter over medium heat. Add onion; cook and stir 4-5 minutes or until tender. Stir in flour, parsley and seasonings until blended; gradually whisk in the chicken broth. Bring to a boil, stirring constantly; cook and stir 1-2 minutes or until slightly thickened.
2. Add the turkey, one slice at a time; heat through. Serve over bread.
PER SERVING *2 open-faced sandwiches equals 361 cal., 14 g fat (7 g sat. fat), 60 mg chol., 1,462 mg sodium, 33 g carb., 2 g fiber, 25 g pro.*

KALE & BEAN SOUP

EAT SMART
Kale & Bean Soup
Full of wholesome vegetables, this chunky soup soothes you body and soul.
—**BETH SOLLARS** DELRAY BEACH, FL

PREP: 20 MIN. • **COOK:** 70 MIN.
MAKES: 8 SERVINGS (2½ QUARTS)

- 2 medium onions, chopped
- 2 cups cubed peeled potatoes
- 1 tablespoon olive oil
- 4 garlic cloves, minced
- 1 bunch kale, trimmed and coarsely chopped
- 3½ cups vegetable broth
- 1 can (28 ounces) diced tomatoes, undrained
- 1½ cups water
- 1 teaspoon Italian seasoning
- 1 teaspoon paprika
- ½ teaspoon pepper
- 1 bay leaf
- 1 can (15 ounces) white kidney or cannellini beans, rinsed and drained

1. In a Dutch oven, saute onions and potatoes in oil until tender. Add garlic; cook 1 minute longer. Stir in kale, broth, tomatoes, water, seasoning, paprika, pepper and bay leaf. Bring to a boil. Reduce heat; cover and simmer for 50-60 minutes or until kale is tender.
2. Cool slightly. Discard the bay leaf. In a blender, process 3 cups soup until smooth. Return to the pan; add beans and heat through.
PER SERVING *1¼ cups equals 152 cal., 2 g fat (trace sat. fat), 0 chol.,*
622 mg sodium, 29 g carb., 6 g fiber, 5 g pro. **Diabetic Exchanges:** *2 vegetable, 1 starch, 1 lean meat.*

FAST FIX
Ham & Corn Chowder
Simmer up a home-style chowder loaded with chunks of ham, potatoes and corn.
—**MARION ST. JEAN** HOMOSASSA, FL

START TO FINISH: 25 MIN.
MAKES: 6 SERVINGS

- 1 can (10¾ ounces) reduced-fat reduced-sodium condensed cream of celery soup, undiluted
- 1½ cups fat-free milk
- 1 can (15¼ ounces) whole kernel corn, drained
- 1 can (14¾ ounces) cream-style corn
- ½ cup cubed fully cooked ham
- 2 tablespoons dried minced onion
- 2 tablespoons minced fresh parsley
- 1 can (14½ ounces) diced potatoes, drained
  Sour cream, shredded cheddar cheese and/or paprika, optional

1. In a large saucepan, combine the cream of celery soup and milk. Heat through, stirring frequently. Stir in the corn, ham, onion and parsley. Bring to a boil. Reduce heat; cover and simmer for 5 minutes.
2. Stir in the potatoes; heat through. Garnish with sour cream, cheddar cheese and/or paprika if desired.
PER SERVING *1 cup (calculated without garnishes) equals 202 cal., 3 g fat (1 g sat. fat), 9 mg chol., 909 mg sodium, 35 g carb., 3 g fiber, 8 g pro.*

HAM & CORN CHOWDER

Creamy Eggplant & Mushroom Monte Cristo

As a child, I wouldn't eat vegetables. As a parent, I try to figure out creative ways to sneak them onto my son's plate. I'm happy to say this toasted eggplant and mushroom sandwich was a hit!

—MACEY ALLEN GREEN FOREST, AR

START TO FINISH: 30 MIN.
MAKES: 4 SERVINGS

- 5 tablespoons olive oil, divided
- 6 slices eggplant (½ inch thick), halved
- 2½ cups sliced fresh shiitake or baby portobello mushrooms (about 6 ounces)
- 1 large garlic clove, minced
- ½ teaspoon salt
- ¼ teaspoon pepper
- 2 large eggs
- 2 tablespoons 2% milk
- ½ cup garlic-herb spreadable cheese (about 3 ounces)
- 8 slices wide-loaf white bread

1. In a large nonstick skillet, heat 1 tablespoon olive oil over medium heat. Add eggplant; cook 2-3 minutes on each side or until tender and lightly browned. Remove from pan.

2. In the same pan, heat 2 tablespoons olive oil over medium heat. Add the mushrooms; cook and stir 2-3 minutes or until tender. Add the garlic, salt and pepper; cook 1 minute longer. Remove from pan; wipe skillet clean.

3. In a shallow bowl, whisk eggs and milk until blended. Spread 1 tablespoon herb cheese over each slice of bread. Layer four slices with eggplant and mushrooms; top with remaining bread.

4. In same pan, heat 1 tablespoon oil over medium heat. Carefully dip both sides of the sandwiches in egg mixture, allowing each side to soak 5 seconds. Place two sandwiches in skillet; toast 2-3 minutes on each side or until golden brown. Repeat with remaining oil and sandwiches.

PER SERVING *1 sandwich equals 573 cal., 36 g fat (13 g sat. fat), 129 mg chol., 939 mg sodium, 52 g carb., 6 g fiber, 15 g pro.*

Warm Greek Chicken Wraps

When I prepared this recipe for one of my cooking classes, the students loved it.

—KIZMET BYRD
FORT WAYNE, IN

START TO FINISH: 20 MIN.
MAKES: 6 SERVINGS

- 2½ cups frozen grilled chicken breast strips
- 1 cup (4 ounces) crumbled feta cheese
- 1 small sweet red pepper, chopped
- ½ cup soft sun-dried tomato halves (not packed in oil), chopped
- ½ cup fat-free zesty Italian salad dressing
- ½ cup chopped ripe olives
- 2 cups fresh baby spinach
- 6 whole wheat tortillas (8 inches), warmed

1. Prepare chicken strips according to the package directions. Cut chicken into ½-in. pieces; place in a large bowl. Add feta cheese, red pepper, sun-dried tomatoes, Italian salad dressing and olives; toss to combine.

2. Place the spinach down the center of tortillas; top with chicken mixture. Roll up tightly and serve.

PER SERVING *1 wrap equals 291 cal., 9 g fat (3 g sat. fat), 50 mg chol., 977 mg sodium, 31 g carb., 5 g fiber, 18 g pro.*

WARM GREEK CHICKEN WRAPS

BBQ BACON BURGER

FAST FIX ▶
BBQ Bacon Burger

Every family seems to have a hamburger of choice. Here is ours! It's piled high with bacon and crunchy onion rings.

—PAULA HOMER NAMPA, ID

START TO FINISH: 30 MIN.
MAKES: 6 SERVINGS

- 12 frozen onion rings
- 2 pounds ground beef
- ¼ teaspoon garlic salt
- ¼ teaspoon pepper
- 6 slices pepper jack cheese
- 6 hamburger buns, split and toasted
- 1 cup barbecue sauce
- 6 cooked bacon strips
  Optional toppings: lettuce leaves, sliced tomato and dill pickles

1. Bake onion rings according to package directions. Meanwhile, in a large bowl, combine beef, garlic salt and pepper; mix lightly but thoroughly. Shape into six ¾-in.-thick patties.
2. In a large nonstick skillet, cook the burgers over medium heat 5-7 minutes on each side or until a thermometer reads 160°, adding the cheese during the last minute of cooking. Serve on hamburger buns with barbecue sauce, bacon, onion rings and toppings as desired.
PER SERVING *1 burger (calculated without optional toppings) equals 768 cal., 39 g fat (15 g sat. fat), 127 mg chol., 1,275 mg sodium, 60 g carb., 2 g fiber, 42 g pro.*

Favorite Hamburger Stew

A woman at our church introduced me to this satisfying supper when I needed a way to use up home-canned tomatoes. My husband raves about the meaty stew.

—MARCIA CLAY TRUMAN, MN

PREP: 20 MIN. • **COOK:** 65 MIN.
MAKES: ABOUT 5 BATCHES (15 CUPS TOTAL)

- 2 pounds ground beef
- 2 medium onions, chopped
- 4 cans (14½ ounces each) stewed tomatoes, undrained
- 8 medium carrots, thinly sliced
- 4 celery ribs, thinly sliced
- 2 medium potatoes, peeled and cubed
- 2 cups water
- ½ cup uncooked long grain rice
- 1 to 2 tablespoons salt
- 1 to 2 teaspoons pepper
  ADDITIONAL INGREDIENT (FOR EACH BATCH OF STEW)
- 1 cup water

1. In a Dutch oven, cook the beef and onions over medium heat until meat is no longer pink, breaking meat into crumbles; drain. Add the tomatoes, carrots, celery, potatoes, water, rice, salt and pepper; bring to a boil. Reduce heat; cover and simmer for 30 minutes or until vegetables and rice are tender.
2. Uncover; simmer 20-30 minutes longer or until thickened. Freeze in 3-cup portions for up to 3 months.
TO USE FROZEN STEW *Thaw in the refrigerator for 24 hours. Transfer to a saucepan; add water. Cook until hot and bubbly.*
PER SERVING *1 cup equals 165 cal., 6 g fat (2 g sat. fat), 30 mg chol., 584 mg sodium, 16 g carb., 2 g fiber, 12 g pro.*

EAT SMART **SLOW COOKER** 🍲

Spiced Split Pea Soup

A hint of curry adds the perfect amount of kick to this split pea soup. I just toss the ingredients into the slow cooker, switch it on and go about my day.

—SUE MOHRE MOUNT GILEAD, OH

PREP: 25 MIN. • **COOK:** 7 HOURS
MAKES: 10 SERVINGS (2½ QUARTS)

- 4 cups reduced-sodium chicken broth
- 1 cup dried green split peas
- 2 medium potatoes, chopped
- 2 medium carrots, halved and thinly sliced
- 1 medium onion, chopped
- 1 celery rib, thinly sliced
- 3 garlic cloves, minced
- 3 bay leaves
- 4 teaspoons curry powder
- 1 teaspoon ground cumin
- ½ teaspoon coarsely ground pepper
- ½ teaspoon ground coriander
- 1 can (28 ounces) diced tomatoes, undrained

In a 4-qt. slow cooker combine the first 12 ingredients. Cover; cook on low for 7-9 hours or until peas are tender. Add tomatoes; heat through. Discard bay leaves.

PER SERVING *1 cup equals 139 cal., trace fat (trace sat. fat), 0 chol., 347 mg sodium, 27 g carb., 8 g fiber, 8 g pro. Diabetic Exchanges: 1 starch, 1 lean meat, 1 vegetable.*

SPICED SPLIT PEA SOUP

ZUCCHINI PIZZA LOAVES

> Full of gooey cheese, zesty seasonings and turkey pepperoni, Zucchini Pizza Loaves will get even the picky eaters you know coming back for a second slice.
> **—TRISHA KRUSE** EAGLE, ID

Zucchini Pizza Loaves

PREP: 30 MIN. • **BAKE:** 30 MIN.
MAKES: 2 LOAVES (4 SERVINGS EACH)

- 2 medium zucchini, thinly sliced
- 1 medium onion, finely chopped
- 1 cup sliced fresh mushrooms
- 2 teaspoons olive oil
- 2 garlic cloves, minced
- 1 can (8 ounces) no-salt-added tomato sauce
- 1 medium tomato, seeded and chopped
- 1 can (2¼ ounces) sliced ripe olives, drained
- 2 teaspoons Italian seasoning
- 2 tubes (11 ounces each) refrigerated crusty French loaf
- 3 slices provolone cheese, chopped
- 1 ounce sliced turkey pepperoni, julienned
- 1 cup (4 ounces) shredded part-skim mozzarella cheese

1. In a large skillet, saute zucchini, onion, mushrooms in oil until tender. Add garlic; cook 1 minute longer. Stir in tomato sauce, tomato, olives and Italian seasoning; remove from heat.

2. Unroll one loaf of dough, starting at seam. Pat into a 14x12-in. rectangle. Sprinkle half of the provolone and pepperoni to within ½ in. of edges. Spread with half of zucchini mixture; sprinkle with half of the mozzarella.

3. Roll up jelly-roll style, starting with a long side; pinch seams to seal. Place seam side down on a baking sheet coated with cooking spray. Repeat with remaining dough, pepperoni, cheeses and zucchini mixture.

4. Bake at 350° for 30-35 minutes or until golden brown. Slice; serve warm.

PER SERVING *1 slice equals 322 cal., 10 g fat (5 g sat. fat), 20 mg chol., 801 mg sodium, 42 g carb., 3 g fiber, 15 g pro.*

Andouille-Shrimp Cream Soup

Inspired by southern Louisiana corn stew, this recipe features a flavorful combination of andouille sausage, shrimp and spices. It's a great taste of the South!

—JUDY ARMSTRONG PRAIRIEVILLE, LA

PREP: 20 MIN. • **COOK:** 30 MIN.
MAKES: 7 SERVINGS

- ½ pound fully cooked andouille sausage links, thinly sliced
- 1 medium onion, chopped
- 2 celery ribs, thinly sliced
- 1 medium sweet red pepper, chopped
- 1 medium green pepper, chopped
- 1 jalapeno pepper, seeded and chopped
- ¼ cup butter, cubed
- 3 garlic cloves, minced
- 2 cups fresh or frozen corn, thawed
- 4 plum tomatoes, chopped
- 1 cup vegetable broth
- 2 tablespoons minced fresh thyme or 2 teaspoons dried thyme
- 1 teaspoon chili powder
- ½ teaspoon salt
- ½ teaspoon pepper
- ¼ to ½ teaspoon cayenne pepper
- 1 pound uncooked medium shrimp, peeled and deveined
- 1 cup heavy whipping cream

1. In a large skillet, saute the first six ingredients in the butter until the vegetables are tender. Add the garlic; cook 1 minute longer.

2. Add the corn, plum tomatoes, vegetable broth, thyme, chili powder, salt, pepper and cayenne. Bring to a boil. Reduce heat; simmer, uncovered, for 10 minutes.

3. Stir in shrimp and heavy whipping cream. Bring to a gentle boil. Simmer, uncovered, for 8-10 minutes or until shrimp turn pink.

NOTE *Wear disposable gloves when cutting hot peppers; the oils can burn skin. Avoid touching your face.*

PER SERVING *1 cup equals 390 cal., 27 g fat (15 g sat. fat), 185 mg chol., 751 mg sodium, 20 g carb., 4 g fiber, 21 g pro.*

EAT SMART
Hearty Beef & Sweet Potato Stew

I have fond memories of learning to cook from my grandparents. Beef stew always reminds me of their delicious meals.

—RENÉE GREENE MURPHY SMITHTOWN, NY

PREP: 40 MIN. • **BAKE:** 2 HOURS
MAKES: 8 SERVINGS (2½ QUARTS)

- 3 tablespoons canola oil, divided
- 1½ pounds boneless beef chuck steak, cut into 1-inch pieces
- 2 medium onions, chopped
- 2 garlic cloves, minced
- 2 cans (14½ ounces each) reduced-sodium beef broth
- ⅓ cup dry red wine or additional reduced-sodium beef broth
- 1 tablespoon minced fresh thyme or 1 teaspoon dried thyme
- 1 tablespoon Worcestershire sauce
- 1 teaspoon salt
- ¾ teaspoon pepper
- 3 tablespoons cornstarch
- 3 tablespoons cold water
- 1¼ pounds sweet potatoes (about 2 medium), cut into 1-inch cubes
- 1 pound baby portobello mushrooms, halved
- 4 medium carrots, cut into ½-inch slices
- 2 medium parsnips, cut into ½-inch slices
- 1 medium turnip, cut into ¾-inch cubes

1. Preheat the oven to 325°. In an ovenproof Dutch oven, heat 2 tablespoons oil over medium-high heat. Brown beef in batches. Remove with a slotted spoon.

2. Add the remaining oil to pan. Add onions; cook and stir 2-3 minutes or until tender. Add garlic; cook 1 minute longer. Add broth and wine, stirring to remove browned bits from pan. Stir in thyme, Worcestershire sauce, salt and pepper. Return beef to pan; bring to a boil. Bake, covered, 1¼ hours.

3. In a small bowl, mix the cornstarch and cold water until smooth; gradually stir into stew. Add the sweet potatoes, baby portobello mushrooms, carrots, parsnips and turnip to the pan. Bake, covered, 45-60 minutes longer or until the beef and vegetables are tender. If desired, strain cooking juices; skim fat. Return cooking juices to Dutch oven.

PER SERVING *1¼ cups equals 354 cal., 14 g fat (4 g sat. fat), 57 mg chol., 586 mg sodium, 36 g carb., 6 g fiber, 22 g pro.* **Diabetic Exchanges:** *3 lean meat, 3 vegetable, 1 starch, 1 fat.*

HEARTY BEEF & SWEET POTATO STEW

LYNNE GERMAN'S SMOKY BAKED BEANS
PAGE 53

Side Dishes & Condiments

Complement any main course—from a holiday ham to burgers off the grill—with the amazing accompaniments here. You'll find pasta, veggies, rice and more to **round out every menu.**

SHELLY GRAVER'S GRILLED VEGGIES WITH MUSTARD VINAIGRETTE *PAGE 50*

CATHERINE CASSIDY'S GRANDMA'S CRANBERRY STUFF *PAGE 53*

REBEKAH CHAPPEL'S SWISS CHARD WITH ONIONS & GARLIC *PAGE 58*

Scalloped Portobello & Cauliflower

When you're bored with your usual side dishes, shake things up with cauliflower and portobello mushrooms. Add rolls and a light salad for a meatless meal.

—**DONNA NOEL** GRAY, ME

PREP: 35 MIN. • **BAKE:** 35 MIN.
MAKES: 8 SERVINGS

- 1 large head cauliflower, broken into florets (about 7 cups)
- 1 pound sliced baby portobello mushrooms
- ¾ cup water
- 6 tablespoons butter, divided
- 4 shallots, finely chopped
- ¼ cup all-purpose flour
- ½ teaspoon salt
- ¼ teaspoon paprika
- 1¼ cups half-and-half cream
- ¾ cup shredded white cheddar cheese
- ¼ cup panko (Japanese) bread crumbs

1. Preheat the oven to 350°. Place 1 in. of water and the cauliflower in a 6-qt. stockpot; bring to a boil. Cook, covered, 7-10 minutes or until tender. Drain.
2. In a large saucepan, combine the portobello mushrooms and water; bring to a boil. Reduce the heat; simmer, covered, 10 minutes. Drain portobello mushrooms, reserving ⅓ cup cooking liquid.
3. In the same saucepan, heat 3 tablespoons butter over medium heat until hot. Add the shallots and drained mushrooms; cook and stir until shallots are tender and lightly browned. Stir in flour, salt and paprika until blended; gradually stir in cream and reserved mushroom liquid. Bring to a boil, stirring constantly; cook and stir 2-3 minutes or until thickened.
4. Place the cauliflower in a greased 1½-qt. or 11x7-in. baking dish; cover with mushroom sauce. Sprinkle with cheese, then bread crumbs. Dot with remaining butter. Bake, uncovered, 35-40 minutes or until bubbly and golden brown.
PER SERVING ¾ cup equals 169 cal., 8 g fat (5 g sat. fat), 30 mg chol., 275 mg sodium, 17 g carb., 3 g fiber, 9 g pro.

Orzo-Lentil Rice

A versatile medley of small orzo pasta, lentils, rice and more makes a perfect partner for grilled beef, pork—just about any main course you choose.

—**MISTY SCONDRAS** DALTON, PA

PREP: 15 MIN. • **COOK:** 40 MIN.
MAKES: 8 SERVINGS

- 1 small onion, chopped
- 1 celery rib, chopped
- ¼ cup finely chopped carrot
- ¼ cup finely chopped sweet red pepper
- 4 teaspoons butter
- 5 cups water
- ½ cup dried lentils, rinsed
- 1 teaspoon salt
- ½ teaspoon ground cumin
- ¼ teaspoon dried rosemary, crushed
- ¼ teaspoon dried thyme
- ¼ teaspoon rubbed sage
- ¼ teaspoon pepper
- 1 cup uncooked orzo pasta
- 1 cup uncooked long grain rice

1. In a large saucepan, saute the onion, celery, carrot and red pepper in butter until tender. Stir in the water, lentils and seasonings. Bring to a boil. Reduce heat; cover and simmer for 15 minutes.
2. Stir in pasta and rice. Bring to a boil; cover and cook 15-20 minutes longer or until the pasta and rice are tender.
PER SERVING ¾ cup equals 244 cal., 3 g fat (1 g sat. fat), 5 mg chol., 320 mg sodium, 46 g carb., 5 g fiber, 8 g pro.

ORZO-LENTIL RICE

I'm always looking for new recipes that would appeal to my husband, who's a real meat-and-potatoes guy. My Loaded Twice-Baked Potato Casserole mixes mashed spuds with bacon.
—**CYNTHIA GERKEN** NAPLES, FL

Loaded Twice-Baked Potato Casserole

PREP: 1½ HOURS • **BAKE:** 30 MIN.
MAKES: 8 SERVINGS

- 4 **large baking potatoes (about 3¼ pounds)**
- 1 **tablespoon olive oil**
- ¾ **teaspoon salt, divided**
- ¾ **teaspoon pepper, divided**
- ¼ **cup butter, cubed**
- ⅔ **cup heavy whipping cream**
- ¼ **cup sour cream**
- 2 **cups (8 ounces) shredded cheddar cheese, divided**
- 6 **bacon strips, cooked and crumbled, divided**
- 2 **green onions, divided**
  Additional sour cream, optional

1. Preheat oven to 375°. Scrub the potatoes; pierce several times with a fork. Brush with olive oil; sprinkle with ½ teaspoon salt and ¼ teaspoon pepper. Place in a foil-lined 15x10x1-in. baking pan; bake 1-1¼ hours or until tender. Cool slightly.
2. In a small saucepan, melt butter over medium heat. Whisk in cream and ¼ cup sour cream. Add 1½ cups cheese; stir until melted. Remove from heat; cover to keep warm.
3. When potatoes are cool enough to handle, cut each potato lengthwise in half. Scoop out pulp and place in a large bowl. Cut two potato skin shells into 1-in. pieces; save remaining skins for another use.
4. Mash pulp with the remaining salt and pepper. Stir in the cheese mixture, half of the bacon and 2 tablespoons

LOADED TWICE-BAKED POTATO CASSEROLE

green onion. Transfer to a greased 1½-qt. baking dish. Top with the cut-up potato skins. Sprinkle with remaining cheese and bacon.
5. Bake 30-35 minutes or until the casserole is heated through and lightly browned. Sprinkle with the remaining green onion. If desired, serve with additional sour cream.
PER SERVING *½ cup (calculated without additional sour cream) equals 367 cal., 27 g fat (16 g sat. fat), 84 mg chol., 458 mg sodium, 20 g carb., 2 g fiber, 12 g pro.*

⑤ INGREDIENTS
Simple Orange-Glazed Beets
In our house, we prefer our beets prepared simply—with a little butter, salt and an orange marmalade glaze.
—**MARY BETH JUNG** HENDERSONVILLE, NC

PREP: 10 MIN. • **COOK:** 30 MIN.
MAKES: 4 SERVINGS

- 1 **pound small fresh beets (about 4)**
- ⅓ **cup orange marmalade**
- 1 **tablespoon butter**
  Dash salt

1. Scrub the beets and trim the tops to 1 in. Place in a large saucepan; add water to cover. Bring to a boil. Reduce heat; simmer, covered, 25-30 minutes or until tender. Drain; cool slightly.
2. Peel and cut beets into ¼-in. slices. In the same pan, combine the orange marmalade, butter and salt; cook and stir over medium-low heat until blended. Add the beets; heat through, stirring to coat.
PER SERVING *½ cup equals 141 cal., 3 g fat (2 g sat. fat), 8 mg chol., 164 mg sodium, 29 g carb., 2 g fiber, 2 g pro.*

TOP TIP

When it comes to nutrition, taste and beautiful color, it's hard to beat a beet! Keep in mind that cutting a beet causes its deep red color to bleed, which can create stains that are difficult to remove from clothing, skin or other areas. When preparing beets for a recipe, protect your hands by wearing plastic gloves and cover your work surface.

GRILLED VEGGIES WITH MUSTARD VINAIGRETTE

EAT SMART

Grilled Veggies with Mustard Vinaigrette

Whenever friends are coming over for a cookout, I fire up the grill for this healthy and inviting side dish. It's great with just about any main course. The homemade honey-mustard vinaigrette adds flavor, but the vegetables shine through.

—SHELLY GRAVER LANSDALE, PA

PREP: 20 MIN. • **GRILL:** 15 MIN.
MAKES: 10 SERVINGS (¾ CUP EACH)

- ¼ cup red wine vinegar
- 1 tablespoon Dijon mustard
- 1 tablespoon honey
- ½ teaspoon salt
- ⅛ teaspoon pepper
- ¼ cup canola oil
- ¼ cup olive oil

VEGETABLES

- 2 large sweet onions
- 2 medium zucchini
- 2 yellow summer squash
- 2 large sweet red peppers, halved and seeded
- 1 bunch green onions, trimmed Cooking spray

1. In a small bowl, whisk the first five ingredients. Gradually whisk in oils until blended.

2. Peel and quarter each sweet onion, leaving root ends intact. Cut zucchini and yellow squash lengthwise into ½-in.-thick slices. Lightly spritz the onions, zucchini, yellow squash and remaining vegetables with cooking spray, turning to coat all sides.

3. Grill the sweet onions, covered, over medium heat 15-20 minutes until tender, turning occasionally. Grill the zucchini, squash and peppers, covered, over medium heat 10-15 minutes or until crisp-tender and lightly charred, turning once. Grill the green onions, covered, 2-4 minutes or until lightly charred, turning once.

4. Cut the vegetables into bite-size pieces; place in a large bowl. Add ½ cup vinaigrette and toss to coat. Serve with remaining vinaigrette.

PER SERVING *¾ cup equals 155 cal., 12 g fat (1 g sat. fat), 0 chol., 166 mg sodium, 13 g carb., 2 g fiber, 2 g pro.* **Diabetic Exchanges:** *2½ fat, 1 vegetable, ½ starch.*

EAT SMART

Oven-Roasted Spiced Carrots

I fixed carrots this way for dinner, and my kids wanted to eat every piece on the plate. They didn't care that it was a veggie!

—JOAN DUCKWORTH LEE'S SUMMIT, MO

PREP: 15 MIN. • **BAKE:** 25 MIN.
MAKES: 8 SERVINGS

- 2 pounds medium carrots, cut into 2-inch pieces
- 3 tablespoons olive oil
- ½ teaspoon salt
- ½ teaspoon ground coriander
- ½ teaspoon ground cumin
- ½ teaspoon pepper
- ¼ teaspoon chili powder
- ¼ teaspoon paprika
- ⅛ teaspoon ground ginger
- ⅛ teaspoon ground cinnamon
  Dash ground cloves
  Dash cayenne pepper

1. Preheat oven to 400°. In a large bowl, toss the carrots with olive oil. Mix seasonings; sprinkle over carrots and toss to coat.

2. Arrange the carrots in a single layer in a 15x10x1-in. baking pan coated with cooking spray. Roast 25-30 minutes or until lightly browned and crisp-tender, stirring occasionally.

PER SERVING *¾ cup equals 93 cal., 5 g fat (1 g sat. fat), 0 chol., 228 mg sodium, 11 g carb., 3 g fiber, 1 g pro.* **Diabetic Exchanges:** *1 vegetable, 1 fat.*

OVEN-ROASTED SPICED CARROTS

LEMON-PARMESAN PASTA TOPPER

Roasted Brussels Sprouts with Cranberries & Almonds

If Brussels sprouts seem bitter to you, roast them to bring out their sweetness. We sprinkle on dried cranberries and toasted almonds as the finishing touch.

—**CLAUDIA LAMASCOLO** MELBOURNE, FL

PREP: 10 MIN. • **BAKE:** 30 MIN.
MAKES: 8 SERVINGS

- 3 **pounds fresh Brussels sprouts, trimmed and halved**
- ¼ **cup olive oil**
- ¾ **teaspoon salt**
- ¼ **teaspoon garlic powder**
- ¼ **teaspoon pepper**
- 1 **cup balsamic vinegar**
- ½ **cup sugar**
- 1 **cup dried cranberries**
- ½ **cup sliced almonds, toasted**

1. Preheat oven to 400°. In a large bowl, toss the Brussels sprouts with oil, salt, garlic powder and pepper. Transfer to a greased 15x10x1-in. baking pan. Roast 30-35 minutes or until tender, stirring occasionally.

2. In a small saucepan, combine the vinegar and sugar; bring to a boil, stirring to dissolve sugar. Reduce heat; simmer, uncovered, 15-20 minutes or until syrupy, stirring occasionally.

3. To serve, place sprouts in a serving dish; drizzle with glaze and toss to coat. Sprinkle with berries and almonds.

NOTE *To toast nuts, bake in a shallow pan in a 350° oven for 5-10 minutes or cook in a skillet over low heat until lightly browned, stirring occasionally.*

PER SERVING *¾ cup equals 284 cal., 10 g fat (1 g sat. fat), 0 chol., 260 mg sodium, 48 g carb., 7 g fiber, 6 g pro.*

(5) INGREDIENTS FAST FIX

Lemon-Parmesan Pasta Topper

Make extra batches of this quick blend to pass around the table on pasta night.

—**KAREN BERNER** NEW CANAAN, CT

START TO FINISH: 5 MIN.
MAKES: 1 SERVING

- 2 **tablespoons grated Parmesan cheese**
- 1 **tablespoon grated lemon peel**
- 2 **garlic cloves, minced**
  Hot cooked pasta
  Pasta sauce, optional

Toss Parmesan cheese with lemon peel and garlic. Sprinkle over pasta and, if desired, sauce.

PER SERVING *3 tablespoons equals 55 cal., 3 g fat (2 g sat. fat), 9 mg chol., 154 mg sodium, 3 g carb., 1 g fiber, 4 g pro.*

TOP TIP

I shake steamed Brussels sprouts in ¾ cup flour, ¼ cup grated Parmesan, and pepper to taste. I dunk them in beaten egg, then in the flour mixture again. After refrigerating for 1 hour, I fry them until golden. Delicious!

—**RUTH C.** GLENDALE HEIGHTS, IL

ROASTED BRUSSELS SPROUTS WITH CRANBERRIES & ALMONDS

Spicy Ketchup

When this zesty ketchup is bubbling on the stove, the aroma takes me back to my childhood. One taste and I'm home again.

—**KAREN NAIHE** KAMUELA, HI

PREP: 30 MIN.
COOK: 1½ HOURS + CHILLING
MAKES: 1 CUP

- 1 **tablespoon olive oil**
- 1 **medium onion, chopped**
- 3 **pounds tomatoes (about 11 medium), coarsely chopped**
- 1 **cinnamon stick (3 inches)**
- ¾ **teaspoon celery seed**
- ½ **teaspoon mustard seed**
- ¼ **teaspoon whole allspice**
- ⅓ **cup sugar**
- 1 **teaspoon salt**
- ¾ **cup red wine vinegar**
- 1½ **teaspoons smoked paprika**
- 1½ **teaspoons Sriracha Asian hot chili sauce, optional**

1. In a large saucepan, heat oil over medium-high heat. Add onion; cook and stir until tender. Stir in tomatoes; cook, uncovered, over medium heat 25-30 minutes or until tomatoes are softened.

2. Press the tomato mixture through a fine-mesh strainer; discard solids. Return mixture to pot; bring to a boil. Cook, uncovered, until the liquid is reduced to 1½ cups, about 10 minutes.

3. Place the cinnamon, celery seed, mustard seed and allspice on a double thickness of cheesecloth. Gather the corners of the cheesecloth to enclose the spices; tie securely with string. Add to the tomatoes. Stir in the sugar and salt; return to a boil. Reduce heat; simmer, uncovered, 20-25 minutes or until thickened.

4. Stir in the remaining ingredients; bring to a boil. Simmer, uncovered, 10-15 minutes longer or until desired consistency, stirring occasionally. Discard spice bag.

5. Transfer to a covered container; cool slightly. Refrigerate until cold. Store in refrigerator for up to 1 week.

PER SERVING *1 tablespoon equals 46 cal., 1 g fat (trace sat. fat), 0 chol., 152 mg sodium, 9 g carb., 1 g fiber, 1 g pro.* **Diabetic Exchange:** *½ starch.*

SWEET & WHITE SCALLOPED POTATOES

Sweet & White Scalloped Potatoes

I love sweet potatoes and scalloped potatoes. One day I was craving both, so I combined them. It's a nice option when you want to change up a special menu—or just indulge in comfort food.

—**YVONNE STARLIN** HERMITAGE, TN

PREP: 20 MIN. • **BAKE:** 45 MIN.
MAKES: 8 SERVINGS

- 3 **medium sweet potatoes, peeled and thinly sliced**
- 3 **medium russet potatoes, peeled and thinly sliced**
- 3½ **cups heavy whipping cream**
- 2 **tablespoons all-purpose flour**
- 4 **teaspoons minced fresh thyme**
- 3 **small garlic cloves, minced**
- 1 **teaspoon salt**
- ¼ **teaspoon pepper**

1. Arrange potatoes in a greased 13x9-in. baking dish. In a small saucepan, combine heavy whipping cream, flour, thyme, garlic, salt and pepper. Bring to a gentle boil. Remove from the heat; pour over potatoes.

2. Cover; bake at 400° for 20 minutes. Uncover; bake 25-30 minutes longer or until the potatoes are tender and the top is golden brown.

PER SERVING *1 cup equals 459 cal., 39 g fat (24 g sat. fat), 143 mg chol., 341 mg sodium, 26 g carb., 2 g fiber, 4 g pro.*

Smoky Baked Beans

They'll be standing in line for a scoop of these saucy baked beans full of campfire flavor. Keep the recipe in mind for just about any get-together, from a Fourth of July cookout in the backyard to a football party around the TV in fall.
—**LYNNE GERMAN** WOODLAND HILLS, CA

PREP: 25 MIN. • **COOK:** 7 HOURS
MAKES: 16 SERVINGS

- 1 pound bulk spicy pork sausage
- 1 medium onion, chopped
- 1 can (31 ounces) pork and beans
- 1 can (16 ounces) kidney beans, rinsed and drained
- 1 can (16 ounces) butter beans, rinsed and drained
- 1 can (15½ ounces) navy beans, rinsed and drained
- 1 can (15 ounces) black beans, rinsed and drained
- 1 can (10 ounces) diced tomatoes and green chilies, drained
- ½ cup hickory smoke-flavored barbecue sauce
- ½ cup ketchup
- ½ cup packed brown sugar
- 1 teaspoon ground mustard
- 1 teaspoon steak seasoning
- 1 teaspoon Liquid Smoke, optional

1. In a large skillet, cook sausage and onion over medium heat until meat is no longer pink, breaking meat into crumbles; drain.

2. In a 5-qt. slow cooker, combine the beans, tomatoes and sausage mixture. In a small bowl, combine the barbecue sauce, ketchup, brown sugar, mustard, steak seasoning and Liquid Smoke if desired. Stir into bean mixture.

3. Cover; cook on low for 7-8 hours or until heated through.

NOTE *This recipe was tested with McCormick's Montreal Steak Seasoning. Look for it in the spice aisle.*
PER SERVING *¾ cup equals 244 cal., 6 g fat (2 g sat. fat), 10 mg chol., 896 mg sodium, 39 g carb., 8 g fiber, 11 g pro.*

Grandma's Cranberry Stuff

START TO FINISH: 10 MIN.
MAKES: 3 CUPS

- 1 medium navel orange, unpeeled
- 1 package (12 ounces) fresh or frozen cranberries, thawed
- 1 cup sugar
- 1 cup chopped walnuts, toasted

Cut unpeeled orange into wedges, removing any seeds, and place in a food processor. Add cranberries and sugar; pulse until chopped. Add nuts; pulse just until combined.

NOTE *To toast nuts, bake in a shallow pan in a 350° oven for 5-10 minutes or cook in a skillet over low heat until lightly browned, stirring occasionally.*
PER SERVING *¼ cup equals 148 cal., 6 g fat (1 g sat. fat), 0 chol., 1 mg sodium, 23 g carb., 2 g fiber, 2 g pro.*

Cranberries have always been a must on Mom's Thanksgiving table, and now mine, in the form of what we affectionately call Grandma's Cranberry Stuff. A no-fuss concoction made with a whole orange, walnuts and sugar, it's the best possible complement to the salty, savory dishes of the holiday. Thank you, Great-Grandma Kerr! —**CATHERINE CASSIDY** MILWAUKEE, WI

GRANDMA'S CRANBERRY STUFF

EAT SMART ⑤ INGREDIENTS
No-Cook Fresh Tomato Sauce

PREP: 15 MIN. + STANDING
MAKES: 3½ CUPS

- 1½ **pounds assorted fresh tomatoes, coarsely chopped (about 4½ cups)**
- ⅓ **cup minced fresh basil**
- 1 **tablespoon olive oil**
- 2 **garlic cloves, coarsely chopped**
  Salt and pepper to taste
  Hot cooked angel hair pasta or spaghetti
  Grated Parmesan cheese

1. In a large bowl, toss tomatoes with basil, oil and garlic; season with salt and pepper to taste. Let stand at room temperature 30-60 minutes or until juices are released from tomatoes, stirring occasionally.

2. Serve the tomato sauce with hot cooked pasta. Sprinkle with grated Parmesan cheese.

PER SERVING *¾ cup (calculated without pasta and cheese) equals 64 cal., 4 g fat (1 g sat. fat), 0 chol., 9 mg sodium, 7 g carb., 2 g fiber, 2 g pro.* **Diabetic Exchanges:** *1 vegetable, 1 fat.*

Rely on No-Cook Fresh Tomato Sauce to make a box of angel hair or a store-bought pizza crust a little more special. You can use up your garden tomatoes, too.
—**JULIANNE SCHNUCK** MILWAUKEE, WI

NO-COOK FRESH TOMATO SAUCE

GRILLED STREET CORN

EAT SMART ⑤ INGREDIENTS
Grilled Street Corn

I wanted the perfect side to go with my grandmother's legendary tacos, and this chile-lime grilled corn was just right.
—**ASHLEY CRAINSHAW** SHAWNEE, KS

PREP: 15 MIN. • **GRILL:** 20 MIN.
MAKES: 6 SERVINGS

- 6 **medium ears sweet corn**
- ½ **cup sour cream**
- ¼ **cup grated Parmesan cheese**
- 1 **tablespoon lime juice**
- ½ **teaspoon chili powder**
- ¼ **teaspoon salt**
- ⅛ **teaspoon pepper**

1. Carefully peel back the corn husks to within 1 in. of bottoms; remove silk. Rewrap the corn in husks; secure with kitchen string. Rinse corn under water, moistening husks. Grill corn, covered, over medium heat 20-25 minutes or until tender, turning often.

2. In a small bowl, mix the remaining ingredients until blended. Cut string from corn and peel back husks. Spread corn with sour cream mixture.

PER SERVING *1 ear of corn with about 1 tablespoon sour cream mixture equals 143 cal., 6 g fat (3 g sat. fat), 16 mg chol., 180 mg sodium, 20 g carb., 2 g fiber, 5 g pro.* **Diabetic Exchanges:** *1 starch, 1 fat.*

Green Beans with Roasted Grape Tomatoes

When your summertime vegetable crop is ripe for the picking, toss together this delicious but easy-to-fix dish.

—**MICHAELA ROSENTHAL** INDIO, CA

PREP: 10 MIN. • **BAKE:** 35 MIN.
MAKES: 10 SERVINGS

- 2 **teaspoons olive oil**
- ¼ **teaspoon grated lemon peel**
- 2 **pints grape tomatoes**
- ¼ **teaspoon celery salt**
  Dash white pepper
- 1½ **pounds fresh green beans, trimmed**
- 2 **tablespoons grated Romano or Parmesan cheese**

1. In a small bowl, combine the oil and lemon peel. Place the tomatoes in a greased 15x10x1-in. baking pan; drizzle with oil mixture. Sprinkle with the celery salt and pepper; toss to coat. Bake at 350° for 35-40 minutes or until very tender, stirring once.
2. Meanwhile, place beans in steamer basket; place in a saucepan over 1 in. of water. Bring to a boil; cover and steam for 7-8 minutes or until crisp-tender. Transfer to a serving plate.
3. Place the tomatoes over beans; sprinkle with cheese. Serve warm or at room temperature.
PER SERVING ¾ cup equals 45 cal., 2 g fat (trace sat. fat), 2 mg chol., 72 mg sodium, 7 g carb., 3 g fiber, 2 g pro. *Diabetic Exchange: 1 vegetable.*

BAKED THREE-CHEESE MACARONI

GREEN BEANS WITH ROASTED GRAPE TOMATOES

Baked Three-Cheese Macaroni

Mac and cheese is a tradition at our big family events. My version is a rich blend of cheddar, Gruyere and Parmesan.

—**JOAN SULLIVAN** GAMBRILLS, MD

PREP: 20 MIN. • **BAKE:** 30 MIN.
MAKES: 12 SERVINGS (¾ CUP EACH)

- 1 **package (16 ounces) elbow macaroni or fusilli pasta**
- 6 **tablespoons butter, cubed**
- ½ **cup all-purpose flour**
- 4 **cups 2% milk, warmed**
- 4 **cups (16 ounces) shredded Gruyere cheese**
- 2 **cups (8 ounces) shredded extra-sharp cheddar cheese**
- 2 **teaspoons salt**
- ¾ **teaspoon freshly ground pepper**
- ¼ **teaspoon freshly ground nutmeg**
- 1½ **cups panko (Japanese) bread crumbs**
- ½ **cup grated Parmesan cheese**
- 2 **tablespoons butter, melted**

1. Preheat oven to 350°. Cook the macaroni in a 6-qt. stockpot according to the package directions for al dente. Drain; return to pot.
2. In a large saucepan, melt 6 tablespoons butter over medium heat. Stir in the flour until smooth; gradually whisk in warmed milk. Bring to a boil, stirring constantly; cook and stir 2-3 minutes or until thickened.
3. Remove from the heat; stir in the Gruyere and cheddar cheeses, salt, pepper and nutmeg. Add to macaroni, tossing to coat.
4. Transfer to a greased 13x9-in. baking dish. Toss the panko bread crumbs with the grated Parmesan cheese and melted butter; sprinkle over the casserole. Bake, uncovered, 30-40 minutes or until bubbly and the top is golden brown.
PER SERVING ¾ cup equals 487 cal., 24 g fat (14 g sat. fat), 76 mg chol., 515 mg sodium, 41 g carb., 2 g fiber, 27 g pro.

Three root vegetables are better than one! In Triple Mash with Horseradish Bread Crumbs, parsnips and Yukon Gold potatoes complement the subtle sweetness of rutabagas.
—LILY JULOW LAWRENCEVILLE, GA

FAST FIX

Triple Mash with Horseradish Bread Crumbs

START TO FINISH: 30 MIN.
MAKES: 12 SERVINGS (⅔ CUP EACH)

- 1¾ pounds Yukon Gold potatoes, peeled and cubed
- 4 medium parsnips (about 1¼ pounds), peeled and cubed
- 2½ cups cubed peeled rutabaga
- 2 teaspoons salt
- ½ cup butter, divided
- 1 cup soft bread crumbs
- 2 tablespoons prepared horseradish
- 1 cup whole milk
- ¼ teaspoon pepper

1. Place potatoes, parsnips, rutabaga and salt in a 6-qt. stockpot; add water to cover. Bring to a boil. Reduce the heat; cook, uncovered, 15-20 minutes or until tender.

2. Meanwhile, in a skillet, heat ¼ cup butter over medium heat. Add bread crumbs; cook and stir 3-5 minutes or until toasted. Stir in horseradish; remove from heat.

3. Drain the vegetables; return to the pot. Mash vegetables over low heat, gradually adding milk, pepper and remaining butter. Transfer to a serving dish; sprinkle with bread crumbs.

PER SERVING ⅔ cup equals 199 cal., 9 g fat (5 g sat. fat), 22 mg chol., 240 mg sodium, 28 g carb., 4 g fiber, 4 g pro.

FAST FIX

Brussels Sprouts in Rosemary Cream Sauce

Brussels sprouts in an herb cream sauce? You've never had them like this—and you may never want them any other way!
—LIZ KOSCHORECK BEREA, KY

START TO FINISH: 30 MIN.
MAKES: 6 SERVINGS

- 1 pound fresh Brussels sprouts (about 4 cups)
- ¼ cup butter, cubed
- 1 tablespoon all-purpose flour
- 1 cup heavy whipping cream
- 1 tablespoon coarsely chopped fresh rosemary
- 2 garlic cloves, minced
- ¾ teaspoon salt
- ¼ cup shredded Parmigiano-Reggiano cheese
  Freshly ground pepper

1. Trim the Brussels sprout stems; using a paring knife, cut an "X" in the bottom of each. Place Brussels sprouts in a large saucepan; add water to cover. Bring to a boil. Reduce heat; simmer, covered, 6-8 minutes or until almost tender. Drain.

2. Meanwhile, in a large saucepan, melt the butter over medium heat. Stir in flour until smooth; gradually whisk in the heavy whipping cream. Bring to a boil, stirring constantly; cook and stir 1-2 minutes or until sauce is thickened.

3. Stir in the rosemary and garlic. Add Brussels sprouts and salt; heat through, stirring to combine. Sprinkle with cheese and pepper.

PER SERVING ⅔ cup equals 256 cal., 24 g fat (15 g sat. fat), 78 mg chol., 445 mg sodium, 9 g carb., 3 g fiber, 5 g pro.

BRUSSELS SPROUTS IN ROSEMARY CREAM SAUCE

HERBY-ALMOND PASTA TOPPER

Roasted Cabbage & Onions

Roasting veggies really brings out their natural flavors, and it works wonders with onions and cabbage. A vinegar and mustard dressing makes this side dish similar to slaw.

—**ANN SHEEHY** LAWRENCE, MA

PREP: 10 MIN. • **COOK:** 30 MIN. + STANDING
MAKES: 6 SERVINGS

- 1 **medium head cabbage (about 2 pounds), coarsely chopped**
- 2 **large onions, chopped**
- ¼ **cup olive oil**
- ¾ **teaspoon salt**
- ¾ **teaspoon pepper**
- 3 **tablespoons minced fresh chives**
- 3 **tablespoons minced fresh tarragon**

DRESSING

- 2 **tablespoons white balsamic vinegar or white wine vinegar**
- 2 **tablespoons olive oil**
- 2 **tablespoons Dijon mustard**
- 1 **tablespoon lemon juice**
- ½ **teaspoon salt**
- ½ **teaspoon pepper**

1. Preheat oven to 450°. Place the cabbage and onions in a large bowl. Drizzle with oil; sprinkle with salt and pepper and toss to coat. Transfer to a shallow roasting pan, spreading evenly. Roast 30-35 minutes or until the vegetables are tender and lightly browned, stirring halfway.

2. Transfer the cabbage mixture to a large bowl. Add the chives and tarragon; toss to combine. In a small bowl, whisk the dressing ingredients until blended. Drizzle over cabbage mixture; toss to coat. Let stand 10 minutes to allow flavors to blend. Serve warm or at room temperature.

PER SERVING ¾ cups equals 183 cal., 14 g fat (2 g sat. fat), 0 chol., 636 mg sodium, 15 g carb., 4 g fiber, 2 g pro.

⑤ INGREDIENTS FAST FIX ▶
Herby-Almond Pasta Topper

When you're tired of the same old pasta, perk it up with a topping of chopped nuts, basil, oregano and thyme.

—**KAREN BERNER** NEW CANAAN, CT

START TO FINISH: 5 MIN.
MAKES: 1 SERVING

- 1 **tablespoon finely chopped almonds**
- 1 **tablespoon minced fresh basil**
- 2 **teaspoons minced fresh oregano**
- 1 **teaspoon minced fresh thyme**
  Hot cooked pasta
  Pasta sauce, optional

Toss almonds with herbs. Sprinkle over pasta and, if desired, sauce.
PER SERVING 1 serving equals 51 cal., 4 g fat (trace sat. fat), 0 chol., trace sodium, 2 g carb., 1 g fiber, 2 g pro.

💬 TOP TIP

When buying cabbage, look for crisp leaves that are firmly packed. The head should feel heavy for its size. Store cabbage tightly wrapped in a plastic bag in the refrigerator for up to two weeks. Remove the core, rinse the cabbage and blot it dry just before using.

ROASTED CABBAGE & ONIONS

SWISS CHARD WITH ONIONS & GARLIC

If you cook for picky eaters who are fussy about both flavor and texture, try a simple side of Roasted Fresh Okra. It goes over well every time.

—ANNA HUMPHRY GREENVILLE, NC

EAT SMART **FAST FIX**

Roasted Fresh Okra

START TO FINISH: 25 MIN.
MAKES: 4 SERVINGS

- 1 pound fresh okra, trimmed and cut lengthwise in half
- 3 tablespoons olive oil
- ½ teaspoon salt
- ¼ teaspoon pepper

Preheat oven to 400°. Toss the okra with the olive oil, salt and pepper. Arrange in a 15x10x1-in. baking pan, cut side up. Roast 12-15 minutes or until okra is tender and bottoms are lightly browned.
PER SERVING *⅔ cup equals 115 cal., 10 g fat (1 g sat. fat), 0 chol., 302 mg sodium, 5 g carb., 3 g fiber, 2 g pro. Diabetic Exchanges: 2 fat, 1 vegetable.*

ROASTED FRESH OKRA

EAT SMART **FAST FIX**

Swiss Chard with Onions & Garlic

My sons often request this tasty Swiss chard. Sometimes I ramp it up a bit by tossing in cooked noodles.
—REBEKAH CHAPPEL PORTALES, NM

START TO FINISH: 25 MIN.
MAKES: 6 SERVINGS

- 2 tablespoons olive oil
- 2 medium onions, chopped
- 6 garlic cloves, sliced
- ½ cup white balsamic vinegar
- 2 bunches Swiss chard, coarsely chopped (about 16 cups)
- ½ cup walnut halves, toasted
- ¼ teaspoon salt
- ¼ teaspoon pepper

1. In a 6-qt. stockpot, heat oil over medium-high heat. Add onions; cook and stir until tender. Add garlic; cook 1 minute longer.
2. Add the white balsamic vinegar, stirring to loosen any browned bits from the pot. Add the remaining ingredients; cook 4-6 minutes or until Swiss chard is tender, stirring occasionally.
NOTE *To toast nuts, bake in a shallow pan in a 350° oven for 5-10 minutes or cook in a skillet over low heat until lightly browned, stirring occasionally.*
PER SERVING *⅔ cup equals 159 cal., 10 g fat (1 g sat. fat), 0 chol., 381 mg sodium, 16 g carb., 3 g fiber, 4 g pro. Diabetic Exchanges: 2 fat, 1 starch.*

Buttery-Horseradish Corn on the Cob

For a July Fourth barbecue, I whipped up a butter and horseradish spread for corn.

—TRISH LOEWEN BAKERSFIELD, CA

START TO FINISH: 30 MIN.
MAKES: 12 SERVINGS

- ¾ cup butter, softened
- ¼ cup shredded pepper jack cheese
- ¼ cup prepared horseradish
- 1 tablespoon dried parsley flakes
- 3 teaspoons salt
- 2 teaspoons balsamic vinegar
- ½ teaspoon pepper
- ¼ teaspoon dried thyme
- 12 medium ears sweet corn, husks removed

1. In a small bowl, mix the first eight ingredients until blended; spread over ears of corn. Wrap each with a piece of heavy-duty foil (about 14 in. square), sealing tightly.

2. Grill corn, covered, over medium heat 15-20 minutes or until tender, turning occasionally. Open the foil carefully to allow steam to escape.

PER SERVING *1 ear of corn equals 203 cal., 14 g fat (8 g sat. fat), 33 mg chol., 732 mg sodium, 20 g carb., 2 g fiber, 4 g pro.*

BROCCOLI WITH GARLIC, BACON & PARMESAN

Want a new way to cook those fresh green florets? Broccoli with Garlic, Bacon & Parmesan uses a few basic ingredients to make an ordinary veggie irresistible.

—ERIN CHILCOAT CENTRAL ISLIP, NY

---

(5) INGREDIENTS FAST FIX ▶
Roasted Red Pepper Pasta Topper

Give plain pasta and sauce a boost in just 5 minutes with this zippy topping.

—KAREN BERNER NEW CANAAN, CT

START TO FINISH: 5 MIN.
MAKES: 1 SERVING

- 3 tablespoons chopped roasted sweet red peppers
- 1 tablespoon chopped fresh parsley
  Dash crushed red pepper flakes
  Hot cooked pasta
  Pasta sauce, optional

Toss the peppers with parsley and red pepper flakes. Sprinkle over pasta and, if desired, sauce.

PER SERVING *3 tablespoons equals 17 cal., trace fat (trace sat. fat), 0 chol., 169 mg sodium, 2 g carb., trace fiber, trace pro.*

EAT SMART FAST FIX ▶
Broccoli with Garlic, Bacon & Parmesan

START TO FINISH: 30 MIN.
MAKES: 8 SERVINGS

- 1 teaspoon salt
- 2 bunches broccoli (about 3 pounds), stems removed, cut into florets
- 6 thick-sliced bacon strips, chopped
- 2 tablespoons olive oil
- 6 to 8 garlic cloves, thinly sliced
- ½ teaspoon crushed red pepper flakes
- ¼ cup shredded Parmesan cheese

1. Fill a 6-qt. stockpot two-thirds full with water; add the salt and bring to a boil. In batches, add broccoli florets and cook 2-3 minutes or until broccoli turns bright green; remove with a slotted spoon.

2. In a large skillet, cook chopped bacon strips over medium heat until crisp, stirring occasionally. Remove the bacon with a slotted spoon; drain on paper towels. Discard the bacon drippings, reserving 1 tablespoon in the pan.

3. Add the olive oil to the bacon drippings; heat over medium heat. Add the garlic and crushed red pepper flakes; cook and stir over medium heat 2-3 minutes or until garlic is tender (do not allow to brown).

4. Add broccoli; cook until broccoli is tender, stirring occasionally. Stir in the bacon; sprinkle with shredded Parmesan cheese.

PER SERVING *¾ cup equals 155 cal., 10 g fat (3 g sat. fat), 11 mg chol., 371 mg sodium, 11 g carb., 4 g fiber, 8 g pro.* **Diabetic Exchanges:** *2 fat, 1 vegetable.*

DAVID NELSON'S
GRAM'S FRIED CHICKEN
PAGE 70

Main Dishes

Home cooks know the **most memorable menus** start with the entree. Here, you'll find everything from **gooey casseroles** to **Sunday-dinner chicken.** Just choose your favorites and enjoy!

CHERYL SNAVELY'S BLACK BEAN & CHICKEN ENCHILADA LASAGNA *PAGE 70*

JEN SMALLWOOD'S BARBECUED SHRIMP & PEACH KABOBS *PAGE 66*

ERICA ALLEN'S CUBAN-STYLE PORK CHOPS *PAGE 76*

FONTINA ROLLED CHICKEN

FAST FIX ▶
Grilled Greek Pita Pizzas

These personal-size flatbread pies really capture the taste of the Mediterranean. They work equally well as a main course or as a substantial appetizer.

—**KRISTEN HEIGL** STATEN ISLAND, NY

START TO FINISH: 20 MIN.
MAKES: 4 SERVINGS

- 1 jar (12 ounces) marinated quartered artichoke hearts, drained and chopped
- 1 cup grape tomatoes, halved
- ½ cup pitted Greek olives, halved
- ⅓ cup chopped fresh parsley
- 2 tablespoons olive oil
- ¼ teaspoon pepper
- ¾ cup hummus
- 4 whole pita breads
- 1 cup (4 ounces) crumbled feta cheese

Place the first six ingredients in a small bowl; toss to combine. Spread hummus over pita breads. Top with artichoke mixture; sprinkle with the feta cheese. Grill the pizzas, covered, over medium heat 4-5 minutes or until the bottoms are golden brown.
PER SERVING *1 pizza equals 585 cal., 34 g fat (8 g sat. fat), 15 mg chol., 1,336 mg sodium, 50 g carb., 6 g fiber, 15 g pro.*

GRILLED GREEK PITA PIZZAS

> Good food has a way of transporting you to far-off places. Eating Fontina Rolled Chicken is like dining in Italy without ever leaving home.
> —**TAMMY REX** NEW TRIPOLI, PA

Fontina Rolled Chicken

PREP: 30 MIN. • **BAKE:** 30 MIN.
MAKES: 4 SERVINGS

- 4 ounces cream cheese, softened
- 1 cup (4 ounces) shredded fontina cheese
- 5 bacon strips, cooked and crumbled
- 4 green onions, chopped
- ¼ cup chopped fresh Italian parsley
- ¼ cup julienned oil-packed sun-dried tomatoes, drained, chopped and patted dry
- ½ teaspoon salt, divided
- ¾ teaspoon pepper, divided
- 1 large egg
- 1½ cups panko (Japanese) bread crumbs
- 1 teaspoon paprika
- 4 boneless skinless chicken breast halves (6 ounces each)
- 1 tablespoon olive oil

1. Preheat oven to 375°. In a bowl, mix the first six ingredients; stir in ¼ teaspoon each salt and pepper. In a shallow bowl, whisk egg and the remaining salt and pepper. In another shallow bowl, toss crumbs with paprika.
2. Carefully pound chicken breasts with a meat mallet to ¼-in. thickness. Spread cheese mixture over chicken. Roll up the chicken from a short side; secure with toothpicks.
3. Dip the chicken in egg, then coat with the crumbs. Place in a foil-lined 15x10x1-in. baking pan, seam side down. Drizzle tops with oil.
4. Bake, uncovered, 30-35 minutes or until golden brown and chicken is no longer pink. Let stand 5 minutes; discard toothpicks before serving.
PER SERVING *1 serving equals 561 cal., 32 g fat (14 g sat. fat), 213 mg chol., 962 mg sodium, 15 g carb., 2 g fiber, 51 g pro.*

Stuffing & Turkey Casserole

Dish out big scoops of this holiday-leftover casserole to serve plates full of comfort.

—DEBBIE FABRE
FORT MYERS, FL

PREP: 15 MIN. • **BAKE:** 45 MIN. + STANDING
MAKES: 12 SERVINGS

- 4 cups leftover stuffing
- 1 cup dried cranberries
- 1 cup chopped pecans
- ¾ cup chicken broth
- 1 large egg, lightly beaten
- 2 cups (8 ounces) shredded part-skim mozzarella cheese
- 1 cup whole-milk ricotta cheese
- 4 cups cubed cooked turkey, divided
- 1 cup (4 ounces) shredded cheddar cheese

1. Preheat oven to 350°. Place the stuffing, berries and pecans in a large bowl; stir in broth. In a small bowl, mix egg and mozzarella and ricotta cheeses.
2. In a greased 13x9-in. baking dish, layer 2 cups turkey, 3 cups stuffing mixture and ricotta mixture. Top with remaining turkey and stuffing mixture. Sprinkle with cheddar cheese.
3. Bake, covered, 40-45 minutes or until heated through. Bake, uncovered, 5 minutes longer. Let stand 10 minutes before serving.
PER SERVING *1 piece equals 418 cal., 24 g fat (8 g sat. fat), 91 mg chol., 640 mg sodium, 26 g carb., 3 g fiber, 27 g pro.*

STUFFING & TURKEY CASSEROLE

NEW ORLEANS-STYLE SPICY SHRIMP

New Orleans-Style Spicy Shrimp

Members of our family attended college in New Orleans and loved all the unique culinary specialties they discovered there. This zesty oven shrimp brings back the traditional cooking of The Big Easy, with just the right touch of spices and heat.

—SUSAN SEYMOUR VALATIE, NY

PREP: 15 MIN. • **BAKE:** 20 MIN.
MAKES: 12 SERVINGS

- 3 medium lemons, sliced
- ⅔ cup butter, cubed
- ½ cup ketchup
- ¼ cup Worcestershire sauce
- 2 tablespoons seafood seasoning
- 2 tablespoons chili garlic sauce
- 2 tablespoons Louisiana-style hot sauce
- 1 tablespoon Italian salad dressing mix
- 4 pounds uncooked shell-on shrimp (31-40 per pound)
- 2 bay leaves
  French bread

1. Preheat the oven to 350°. In a microwave-safe bowl, combine the first eight ingredients. Microwave, covered, on high 2-3 minutes or until butter is melted; stir until blended.
2. Divide the shrimp and bay leaves between two ungreased 13x9-in. baking dishes. Add half of the lemon mixture to each dish; toss to combine.
3. Bake, uncovered, 20-25 minutes or until shrimp turn pink, stirring halfway. Remove bay leaves. Serve with bread.
PER SERVING *1 cup (calculated without bread) equals 242 cal., 12 g fat (7 g sat. fat), 211 mg chol., 940 mg sodium, 7 g carb., trace fiber, 25 g pro.*

SPANISH MARSALA TURKEY BREAST

Just about every cook has a go-to dish to rely on when entertaining guests, and Spanish Marsala Turkey Breast is mine. To prep, I just pop everything in to marinate before roasting.

—**JOHNNA JOHNSON** SCOTTSDALE, AZ

Spanish Marsala Turkey Breast

PREP: 15 MIN. + MARINATING
BAKE: 35 MIN. • **MAKES:** 8 SERVINGS

- 2 skin-on boneless turkey breast halves (about 2 pounds each)
- 1 cup pitted dates, quartered
- ½ cup pitted green olives, halved
- ½ cup red wine vinegar
- ½ cup olive oil
- 1 jar (3½ ounces) capers, drained
- 1 whole garlic bulb, cloves separated, peeled and minced (about ¼ cup)
- ¼ cup dried oregano
- 6 bay leaves
- ½ teaspoon salt
- 1 cup packed brown sugar
- 1 cup Marsala wine

1. Cut each turkey breast half crosswise in half; place in a 2-gal. resealable plastic bag. Add the dates, olives, vinegar, olive oil, capers, garlic, oregano, bay leaves and salt. Seal bag and turn to coat; refrigerate 3-4 hours.
2. Preheat the oven to 350°. Place the turkey in a single layer in a large shallow roasting pan; top with the marinade mixture. Sprinkle the sugar over turkey. Pour wine around turkey. Bake, uncovered, 35-45 minutes or until a thermometer inserted in turkey reads 165°, basting turkey occasionally with pan juices.
3. Remove from oven; let turkey stand 5 minutes before slicing. Discard bay leaves. Serve turkey with date-olive mixture and pan juices.
NOTE *If skin-on boneless turkey breast halves are not available, you may ask your butcher to debone a 5-pound bone-in turkey breast, leaving the skin attached.*
PER SERVING *8 ounces cooked turkey with 2 tablespoons olive mixture and ¼ cup pan juices equals 661 cal., 29 g fat (6 g sat. fat), 132 mg chol., 793 mg sodium, 47 g carb., 3 g fiber, 52 g pro.*

⑤ INGREDIENTS **SLOW COOKER**

Slow Cooker Kalua Pork & Cabbage

Savor the taste of traditional slow-roasted Hawaiian kalua pork at home. It's easy!
—**RHOLINELLE DETORRES** SAN JOSE, CA

PREP: 20 MIN. • **COOK:** 9 HOURS
MAKES: 12 SERVINGS

- 7 bacon strips
- 1 boneless pork shoulder butt roast (3 to 4 pounds), well trimmed
- 1 tablespoon coarse sea salt
- 1 medium head cabbage (about 2 pounds), coarsely chopped

1. Line bottom of a 6-qt. slow cooker with 4 slices bacon. Sprinkle all sides of the roast with salt; place in the slow cooker. Arrange remaining bacon over the top of roast.
2. Cook, covered, on low 8-10 hours or until pork is tender. Add cabbage, spreading cabbage around roast. Cook, covered, 1-1¼ hours longer or until cabbage is tender.
3. Remove the pork to a serving bowl; shred the pork with two forks. Using a slotted spoon, add cabbage to pork; toss to combine. If desired, skim fat from some of the cooking juices and stir into pork mixture or serve on the side.
PER SERVING *1 cup equals 227 cal., 13 g fat (5 g sat. fat), 72 mg chol., 622 mg sodium, 4 g carb., 2 g fiber, 22 g pro.*

SLOW COOKER KALUA PORK & CABBAGE

Jalapeno-Bacon Mac & Cheese

All my recipes use ingredients that are usually available in the pantry of our fire department. I simply adjust the amounts depending on how many people we have on duty that day. Mac and cheese with jalapenos and bacon is always popular.

—NICK KACZOR NEW HUDSON, MI

PREP: 25 MIN. • **BAKE:** 10 MIN.
MAKES: 8 SERVINGS

- 1 package (16 ounces) elbow macaroni
- 3 tablespoons butter
- 3 tablespoons all-purpose flour
- 2 cans (12 ounces each) evaporated milk
- 3 tablespoons yellow mustard
- 3 to 4 tablespoons chopped pickled jalapenos
- 4 cups (16 ounces) shredded cheddar cheese, divided
- ½ pound thick-sliced bacon strips (about 7 strips), cooked and crumbled

1. Preheat oven to 350°. In a 6-qt. stockpot, cook macaroni according to package directions.

2. Meanwhile, in a large saucepan, melt the butter over medium heat. Stir in flour until smooth; gradually whisk in the milk and mustard. Bring to a boil, stirring constantly; cook and stir 1-2 minutes or until thickened. Stir in the jalapenos and 3 cups cheese until cheese is melted. Reserve ¼ cup crumbled bacon; stir the remaining bacon into sauce.

3. Drain macaroni and return to pot; stir in the cheese sauce. Transfer to a greased 13x9-in. baking dish; sprinkle with remaining cheese and reserved bacon. Bake, uncovered, 8-10 minutes or until cheese is melted.

PER SERVING 1⅓ cups equals 636 cal., 34 g fat (20 g sat. fat), 105 mg chol., 759 mg sodium, 53 g carb., 2 g fiber, 31 g pro.

Monterey Chicken with Roasted Veggies

I get so many requests for this baked chicken, which is delicious served with mashed potatoes, rice or fettuccine. Roasting the red peppers and asparagus adds even more flavor.

—GLORIA BRADLEY NAPERVILLE, IL

PREP: 15 MIN. • **BAKE:** 25 MIN.
MAKES: 6 SERVINGS

- 1 pound fresh asparagus, trimmed and cut into 2-inch pieces
- 2 large sweet red peppers, cut into strips
- 1 tablespoon olive oil
- 1½ teaspoons salt, divided
- ¾ teaspoon coarsely ground pepper, divided
- 6 boneless skinless chicken breast halves (6 ounces each)
- 5 tablespoons butter, divided
- ¼ cup all-purpose flour
- 1 cup chicken broth
- 1 cup heavy whipping cream
- ¼ cup white wine or additional chicken broth
- 1½ cups (6 ounces) shredded Monterey Jack cheese, divided

1. Preheat the oven to 400°. Place the asparagus and red peppers in a greased 13x9-in. baking dish; toss with oil, ½ teaspoon salt and ¼ teaspoon pepper. Roast 5-8 minutes or just until crisp-tender. Remove the vegetables from the dish.

2. Season chicken with the remaining salt and pepper. In a large skillet, heat 1 tablespoon butter; brown 3 chicken breasts on both sides. Transfer to same baking dish. Repeat with an additional 1 tablespoon butter and the remaining chicken. Top chicken with vegetables.

3. In same skillet, melt the remaining butter over medium heat. Stir in flour until smooth; gradually whisk in broth, cream and wine. Bring to a boil, stirring constantly; cook and stir 2-3 minutes or until thickened. Stir in 1 cup cheese until melted. Pour over chicken.

4. Bake, uncovered, 25-30 minutes or until a thermometer inserted in the chicken reads 165°. Sprinkle with the remaining cheese.

PER SERVING 1 serving equals 581 cal., 40 g fat (22 g sat. fat), 200 mg chol., 1,093 mg sodium, 11 g carb., 2 g fiber, 44 g pro.

MONTEREY CHICKEN WITH ROASTED VEGGIES

Creative Kabobs

Want new recipes for your summer cookout or outdoor party? **Stick with the ideas here,** from tender chicken to delectable seafood.

Tropical Island Shrimp Kabobs

Shrimp, mango and pineapple make a sunny presentation any time of year. To boost the flavor, we use a marinade featuring coconut milk, lime juice and garlic.

—**MARY LEVERETTE** COLUMBIA, SC

PREP: 25 MIN. + MARINATING • **COOK:** 5 MIN./BATCH
MAKES: 2½ DOZEN

- ½ cup coconut milk
- ⅓ cup minced fresh cilantro
- 2 tablespoons lime juice
- 2 garlic cloves, minced
- 2 teaspoons olive oil
- 1½ teaspoons ground coriander
- ¼ teaspoon salt
- ¼ teaspoon coarsely ground pepper
- 30 uncooked shrimp (26-30 per pound size), peeled and deveined
- 30 mango cubes (about 1 large mango)
- 30 fresh pineapple cubes (about 1½ cups)

1. In a large resealable plastic bag, combine the first eight ingredients. Add the shrimp; seal the bag and turn to coat. Refrigerate 2 hours.
2. Drain shrimp, discarding marinade. On each of 30 metal or soaked wooden appetizer skewers, thread one shrimp, one mango cube and one pineapple cube. Heat a grill pan over medium heat. In batches, cook kabobs 2-3 minutes on each side or until shrimp turn pink.
PER SERVING *1 kabob equals 24 cal., trace fat (trace sat. fat), 20 mg chol., 23 mg sodium, 2 g carb., trace fiber, 3 g pro.*

Barbecued Shrimp & Peach Kabobs

At our backyard get-togethers, everyone gets fired up over these seafood specialties with mellow peaches. The spicy seasonings even helped me win a ribbon at a county fair.

—**JEN SMALLWOOD** PORTSMOUTH, VA

PREP: 25 MIN. • **GRILL:** 10 MIN. • **MAKES:** 4 SERVINGS

- 1 tablespoon packed brown sugar
- 1 teaspoon paprika
- ½ to 1 teaspoon ground ancho chili pepper
- ½ teaspoon ground cumin
- ¼ teaspoon salt
- ¼ teaspoon freshly ground pepper
- ⅛ to ¼ teaspoon cayenne pepper
- 1 pound uncooked shrimp (16-20 per pound), peeled and deveined
- 3 medium peaches, each cut into 8 wedges
- 8 green onions (light green and white portion only), cut into 2-inch pieces
  Olive oil-flavored cooking spray
  Lime wedges

1. Mix brown sugar and seasonings. Place shrimp, peaches and green onions in a large bowl; sprinkle with brown sugar mixture and toss to coat. On four or eight metal or soaked wooden skewers, alternately thread shrimp, peaches and green onions.
2. Lightly spritz both sides of the kabobs with cooking spray. Grill, covered, over medium heat or broil 4 in. from heat 3-4 minutes on each side or until the shrimp turn pink. Squeeze lime wedges over kabobs.
PER SERVING *1 kabob equals 170 cal., 2 g fat (trace sat. fat), 138 mg chol., 289 mg sodium, 18 g carb., 3 g fiber, 20 g pro. Diabetic Exchanges: 3 lean meat, 1 fruit.*

BARBECUED SHRIMP & PEACH KABOBS

CILANTRO & LEMON MARINATED
CHICKEN KABOBS

When preparing my Cilantro & Lemon
Marinated Chicken Kabobs, I cook the
onions first so there's plenty of room on
the grill for the meaty skewers.
—**MOUMITA GHOSH** KOLKATA, INDIA

Cilantro & Lemon Marinated Chicken Kabobs

PREP: 40 MIN. + MARINATING • **GRILL:** 20 MIN. • **MAKES:** 6 SERVINGS

- 1½ **pounds boneless skinless chicken breasts, cut into 1-inch pieces**
- 3 **tablespoons lemon juice**
- 1½ **teaspoons salt**
- ½ **cup water**
- ¼ **cup plain yogurt**
- 1 **cup fresh cilantro leaves**
- ⅓ **cup fresh mint leaves**
- 2 **serrano peppers, sliced**
- 1 **piece fresh gingerroot (1 inch), coarsely chopped**
- 4 **garlic cloves, sliced**
- 3 **medium sweet onions, cut crosswise into ½-inch slices**
- 4 **tablespoons canola oil, divided**
  Lemon wedges

1. In a large bowl, toss the chicken with the lemon juice and salt; let stand 15 minutes.

2. Meanwhile, place water, yogurt, cilantro, mint, peppers, ginger and garlic in a blender; cover and process until smooth. Stir into chicken mixture; refrigerate, covered, 2 hours.

3. Moisten a paper towel with cooking oil; using long-handled tongs, rub on grill rack to coat lightly. Brush the sweet onions with 2 tablespoons oil. Grill, covered, over medium heat or broil 4 in. from heat 10-12 minutes or until tender, turning occasionally.

4. Remove the chicken from marinade; discard marinade. Thread chicken onto six metal or soaked wooden skewers. Grill, covered, over medium heat or broil 4 in. from heat 10-12 minutes or until chicken is no longer pink, turning occasionally and brushing with remaining oil during the last 4 minutes. Serve with grilled onions and lemon wedges.

NOTE *Wear disposable gloves when cutting hot peppers; the oils can burn skin. Avoid touching your face.*

PER SERVING *1 kabob with ½ grilled onion equals 224 cal., 12 g fat (2 g sat. fat), 63 mg chol., 651 mg sodium, 4 g carb., 1 g fiber, 24 g pro.* **Diabetic Exchanges:** *3 lean meat, 2 fat, 1 vegetable.*

Double-Crust Pizza Casserole

In our family, this easy biscuit pizza always solves the "What's for supper?" dilemma.

—**PAT CRANE** PINE CITY, NY

PREP: 20 MIN. • **BAKE:** 20 MIN.
MAKES: 12 SERVINGS

- 2 pounds lean ground beef (90% lean)
- 2 cans (15 ounces each) pizza sauce, divided
- 2 teaspoons dried oregano
- 3 cups biscuit/baking mix
- 1¼ cups 2% milk
- 1 large egg, lightly beaten
- 2 cups (8 ounces) shredded part-skim mozzarella cheese
- 1 cup sliced fresh mushrooms
- 1 medium green pepper, chopped
- 1 medium onion, chopped
- ¼ cup grated Parmesan cheese
- 1 plum tomato, chopped

1. Preheat oven to 400°. In a large skillet, cook beef over medium heat 8-10 minutes or until no longer pink, breaking into crumbles; drain. Stir in 1 can sauce and oregano. Bring to a boil. Reduce heat; simmer, uncovered, 5-6 minutes or until slightly thickened, stirring occasionally. Remove from heat.
2. In a large bowl, combine biscuit mix, milk and egg; stir just until moistened. Spread half of batter onto bottom of a greased 13x9-in. baking pan. Spread with remaining sauce. Top with the mozzarella, mushrooms, pepper, onion and beef mixture. Spoon remaining batter over top; sprinkle with Parmesan.
3. Bake, uncovered, 20-25 minutes or until golden brown. Sprinkle with plum tomato. Let stand 5 minutes before serving.
PER SERVING *1 piece equals 369 cal., 16 g fat (7 g sat. fat), 78 mg chol., 710 mg sodium, 30 g carb., 3 g fiber, 26 g pro.*

TOP TIP

Find dry bread crumbs at the store or make your own using very dry bread or zwieback crackers. Just place them in a plastic bag, crush with a rolling pin and spoon into a measuring cup.

SPAGHETTI MEATBALL BAKE

On some nights, we're in the mood for pasta—and it seems nothing else will do! I came up with saucy Spaghetti Meatball Bake to satisfy our cravings.
—**KIM FORNI** LACONIA, NH

Spaghetti Meatball Bake

PREP: 45 MIN. • **BAKE:** 30 MIN.
MAKES: 10 SERVINGS

- 1½ cups dry bread crumbs, divided
- 3 large eggs, lightly beaten
- 1½ cups cooked spaghetti (3 ounces uncooked), coarsely chopped
- 2 garlic cloves, minced
- 2 teaspoons dried basil
- ¾ teaspoon salt
- 1 teaspoon dried oregano
- 1 teaspoon pepper
- 2 pounds ground beef

SAUCE

- 2 jars (24 ounces each) meatless pasta sauce
- 1 small onion, finely chopped
- 2 garlic cloves, minced
- 2 teaspoons dried basil
- 1 teaspoon dried oregano
- 2 cups (8 ounces) shredded part-skim mozzarella cheese

1. Preheat oven to 375°. Place 1 cup dry bread crumbs in a shallow bowl. In a large bowl, combine the eggs, chopped spaghetti, garlic, seasonings and remaining bread crumbs. Add the beef; mix lightly but thoroughly. Shape into 1½-in. balls.
2. Roll meatballs in bread crumbs; place in a greased 13x9-in. baking dish. Bake 15-20 minutes or until cooked through.
3. In a large saucepan, combine the meatless pasta sauce, onion, garlic and seasonings; bring to a boil over medium heat, stirring occasionally. Pour over the meatballs; sprinkle with the shredded mozzarella cheese. Bake 15-20 minutes longer or until cheese is lightly browned.
PER SERVING *4 meatballs with ½ cup sauce equals 390 cal., 17 g fat (7 g sat. fat), 124 mg chol., 1,074 mg sodium, 29 g carb., 3 g fiber, 29 g pro.*

Cheese Tortellini Primavera

This veggie tortellini is quick enough for a weekday but also nice enough for guests.

—CHRISTINE HADDEN WHITMAN, MA

PREP: 20 MIN. • **COOK:** 20 MIN.
MAKES: 6 SERVINGS

- 4 **cups fresh broccoli florets**
- ¼ **cup plus 2 tablespoons water, divided**
- ½ **pound fresh asparagus, trimmed and cut into 1½-inch pieces**
- 1 **package (20 ounces) refrigerated cheese tortellini**
- 2 **tablespoons all-purpose flour**
- 1 **can (10½ ounces) condensed chicken broth, undiluted**
- 1 **medium sweet orange or yellow pepper**
- 1 **medium zucchini**
- 1 **medium yellow summer squash**
- 3 **tablespoons butter**
- 3 **green onions, chopped**
- 3 **garlic cloves, minced**
- ½ **cup freshly grated Parmesan cheese**
- ¼ **teaspoon pepper**
- ⅛ **teaspoon salt**
  Additional freshly grated Parmesan cheese, optional

1. In a large microwave-safe bowl, combine the broccoli and ¼ cup water; microwave, covered, on high for 2-3 minutes or until tender. Cool slightly; drain. Repeat with asparagus and remaining water.

2. Cook cheese tortellini according to package directions; drain. In a small bowl, whisk flour and chicken broth until smooth.

3. Cut orange pepper, zucchini and yellow squash into ¼-in.-thick strips. In a large skillet, heat the butter over medium heat. Add strips; cook and stir 6-8 minutes or just until crisp-tender. Add onions and garlic; cook 1 minute longer. Stir broth mixture to combine; stir into the vegetables. Bring to a boil. Reduce the heat; simmer, uncovered, 1-2 minutes or until sauce is slightly thickened, stirring occasionally.

4. Add broccoli, asparagus, tortellini, ½ cup cheese, pepper and salt; heat through, tossing gently to combine. If desired, serve with additional cheese.

PER SERVING *1 cup equals 436 cal., 17 g fat (9 g sat. fat), 62 mg chol., 875 mg sodium, 53 g carb., 5 g fiber, 21 g pro.*

Sunday Best Stuffed Pork Chops

When we're having our favorite stuffed pork chops for Sunday dinner, we pass around potatoes, a green salad and steamed broccoli on the side.

—LORRAINE SMITH CARPENTER, WY

PREP: 30 MIN. • **COOK:** 35 MIN.
MAKES: 8 SERVINGS

- 1 **package (6 ounces) pork stuffing mix**
- ¾ **teaspoon seasoned salt**
- ½ **teaspoon garlic powder**
- ½ **teaspoon coarsely ground pepper**
- 1 **can (10¾ ounces) condensed cream of mushroom soup, undiluted**
- ¼ **cup 2% milk**
- 1 **cup (4 ounces) shredded smoked Gouda cheese**
- 1 **small apple, finely chopped**
- ½ **cup chopped pecans, toasted**
- 8 **boneless pork loin chops (6 ounces each)**
- 2 **tablespoons olive oil, divided**
  Minced fresh chives or parsley, optional

1. Prepare the stuffing according to the package directions; cool slightly. In a small bowl, mix the seasonings. In another bowl, whisk soup and milk until blended.

2. Stir cheese, apple and, if desired, pecans into the cooled stuffing. Cut a pocket horizontally in the thickest part of each chop. Fill with stuffing mixture. Brush the outsides of chops with 1 tablespoon oil; sprinkle with seasoning mixture.

3. In a Dutch oven, heat remaining oil over medium heat. Stand chops in pan, stuffing side up and spacing evenly. Pour the soup mixture around chops; bring to a boil. Reduce heat; simmer, covered, 35-40 minutes or until pork is no longer pink and a thermometer inserted in stuffing reads 165°.

4. Remove from the heat; let stand 5 minutes. Transfer chops to a serving dish. Spoon sauce over top. If desired, sprinkle with chives.

NOTE *To toast nuts, bake in a shallow pan in a 350° oven for 5-10 minutes or cook in a skillet over low heat until lightly browned, stirring occasionally.*
PER SERVING *1 stuffed pork chop with 3 tablespoons sauce equals 532 cal., 30 g fat (11 g sat. fat), 116 mg chol., 973 mg sodium, 22 g carb., 2 g fiber, 40 g pro.*

SUNDAY BEST STUFFED PORK CHOPS

Black Bean & Chicken Enchilada Lasagna

About twice a month, I put together a big pan of chicken enchiladas, lasagna-style. It's one of my standbys because assembly is easy and my whole family gives it a thumbs up.

—**CHERYL SNAVELY** HAGERSTOWN, MD

PREP: 30 MIN. • **BAKE:** 25 MIN. + STANDING
MAKES: 8 SERVINGS

- 2 **cans (10 ounces each) enchilada sauce**
- 12 **corn tortillas (6 inches)**
- 2 **cups coarsely shredded rotisserie chicken**
- 1 **small onion, chopped**
- 1 **can (15 ounces) black beans, rinsed and drained**
- 3 **cans (4 ounces each) whole green chilies, drained and coarsely chopped**
- 3 **cups (12 ounces) crumbled queso fresco or shredded Mexican cheese blend**
- 2 **medium ripe avocados**
- 2 **tablespoons sour cream**
- 2 **tablespoons lime juice**
- ½ **teaspoon salt**
  Chopped fresh tomatoes and cilantro

1. Preheat the oven to 350°. Spread ½ cup enchilada sauce into a greased 13x9-in. baking dish; top with four tortillas, 1 cup chicken, ¼ cup onion, ¼ cup beans, ⅓ cup green chilies and 1 cup cheese. Repeat layers. Drizzle with ½ cup enchilada sauce; top with the remaining tortillas, onion, beans, chilies, sauce and cheese.

2. Bake, uncovered, 25-30 minutes or until bubbly and cheese is melted. Let stand 10 minutes before serving.

3. Meanwhile, quarter, peel and pit one avocado; place the avocado in a food processor. Add sour cream, lime juice and salt; process until smooth. Peel, pit and cut remaining avocado into small cubes.

4. Top the lasagna with the tomatoes, cilantro and cubed avocado. Serve with the avocado sauce.

PER SERVING *1 piece with 1 tablespoon sauce (calculated without tomatoes) equals 407 cal., 18 g fat (7 g sat. fat), 64 mg chol., 857 mg sodium, 39 g carb., 8 g fiber, 28 g pro.*

As a boy, I wolfed down my grandma's specialty. I never discovered her secret ingredients—but I think my Gram's Fried Chicken recipe is close!

—**DAVID NELSON** LINCOLNTON, NC

Gram's Fried Chicken

PREP: 20 MIN. + CHILLING • **COOK:** 10 MIN.
MAKES: 4 SERVINGS

- 1 **large egg**
- 1 **cup 2% milk**
- 2 **cups mashed potato flakes**
- 1 **tablespoon garlic powder**
- 1 **tablespoon each dried oregano, parsley flakes and minced onion**
- ½ **teaspoon salt**
- ¼ **teaspoon coarsely ground pepper**
- 4 **boneless skinless chicken breast halves (6 ounces each)**
  Oil for frying

1. In a shallow bowl, whisk egg and milk. In another shallow bowl, toss the mashed potato flakes with seasonings. Remove half of the mixture and reserve (for a second coat of breading).

2. Pound chicken with a meat mallet to ½-in. thickness. Dip the chicken in egg mixture, then in potato mixture, patting to help coating adhere. Arrange chicken in an even layer on a large plate. Cover and refrigerate the chicken and remaining egg mixture 1 hour. Discard remaining used potato mixture.

3. In a 12-in. cast-iron or other deep skillet, heat ½ in. of oil over medium heat to 350°. For the second coat of breading, dip chicken in the remaining egg mixture, then in the unused potato mixture; pat to coat. Fry the chicken 4-5 minutes on each side or until golden brown and no longer pink. Drain on paper towels.

PER SERVING *1 chicken breast half equals 469 cal., 28 g fat (3 g sat. fat), 121 mg chol., 269 mg sodium, 16 g carb., 2 g fiber, 38 g pro.*

BLACK BEAN & CHICKEN ENCHILADA LASAGNA

Carolina Cheese Shrimp & Grits

Shrimp and grits are popular in our house. For a change of pace, I stirred things up using cheddar and Cajun seasoning.
—**CHARLOTTE PRICE** RALEIGH, NC

PREP: 15 MIN. • **COOK:** 2¾ HOURS
MAKES: 6 SERVINGS

- 1 cup uncooked stone-ground grits
- 1 large garlic clove, minced
- ½ teaspoon salt
- ¼ teaspoon pepper
- 4 cups water
- 2 cups (8 ounces) shredded cheddar cheese
- ¼ cup butter, cubed
- 1 pound peeled and deveined cooked shrimp (31-40 per pound)
- 2 medium tomatoes, seeded and finely chopped
- 4 green onions, finely chopped
- 2 tablespoons chopped fresh parsley
- 4 teaspoons lemon juice
- 2 to 3 teaspoons Cajun seasoning

1. Place the first five ingredients in a 3-qt. slow cooker; stir to combine. Cook, covered, on high 2½-3 hours or until water is absorbed and grits are tender, stirring every 45 minutes.
2. Stir in the cheese and butter until melted. Stir in remaining ingredients; cook, covered, on high 15-30 minutes or until heated through.
PER SERVING 1⅓ cups equals 417 cal., 22 g fat (13 g sat. fat), 175 mg chol., 788 mg sodium, 27 g carb., 2 g fiber, 27 g pro.

CAROLINA CHEESE SHRIMP & GRITS

BEEF PAPRIKASH WITH FIRE-ROASTED TOMATOES

Beef Paprikash with Fire-Roasted Tomatoes

Served with noodles, this Hungarian beef roast makes a wonderful Sunday dinner.
—**GLORIA BRADLEY** NAPERVILLE, IL

PREP: 15 MIN. • **COOK:** 1¾ HOURS
MAKES: 8 SERVINGS

- ⅓ cup all-purpose flour
- 2 tablespoons sweet Hungarian or regular paprika, divided
- 1¼ teaspoons salt, divided
- 2 pounds boneless beef chuck roast, cut into 1-inch pieces
- 2 tablespoons canola oil, divided
- 1 large onion, chopped
- 1 small sweet red pepper, finely chopped
- 2 cans (8 ounces each) tomato sauce
- 1 can (14½ ounces) fire-roasted diced tomatoes, undrained
- 1 can (14½ ounces) beef broth
- 1 package (16 ounces) kluski or other egg noodles
- 3 tablespoons butter
  Minced fresh parsley, optional

1. In a small bowl, mix the flour, 1 tablespoon paprika and ½ teaspoon salt. Sprinkle over the beef and toss to coat; shake off excess.
2. In a Dutch oven, heat 1 tablespoon oil over medium heat. Brown the beef in batches, adding the remaining oil as needed. Remove from the pan with a slotted spoon, reserving the drippings in the pan.
3. Add onion and pepper to drippings; cook and stir 4-5 minutes or until tender. Stir in tomato sauce, tomatoes, broth and the remaining 1 tablespoon paprika and ¾ teaspoon salt; bring to a boil. Reduce heat; simmer, covered, 1½-2 hours or until beef is tender.
4. Cook the noodles according to the package directions. Drain; return to the pot. Add butter and toss to coat. Serve with stew. If desired, sprinkle with parsley.
PER SERVING 1 cup stew with ¾ cup cooked noodles equals 534 cal., 21 g fat (8 g sat. fat), 133 mg chol., 953 mg sodium, 51 g carb., 4 g fiber, 33 g pro.

Mom's Chicken Tetrazzini

Rotisserie chicken turns baked spaghetti into a hearty meal our whole family craves. Sometimes I substitute leftover turkey.

—**JENNIFER PETRINO** NEWNAN, GA

PREP: 35 MIN. • **BAKE:** 25 MIN. + STANDING
MAKES: 6 SERVINGS

- 8 ounces uncooked spaghetti
- 2 teaspoons plus 3 tablespoons butter, divided
- 8 bacon strips, chopped
- 2 cups sliced fresh mushrooms
- 1 small onion, chopped
- 1 small green pepper, chopped
- ⅓ cup all-purpose flour
- ¼ teaspoon salt
- ¼ teaspoon pepper
- 3 cups chicken broth
- 3 cups coarsely shredded rotisserie chicken
- 2 cups frozen peas (about 8 ounces)
- 1 jar (4 ounces) diced pimientos, drained
- ½ cup grated Romano or Parmesan cheese

1. Preheat oven to 375°. Cook the spaghetti according to the package directions for al dente. Drain; transfer to a greased 13x9-in. baking dish. Add 2 teaspoons butter and toss to coat.

2. Meanwhile, in a large skillet, cook bacon over medium heat until crisp, stirring occasionally. Remove with a slotted spoon; drain on paper towels. Discard bacon drippings, reserving 1 tablespoon in pan. Add mushrooms, onion and green pepper to drippings; cook and stir over medium-high heat 5-7 minutes or until tender. Remove from the pan.

3. In same pan, heat the remaining butter over medium heat. Stir in the flour, salt and pepper until smooth; gradually whisk in the chicken broth. Bring to a boil, stirring occasionally; cook and stir 3-5 minutes or until slightly thickened. Add chicken, peas, pimientos and mushroom mixture; heat through, stirring occasionally. Spoon over pasta. Sprinkle with bacon and cheese.

4. Bake, uncovered, 25-30 minutes or until golden brown. Let stand 10 minutes before serving.

PER SERVING *1½ cups equals 533 cal., 23 g fat (10 g sat. fat), 107 mg chol., 1,133 mg sodium, 44 g carb., 4 g fiber, 38 g pro.*

Maple-Roasted Chicken & Acorn Squash

When I became a new mom, my mother helped me find easy recipes. This oven dinner was a happy discovery.

—**SARA EILERS** SURPRISE, AZ

PREP: 15 MIN. • **BAKE:** 35 MIN.
MAKES: 6 SERVINGS

- 1 medium acorn squash
- 4 medium carrots, chopped (about 2 cups)
- 1 medium onion, cut into 1-inch pieces
- 6 bone-in chicken thighs (about 2¼ pounds)
- ½ cup maple syrup
- 1 teaspoon salt
- ½ teaspoon coarsely ground pepper

1. Preheat oven to 450°. Cut squash lengthwise in half; remove and discard seeds. Cut each half crosswise into ½-in. slices; discard the ends. Place squash, carrots and onion in a greased 13x9-in. baking pan; top with chicken, skin side down. Roast 10 minutes.

2. Turn the chicken over; drizzle with maple syrup and sprinkle with salt and pepper. Roast 25-30 minutes longer or until a thermometer inserted in the chicken reads 170°-175° and the vegetables are tender.

PER SERVING *1 serving equals 363 cal., 14 g fat (4 g sat. fat), 81 mg chol., 497 mg sodium, 36 g carb., 3 g fiber, 24 g pro.* **Diabetic Exchanges:** *3 lean meat, 2 starch, 1 vegetable.*

MAPLE-ROASTED CHICKEN & ACORN SQUASH

PIRATE PASTA SHELLS

My grandfather loved telling stories of the sea. When he made his Pirate Pasta Shells, he'd have a little fun by forming X's on top to mark the buried treasure!
—**KATHY NOLL** LAURELDALE, PA

Pirate Pasta Shells

PREP: 25 MIN. • **BAKE:** 30 MIN.
MAKES: 12 SERVINGS

- 1 **package (12 ounces) jumbo pasta shells**
- 3 **logs (11 ounces each) fresh goat cheese or 2 cartons (15 ounces each) whole-milk ricotta cheese**
- 1 **cup minced fresh basil**
- ½ **cup grated Parmesan cheese**
- 2 **garlic cloves, minced**
- ½ **teaspoon salt**
- 1 **jar (24 ounces) marinara sauce**
- 1 **cup (4 ounces) shredded part-skim mozzarella cheese**
  Zucchini strips, optional
  Additional marinara sauce, optional

1. Preheat oven to 425°. Cook jumbo pasta shells according to the package directions for al dente; drain.

2. Meanwhile, in a large bowl, mix goat cheese, basil, grated Parmesan cheese, minced garlic and salt. Spread 1¼ cups marinara sauce into a greased 13x9-in. baking dish.

3. Fill each jumbo pasta shell with 1 rounded tablespoon cheese mixture; arrange over the marinara sauce. Pour the remaining marinara sauce over the pasta shells. Sprinkle with the mozzarella cheese. If desired, make X's over the top using crisscrossed zucchini strips.

4. Bake, covered, 25 minutes. Bake, uncovered, 5-10 minutes longer or until heated through and the cheese is melted. If desired, warm additional marinara sauce and serve with the pasta shells.

PER SERVING *3 stuffed shells equals 305 cal., 13 g fat (8 g sat. fat), 61 mg chol., 762 mg sodium, 29 g carb., 2 g fiber, 16 g pro.*

Apple Roasted Pork with Cherry Balsamic Glaze

I tried using roasted apples, sweet cherries and onions to dress up an ordinary pork roast and was thrilled with the results. I've prepared it many times since.
—**JOSH DOWNEY** MCHENRY, IL

PREP: 30 MIN. • **BAKE:** 50 MIN.+ STANDING
MAKES: 8 SERVINGS

- 1 **boneless pork loin roast (3 pounds)**
- 1½ **teaspoons salt, divided**
- ¾ **teaspoon pepper, divided**
- ¼ **cup olive oil, divided**
- 3 **medium apples, sliced**
- 1½ **cups unsweetened apple juice**
- 6 **medium onions, sliced (about 5 cups)**
- 3 **tablespoons balsamic vinegar**
- 1½ **cups frozen pitted dark sweet cherries**
- ½ **cup cherry juice**

1. Preheat oven to 350°. Sprinkle the pork roast with 1 teaspoon salt and ½ teaspoon pepper. In an ovenproof Dutch oven, heat 2 tablespoons oil over medium-high heat; brown the roast on all sides. Add apples and apple juice to pan. Roast 50-60 minutes or until a thermometer inserted in the pork reads 145°, basting occasionally with pan juices.

2. Meanwhile, in a large skillet, heat the remaining oil over medium heat. Add the onions and the remaining salt and pepper; cook and stir 8-10 minutes or until softened. Reduce the heat to medium-low; cook 35-40 minutes or until deep golden brown, stirring occasionally. Keep warm.

3. Remove the roast and apples to a serving plate; tent with foil. Let roast stand 10 minutes before slicing.

4. Skim fat from pork pan juices. Place over medium-high heat; add balsamic vinegar and cook 1 minute, stirring to loosen the browned bits from the pan. Stir in cherries and cherry juice. Bring to a boil; cook 10-15 minutes or until the mixture is reduced to about 1 cup. Serve pork, apples and onions with cherry glaze.

PER SERVING *1 serving equals 387 cal., 15 g fat (4 g sat. fat), 85 mg chol., 498 mg sodium, 29 g carb., 3 g fiber, 34 g pro.*

ARTICHOKE FLORENTINE PASTA

Grilled Cheese & Tomato Soup Bake

Put a classic combination—grilled cheese sandwiches and tomato soup—together in a pan. No dipping required!

—**MORGAN SEGER** ANSONIA, OH

PREP: 25 MIN. • **BAKE:** 25 MIN. + STANDING
MAKES: 6 SERVINGS

- 3 ounces reduced-fat cream cheese
- 1½ teaspoons dried basil, divided
- 12 slices Italian, sourdough or rye bread (½ inch thick)
- 6 slices part-skim mozzarella cheese
- 6 tablespoons butter, softened
- ½ cup tomato paste
- 1 garlic clove, minced
- ¼ teaspoon salt
- ¼ teaspoon pepper
- 1¾ cups 2% milk
- 2 large eggs
- 1 cup (4 ounces) shredded Italian cheese blend or part-skim mozzarella cheese

1. Preheat the oven to 350°. In a small bowl, mix cream cheese and 1 teaspoon basil until blended; spread onto six bread slices. Top with the mozzarella cheese and remaining bread. Spread outsides of sandwiches with butter. Arrange in a greased 13x9-in. baking dish.
2. In a small saucepan, combine the tomato paste, garlic, salt, pepper and remaining basil; cook and stir over medium heat 1 minute. Gradually whisk in milk; bring to a boil. Reduce heat; simmer, uncovered, 4-5 minutes or until thickened, stirring frequently. Remove from heat.
3. Whisk the eggs in a large bowl; gradually whisk in a third of the milk mixture. Stir in the remaining milk mixture; pour over the sandwiches. Sprinkle with Italian cheese blend.
4. Bake, uncovered, 25-30 minutes or until golden brown and cheese is melted. Let casserole stand 10 minutes before serving.
PER SERVING *1 sandwich equals 485 cal., 29 g fat (17 g sat. fat), 137 mg chol., 918 mg sodium, 33 g carb., 2 g fiber, 23 g pro.*

Artichoke Florentine Pasta

When it comes to a meatless main course, penne pasta with artichokes and a creamy sauce is a rich, satisfying choice.

—**NANCY BECKMAN** HELENA, MT

PREP: 20 MIN. • **COOK:** 15 MIN.
MAKES: 8 SERVINGS

- 1 package (16 ounces) penne pasta
- 6 tablespoons butter, divided
- 4 garlic cloves, minced
- 12 ounces fresh baby spinach (about 16 cups)
- ¼ cup all-purpose flour
- 3 cups 2% milk
- ¾ cup grated Parmesan cheese
- 1 package (8 ounces) reduced-fat cream cheese
- ½ cup white wine or reduced-sodium chicken broth
- 1 teaspoon salt
- ½ teaspoon pepper
- ¼ teaspoon cayenne pepper
- 2 cans (14 ounces each) water-packed artichoke hearts, drained and coarsely chopped
- ⅓ cup Italian-style panko (Japanese) bread crumbs

1. Cook the penne pasta according to package directions. In a 6-qt. Dutch oven, melt 2 tablespoons butter over medium-high heat. Add garlic; cook and stir 30 seconds. Add the spinach; cook and stir 1-2 minutes or just until wilted. Remove from pot.
2. In same pot, melt remaining butter over medium heat. Stir in flour until smooth; gradually whisk in milk. Bring to a boil, stirring constantly; cook and stir 2-3 minutes or until thickened. Add Parmesan cheese, cream cheese, wine and seasonings; stir until smooth. Stir in artichoke hearts; heat through.
3. Drain the penne pasta; add to the sauce, tossing to coat. Stir in spinach mixture. Transfer to a serving dish; sprinkle with panko bread crumbs. Serve immediately.
PER SERVING *1½ cups equals 523 cal., 21 g fat (12 g sat. fat), 57 mg chol., 993 mg sodium, 61 g carb., 3 g fiber, 21 g pro.*

SLOW COOKER BARBACOA

Slow Cooker Barbacoa

My husband adores beef roast simmered in lime juice, chipotle and cumin.
—**AUNDREA McCORMICK**
CHARLES TOWN, WV

PREP: 45 MIN. • **COOK:** 7 HOURS
MAKES: 8 SERVINGS

- ¼ **cup lime juice**
- ¼ **cup cider vinegar**
- 3 **chipotle peppers in adobo sauce**
- 4 **garlic cloves, thinly sliced**
- 4 **teaspoons ground cumin**
- 3 **teaspoons dried oregano**
- ¾ **teaspoon salt**
- 1½ **teaspoons pepper**
- ½ **teaspoon ground cloves**
- 1 **cup reduced-sodium chicken broth**
- 1 **boneless beef chuck roast (3 to 4 pounds)**
- 3 **bay leaves**

RICE

- 3 **cups water**
- 2 **cups uncooked jasmine rice, rinsed and drained**
- 3 **tablespoons butter**
- 1½ **teaspoons salt**
- ½ **cup minced fresh cilantro**
- 2 **tablespoons lime juice**

1. Place the first nine ingredients in a blender; cover and process until smooth. Add broth; pulse to combine.
2. Place the roast and bay leaves in a 4- or 5-qt. slow cooker; pour sauce over top. Cook, covered, on low 7-9 hours or until meat is tender.
3. Prepare the rice about 30 minutes before serving. In a large saucepan, combine water, rice, butter and salt; bring to a boil. Reduce heat; simmer,

covered, 12-15 minutes or until liquid is absorbed and rice is tender. Remove from heat; gently stir in the cilantro and lime juice.
4. Remove roast from slow cooker; cool slightly. Discard bay leaves and skim fat from cooking juices. Shred the beef with two forks; return to the slow cooker. Serve with rice.
PER SERVING *½ cup beef mixture with ⅔ cup cooked rice equals 513 cal., 21 g fat (9 g sat. fat), 122 mg chol., 882 mg sodium, 40 g carb., 1 g fiber, 37 g pro.*

Roast Spiced Chicken

I still have Mom's recipe card for this dish. It's been in our family for over 50 years.
—**CINDY KANWAR** BLACKLICK, OH

PREP: 20 MIN.
BAKE: 1½ HOURS + STANDING
MAKES: 12 SERVINGS

- 3 **teaspoons dried thyme**
- 2 **teaspoons salt**
- 2 **teaspoons seasoned salt**
- 2 **teaspoons pepper**
- ½ **teaspoon garlic powder**
- ⅔ **cup butter, cubed**
- ⅓ **cup lemon juice**
- 2 **tablespoons Dijon mustard**
- 1½ **teaspoons paprika**
- ½ **teaspoon garlic salt**
- 1 **roasting chicken (6 to 7 pounds)**

1. Preheat oven to 425°. In a small bowl, mix the first five ingredients. In a small saucepan, melt butter; stir in lemon juice, mustard, paprika and garlic salt. Keep warm.
2. Sprinkle half of the thyme mixture inside chicken. Place chicken on a rack in a shallow roasting pan, breast side up. Tuck wings under chicken; tie the drumsticks together.
3. Brush the outside of chicken with ½ cup butter mixture; sprinkle with the remaining thyme mixture. Roast 1 hour, basting every 15 minutes with the remaining butter mixture. (Cover loosely with foil if the chicken browns too quickly.)
4. Roast 30-60 minutes longer or until a thermometer inserted in the thickest part of thigh reads 170°-175°. Remove the chicken from oven; tent with foil. Let stand 15 minutes before carving.
PER SERVING *1 serving equals 390 cal., 27 g fat (11 g sat. fat), 132 mg chol., 918 mg sodium, 2 g carb., trace fiber, 33 g pro.*

ROAST SPICED CHICKEN

CUBAN-STYLE PORK CHOPS

Bacon Tortellini Bake

Using convenient refrigerated tortellini, I whipped up an easy casserole for dinner. Bacon and broccoli add flavor and crunch.

—**AMY LENTS** GRAND FORKS, ND

PREP: 25 MIN. • **BAKE:** 15 MIN.
MAKES: 6 SERVINGS

- 1 package (20 ounces) refrigerated cheese tortellini
- 3 cups small fresh broccoli florets
- ½ pound bacon strips, cut into 1-inch pieces
- 2 garlic cloves, minced
- 1 tablespoon all-purpose flour
- 1 teaspoon dried basil
- ½ teaspoon salt
- ⅛ teaspoon coarsely ground pepper
- 2 cups 2% milk
- ¾ cup shredded part-skim mozzarella cheese, divided
- ¾ cup grated Parmesan cheese, divided
- 2 teaspoons lemon juice

1. Preheat oven to 350°. Cook tortellini according to package directions, adding broccoli during the last 2 minutes; drain.
2. Meanwhile, in a large skillet, cook bacon over medium heat until crisp, stirring occasionally. Remove with a slotted spoon; drain on paper towels. Discard bacon drippings, reserving 1 tablespoon in pan.
3. Reduce the heat to medium-low. Add the garlic to the drippings in pan; cook and stir 1 minute. Stir in flour, basil, salt and pepper until blended; gradually whisk in the milk. Bring to a boil, stirring constantly; cook and stir 3-5 minutes or until slightly thickened. Remove from heat.
4. Stir in ½ cup mozzarella cheese, ½ cup Parmesan cheese and lemon juice. Add the tortellini mixture and bacon; toss to combine. Transfer to a greased 13x9-in. baking dish; sprinkle with the remaining cheeses. Bake, uncovered, 15-20 minutes or until heated through and broccoli is tender.
FREEZE OPTION *Sprinkle remaining cheeses over unbaked casserole. Cover and freeze. To use, partially thaw in refrigerator overnight. Remove from refrigerator 30 minutes before baking. Preheat oven to 350°. Bake casserole as directed, increasing time as necessary to heat through and for a thermometer inserted in center to read 165°.*
PER SERVING *1 cup equals 522 cal., 23 g fat (11 g sat. fat), 80 mg chol., 1,084 mg sodium, 52 g carb., 4 g fiber, 29 g pro.*

EAT SMART

Cuban-Style Pork Chops

These are like Cuban sandwiches without the bread. Serve popular toppings such as pickles, mayo and mustard at the table.

—**ERICA ALLEN** TUCKERTON, NJ

PREP: 15 MIN. + MARINATING
GRILL: 10 MIN. • **MAKES:** 4 SERVINGS

- 1 tablespoon Dijon mustard
- 1 tablespoon lime juice
- 1 teaspoon adobo seasoning
- 4 boneless pork loin chops (4 ounces each)
- 4 slices deli ham (about 3 ounces)
- 4 slices Swiss cheese
- 2 tablespoons chopped fresh cilantro
  Optional ingredients: mayonnaise, additional Dijon mustard and thinly sliced dill pickles

1. Mix the Dijon mustard, lime juice and adobo seasoning. Lightly pound the pork chops with a meat mallet to ½-in. thickness; spread both sides with mustard mixture. Refrigerate, covered, 3-4 hours.
2. Grill pork, covered, over medium heat 3 minutes. Turn the pork and top with ham; grill 2 minutes longer. Top with cheese and cilantro; grill, covered, 30-60 seconds longer or until cheese is melted and a thermometer inserted in chops reads 145°. Let stand 5 minutes before serving. If desired, serve with mayonnaise, mustard and pickles.
PER SERVING *1 serving (calculated without optional ingredients) equals 247 cal., 12 g fat (5 g sat. fat), 84 mg chol., 700 mg sodium, 2 g carb., trace fiber, 31 g pro.* **Diabetic Exchanges:** *4 lean meat, ½ fat.*

BACON TORTELLINI BAKE

Nana's Italian Roulade

Here's a cherished family recipe that was passed down by my great-aunt from Sicily.
—ROSEANNE MCDONLAD DAYS CREEK, OR

PREP: 30 MIN. • **COOK:** 1½ HOURS
MAKES: 8 SERVINGS

- 6 bacon strips
- 2 garlic cloves, minced
- ¾ teaspoon Italian seasoning
- ½ teaspoon salt
- ½ teaspoon pepper
- 1 beef flank steak (1½-2 pounds)
- ¼ cup grated Parmesan cheese
- 3 large hard-cooked eggs, sliced
- ¼ cup minced fresh parsley
- 2 tablespoons olive oil
- 3 jars (24 ounces each) meatless pasta sauce
  Hot cooked spaghetti
  Additional minced fresh parsley

1. Preheat the oven to 350°. Place the bacon on a microwave-safe plate lined with paper towels. Cover with additional paper towels; microwave on high 3-5 minutes or until partially cooked but not crisp. In a small bowl, mix the garlic, Italian seasoning, salt and pepper.

2. Starting at one long side, cut the steak horizontally in half to within ½ in. of opposite side. Open the steak flat; cover with plastic wrap. Pound with a meat mallet to ¼-in. thickness; remove plastic wrap.

3. Spread garlic mixture over steak; sprinkle with Parmesan cheese. Layer with the eggs and bacon to within 1 in. of the edges; sprinkle with the parsley. Starting with a long side of steak, roll up jelly-roll style (along the grain); tie at 1½-in. intervals with kitchen string.

4. In a Dutch oven, heat the oil over medium-high heat. Brown the roulade on all sides. Pour pasta sauce over top. Bake, covered, 1½-1¾ hours or until meat is tender.

5. Remove roulade from pot; remove string and cut into slices. Serve with sauce over spaghetti. Sprinkle with additional parsley.

PER SERVING *1 slice with ¾ cup sauce (calculated without spaghetti) equals 331 cal., 15 g fat (5 g sat. fat), 119 mg chol., 1,491 mg sodium, 24 g carb., 4 g fiber, 26 g pro.*

I learned to make Chicken-Fried Steak & Gravy by watching my grandmother. I taught my daughters and plan to do the same for my granddaughters, too.
—DONNA CATER FORT ANN, NY

CHICKEN-FRIED STEAK & GRAVY

⑤ INGREDIENTS FAST FIX
Chicken-Fried Steak & Gravy

START TO FINISH: 30 MIN.
MAKES: 4 SERVINGS

- 1¼ cups all-purpose flour, divided
- 2 large eggs
- 1½ cups 2% milk, divided
- 4 beef cubed steaks (6 ounces each)
- 1¼ teaspoons salt, divided
- 1 teaspoon pepper, divided
  Oil for frying
- 1 cup water

1. Place 1 cup flour in a shallow bowl. In a separate shallow bowl, whisk the eggs and ½ cup milk until blended. Sprinkle the steaks with ¾ teaspoon each salt and pepper. Dip in the flour to coat both sides; shake off the excess. Dip in the egg mixture, then again in the flour.

2. In a large skillet, heat ¼ in. of oil over medium heat. Add the steaks; cook 4-6 minutes on each side or until golden brown and a thermometer reads 160°. Remove from pan; drain on paper towels. Keep warm.

3. Remove all but 2 tablespoons oil from pan. Stir in the remaining ¼ cup flour, ½ teaspoon salt and ¼ teaspoon pepper until smooth; cook and stir over medium heat 3-4 minutes or until golden brown. Gradually whisk in water and remaining milk. Bring to a boil, stirring constantly; cook and stir 1-2 minutes or until thickened. Serve with steaks.

PER SERVING *1 steak with ⅓ cup gravy equals 563 cal., 28 g fat (5 g sat. fat), 148 mg chol., 839 mg sodium, 29 g carb., 1 g fiber, 46 g pro.*

Artichoke & Lemon Pasta

While sailing in the Mediterranean, we sampled a wonderful lemony pasta that had authentic Greek flavor. I created an at-home version, which our guests have loved.

—**PETER HALFERTY** CORPUS CHRISTI, TX

PREP: 20 MIN. • **COOK:** 20 MIN.
MAKES: 6 SERVINGS

- 2½ teaspoons salt, divided
- ½ pound fresh asparagus, trimmed and cut into 1½-inch pieces
- 4 cups uncooked bow tie pasta (about 12 ounces)
- 3 tablespoons olive oil, divided
- 1 can (14 ounces) water-packed quartered artichoke hearts, well drained
- 2 garlic cloves, minced
- 1 cup crumbled goat cheese
- 2 tablespoons minced fresh parsley
- 1 tablespoon grated lemon peel
- 2 to 3 tablespoons lemon juice
- ⅓ cup grated Parmesan cheese

1. Fill a 6-qt. stockpot three-fourths full with water; add 2 teaspoons salt and bring to a boil. Add asparagus; cook, uncovered, 1-2 minutes or just until crisp-tender. Remove asparagus and immediately drop into ice water. Drain and pat dry.
2. In the same pot of water, cook the bow tie pasta according to the package directions for al dente. Drain, reserving 1 cup pasta water. Return bow tie pasta to the pot.
3. Meanwhile, in a large skillet, heat 1 tablespoon oil over medium-high heat. Add the artichoke hearts; cook and stir 3-4 minutes or until lightly browned. Add garlic; cook 1 minute longer. Add to pasta.
4. Add the asparagus, goat cheese, parsley, lemon peel, lemon juice and the remaining salt and oil; toss to combine, adding enough reserved pasta water to coat. Heat through. Serve with Parmesan cheese.
PER SERVING *1¼ cups equals 343 cal., 14 g fat (5 g sat. fat), 27 mg chol., 919 mg sodium, 43 g carb., 3 g fiber, 14 g pro.*

MUSHROOM & LEEK PIE

Mushroom & Leek Pie

Here in the Pacific Northwest, we bake a savory pie that's so good as a main dish.
—**VICKIE WOODS** SALEM, OR

PREP: 30 MIN. + CHILLING • **BAKE:** 30 MIN.
MAKES: 8 SERVINGS

- Pastry for single-crust pie (9 inches)
- 12 ounces fresh chanterelle, baby portobello or oyster mushrooms, or a combination
- 3 tablespoons butter, divided
- 1 medium leek (white portion only), halved and sliced
- ½ teaspoon salt
- ¼ teaspoon pepper
- 1 cup (4 ounces) shredded cheddar cheese
- 4 large eggs
- 3 tablespoons heavy whipping cream
- Minced fresh parsley, optional

1. Preheat oven to 375°. On a lightly floured surface, roll the pastry dough to a ⅛-in.-thick circle; transfer to a 9-in. pie plate. Trim pastry to ½ in. beyond the rim of plate; flute the edge. Refrigerate while preparing filling.
2. Wipe the mushrooms clean with a damp tea towel. Trim the stems; quarter or slice large mushrooms.
3. In a large skillet, heat 1 tablespoon butter over medium-high heat. Add the leek; cook and stir 2-3 minutes or until tender. Remove from pan.
4. In the same pan, heat remaining butter over medium-high heat. Add mushrooms; cook 4-6 minutes or until tender and liquid has evaporated. Stir in leek, salt and pepper. Cool slightly.
5. Sprinkle ½ cup cheddar cheese onto bottom of pastry-lined pie plate. Top with mushroom mixture; sprinkle with remaining cheese. In a large bowl, whisk eggs and cream until blended; pour over top.
6. Bake the pie on a lower oven rack 30-35 minutes or until a knife inserted near center comes out clean. If desired, sprinkle with parsley before serving.
PASTRY FOR SINGLE-CRUST PIE (9 INCHES) *Combine 1¼ cups of all-purpose flour and ¼ teaspoon salt; cut in ½ cup cold butter until crumbly. Gradually add 3-5 tablespoons ice water, tossing with a fork until dough holds together when pressed. Wrap in plastic wrap and refrigerate 1 hour.*
PER SERVING *1 piece equals 338 cal., 25 g fat (15 g sat. fat), 157 mg chol., 470 mg sodium, 18 g carb., 1 g fiber, 10 g pro.*

Chicken-Chile Relleno Tacos

A local restaurant serves awesome charred tacos that are a lot like these. Their marinade recipe's a secret, so I did some experimenting and made my own.
—**DENISE KLIBERT** SHREVEPORT, LA

PREP: 30 MIN. + MARINATING
GRILL: 30 MIN. + STANDING
MAKES: 8 SERVINGS

- ⅓ cup olive oil
- ⅓ cup lime juice
- ⅓ cup red wine vinegar
- 2 teaspoons sugar
- 2 teaspoons salt
- 2 teaspoons pepper
- 1 cup coarsely chopped fresh cilantro
- 2 tablespoons finely chopped chipotle peppers in adobo sauce
- 2 pounds boneless skinless chicken thighs

TACOS

- 4 poblano peppers
- 1 tablespoon olive oil
- 8 flour tortillas (8 inches)
- 2 cups (8 ounces) shredded Monterey Jack cheese

1. In a small bowl, whisk the first six ingredients until blended; stir in the cilantro and chipotle peppers. Transfer ⅔ cup marinade to a large resealable plastic bag. Add chicken; seal bag and turn to coat. Refrigerate 8 hours or overnight. Cover and refrigerate the remaining marinade for tossing with grilled chicken.

2. Brush poblanos with 1 tablespoon oil. Grill peppers, covered, over high heat 8-10 minutes or until all sides are blistered and blackened, turning as needed. Immediately place peppers in a small bowl; let stand, covered, 20 minutes. Reduce grill temperature to medium heat.

3. Drain chicken, discarding marinade in the bag. Grill chicken, covered, over medium heat 6-8 minutes on each side or until a thermometer reads 170°.

4. Peel off and discard charred skin from peppers. Cut peppers lengthwise in half; carefully remove stems and seeds. Cut chicken into slices. Warm the reserved marinade; add chicken and toss to coat.

5. To assemble, place one pepper half in the center of each tortilla; top with ½ cup chicken and ¼ cup cheese. Fold tortillas in half over filling. Grill, covered, on medium heat 2-3 minutes on each side or until heated through.
PER SERVING *1 taco equals 525 cal., 29 g fat (10 g sat. fat), 101 mg chol., 931 mg sodium, 33 g carb., 3 g fiber, 33 g pro.*

Mom's Meat Loaf

When I first met my husband, he wasn't a fan of meat loaf. Then he tried my mom's amazing recipe, and it won him over.
—**MICHELLE BERAN** CLAFLIN, KS

PREP: 15 MIN. • **BAKE:** 1 HOUR + STANDING
MAKES: 6 SERVINGS

- 2 large eggs, lightly beaten
- ¾ cup 2% milk
- ⅔ cup finely crushed saltines
- ½ cup chopped onion
- 1 teaspoon salt
- ½ teaspoon rubbed sage
- Dash pepper
- 1½ pounds lean ground beef (90% lean)
- 1 cup ketchup
- ½ cup packed brown sugar
- 1 teaspoon Worcestershire sauce

1. Preheat the oven to 350°. In a large bowl, combine the first seven ingredients. Add the ground beef; mix lightly but thoroughly. Shape mixture into an 8x4-in. loaf in an ungreased 15x10x1-in. baking pan.

2. In a small bowl, combine remaining ingredients, stirring to dissolve sugar; remove ½ cup for sauce. Spread the remaining mixture over meat loaf.

3. Bake 60-65 minutes or until a thermometer reads 160°. Let stand 10 minutes before slicing. Serve with the reserved sauce.
PER SERVING *1 slice equals 366 cal., 12 g fat (5 g sat. fat), 135 mg chol., 1,092 mg sodium, 38 g carb., trace fiber, 26 g pro.*

MOM'S MEAT LOAF

MARCIA WHITNEY'S HONEY-SQUASH DINNER ROLLS *PAGE 86*

Breads, Rolls & Muffins

Whether you want to stir up a quick batter or knead a yeast dough, you'll find **something special** in this chapter. These loaves, scones, muffins and more will **please the whole family.**

SHELLY PLATTEN'S CHOCOLATE PEPPERMINT SCONES *PAGE 85*

SARA EICHENLAUB'S CRANBERRY ORANGE MUFFINS *PAGE 88*

ANGIE PRICE'S CONFETTI CORN BREAD *PAGE 92*

Rye Onion Bread

I'll prepare my rye any time of year, but I think the oniony bread is especially good next to a steaming bowl of soup or stew on a chilly winter day.

—**CAROL FEGLEY** LAVELLE, PA

PREP: 40 MIN. + RISING • **BAKE:** 40 MIN.
MAKES: 1 LOAF (16 SLICES)

Cornmeal
2 to 2¾ cups all-purpose flour
1½ cups rye flour
½ cup finely chopped onion
3 tablespoons sugar
2 tablespoons caraway seeds
1 teaspoon salt
1 package (¼ ounce) active dry yeast
1½ cups 2% milk
3 tablespoons butter
1 large egg white
1½ teaspoons water

1. Grease a 9x5-in. loaf pan; sprinkle lightly with cornmeal. Set aside.
2. In a large bowl, combine 1 cup all-purpose flour, rye flour, onion, sugar, caraway seeds, salt and yeast. In a small saucepan, heat the milk and butter to 120°-130°. Add to dry ingredients; beat just until moistened. Stir in enough remaining all-purpose flour to form a firm dough.
3. Turn dough onto a floured surface; knead until smooth and elastic, about 6-8 minutes. Place in a greased bowl, turning once to grease the top. Cover dough and let rise in a warm place until doubled, about 1 hour.
4. Punch the dough down. Shape into a loaf. Place in prepared pan. Cover and let rise until doubled, about 30 minutes. Combine the egg white and water; brush over the loaf. Bake at 350° for 40-45 minutes or until golden brown. Remove from the pan to a wire rack to cool completely.
PER SERVING 1 slice equals 138 cal., 3 g fat (2 g sat. fat), 7 mg chol., 179 mg sodium, 24 g carb., 2 g fiber, 4 g pro. **Diabetic Exchange:** 1½ starch.

CHOCOLATE BANANA BRAN MUFFINS

Chocolate Banana Bran Muffins

Ready in just 25 minutes, these goodies are on the healthier side but still satisfy my chocolate-loving family.

—**TRACY CHAPPELL** HAMIOTA, MB

START TO FINISH: 25 MIN.
MAKES: 1 DOZEN

1 cup all-purpose flour
½ cup sugar
2 tablespoons baking cocoa
1 teaspoon baking powder
1 teaspoon baking soda
½ teaspoon salt
1 cup bran flakes
2 large eggs
1 cup mashed ripe bananas (about 2 medium)
⅓ cup canola oil
¼ cup buttermilk

1. Preheat oven to 400°. In a large bowl, whisk the first six ingredients. Stir in bran flakes. In another bowl, whisk the eggs, mashed bananas, oil and buttermilk until blended. Add to flour mixture; stir just until moistened.
2. Fill foil-lined muffin cups three-fourths full. Bake 12-14 minutes or until a toothpick inserted in center comes out clean. Cool 5 minutes before removing from pan to a wire rack. Serve warm.
PER SERVING 1 muffin equals 169 cal., 7 g fat (1 g sat. fat), 35 mg chol., 278 mg sodium, 24 g carb., 2 g fiber, 3 g pro. **Diabetic Exchanges:** 1½ starch, 1½ fat.

EAT SMART
Garlic Knotted Rolls

PREP: 15 MIN. + RISING • **BAKE:** 15 MIN.
MAKES: 10 ROLLS

- 1 loaf (1 pound) frozen bread dough, thawed
- 1½ teaspoons dried minced onion
- 3 tablespoons butter
- 4 garlic cloves, minced
- ⅛ teaspoon salt
- 1 large egg, beaten
- 1 teaspoon poppy seeds

1. Pat out dough on a work surface; sprinkle with minced onion and knead until combined. Divide dough in half. Shape each half into five balls. To form knots, roll each ball into a 10-in. rope; tie into a knot. Tuck the ends under. Place rolls 2 in. apart on a greased baking sheet.
2. In a small skillet over medium heat, melt butter. Add garlic and salt; cook and stir 1-2 minutes. Brush over rolls. Cover and let rise until doubled, about 30 minutes.
3. Preheat oven to 375°. Brush the tops with the egg; sprinkle with poppy seeds. Bake 15-20 minutes or until golden brown.
PER SERVING *1 roll equals 168 cal., 6 g fat (2 g sat. fat), 30 mg chol., 315 mg sodium, 22 g carb., 2 g fiber, 5 g pro. Diabetic Exchanges: 1½ starch, 1 fat.*

FAST FIX
Maple Cinnamon Biscuits

A breakfast or brunch is always better when you include these heavenly biscuits.

—**MARY RELYEA** CANASTOTA, NY

START TO FINISH: 30 MIN.
MAKES: 1 DOZEN

- 2½ cups all-purpose flour
- 3 tablespoons cinnamon-sugar, divided
- 3 teaspoons baking powder
- ½ teaspoon baking soda
- ½ teaspoon salt
- ½ cup cold butter, cubed
- ½ cup buttermilk
- ½ cup maple syrup
- ½ cup finely chopped pecans
- 2 tablespoons 2% milk

1. In a large bowl, combine the flour, 2 tablespoons cinnamon-sugar, baking powder, baking soda and salt. Cut in cold butter until mixture resembles coarse crumbs. Stir in the buttermilk and maple syrup just until moistened. Fold in pecans.
2. Turn the dough onto a floured surface; knead 8-10 times. Roll out to ½-in. thickness; cut with a floured 2½-in. biscuit cutter.
3. Place biscuits 2 in. apart on an ungreased baking sheet. Brush with the milk; sprinkle with the remaining cinnamon-sugar.
4. Bake at 400° for 12-15 minutes or until golden brown. Serve warm.
PER SERVING *1 biscuit equals 246 cal., 11 g fat (5 g sat. fat), 21 mg chol., 334 mg sodium, 33 g carb., 1 g fiber, 4 g pro.*

MAPLE CINNAMON BISCUITS

RASPBERRY-FILLED POPPY SEED MUFFINS

EAT SMART

Glazed Coconut-Banana Bread

I give my baking a tropical twist with this yummy recipe. Combined with bananas, the coconut and lime icing transport taste buds to an island paradise.

—**KATHERINE NELSON** CENTERVILLE, UT

PREP: 20 MIN. • **BAKE:** 50 MIN.
MAKES: 1 LOAF (16 SLICES)

- ¼ cup butter, softened
- 1 cup sugar
- 2 large eggs
- 1½ cups mashed ripe bananas (2 to 3 medium)
- ¼ cup reduced-fat plain yogurt
- 3 tablespoons unsweetened apple juice
- ½ teaspoon vanilla extract
- 2 cups all-purpose flour
- ¾ teaspoon baking soda
- ½ teaspoon salt
- ½ cup plus 1 tablespoon flaked coconut, divided
- ½ cup confectioners' sugar
- 1 tablespoon lime juice

1. Preheat oven to 350°. Grease and flour a 9x5-in. loaf pan. In a large bowl, beat butter and sugar until crumbly. Add the eggs, one at a time, beating well after each addition. Beat in the bananas, plain yogurt, apple juice and vanilla. In another bowl, whisk flour, baking soda and salt; stir into butter mixture. Fold in ½ cup coconut.
2. Transfer batter to the prepared pan. Sprinkle with the remaining coconut. Bake 50-60 minutes or until a toothpick inserted in center comes out clean. Cool in the pan 10 minutes before removing to a wire rack to cool.
3. In a small bowl, mix confectioners' sugar and lime juice until smooth; spoon over warm bread.
PER SERVING *1 slice equals 193 cal., 5 g fat (3 g sat. fat), 34 mg chol., 174 mg sodium, 35 g carb., 1 g fiber, 3 g pro.*
***Diabetic Exchanges:** 2 starch, 1 fat.*

With a berry center and lemony glaze, Raspberry-Filled Poppy Seed Muffins are packed with tangy flavor. They're quick to fix but taste like an indulgence.
—**CAROLYN SCHMELING** BROOKFIELD, WI

FAST FIX
Raspberry-Filled Poppy Seed Muffins

START TO FINISH: 30 MIN.
MAKES: 1½ DOZEN

- 2¼ cups all-purpose flour
- 1¼ cups sugar
- 2 teaspoons baking powder
- ¼ teaspoon salt
- ⅛ teaspoon baking soda
- 3 large eggs
- ½ cup canola oil
- ½ cup buttermilk
- ¾ cup chopped pecans
- 2 tablespoons grated lemon peel
- 2 teaspoons poppy seeds
- 3 tablespoons seedless raspberry preserves

GLAZE
- ¾ cup confectioners' sugar
- ¼ cup lemon juice

1. In a large bowl, combine flour, sugar, baking powder, salt and baking soda. In another bowl, whisk eggs, oil and buttermilk. Stir into dry ingredients just until moistened. Fold in pecans, lemon peel and poppy seeds.
2. Fill greased or paper-lined muffin cups with a rounded tablespoonful of muffin batter. Drop ½ teaspoon raspberry preserves in the center of each; top with the remaining batter. Bake at 350° for 15-20 minutes or until a toothpick inserted near the center comes out clean.
3. Combine glaze ingredients. Poke holes in warm muffins; drizzle with glaze. Cool for 5 minutes before removing from pans to wire racks. Serve warm.
PER SERVING *1 muffin equals 244 cal., 11 g fat (1 g sat. fat), 36 mg chol., 104 mg sodium, 35 g carb., 1 g fiber, 3 g pro.*

BREAD MACHINE NAAN

Bread Machine Naan

Chewy yeast-raised flatbread is a snap to make in a bread machine. Serve naan with your favorite Indian dishes to soak up all the mouthwatering sauces.
—**SHANNON VENTRESCA** MIDDLEBORO, MA

PREP: 1 HOUR 55 MIN.
COOK: 5 MIN./BATCH. • **MAKES:** 6 SERVINGS

- ¾ cup warm 2% milk (70° to 80°)
- ¾ cup (6 ounces) plain yogurt
- 1 large egg, beaten
- 2 tablespoons canola oil
- 2 teaspoons sugar
- 1 teaspoon salt
- 1 teaspoon baking powder
- 4 cups bread flour
- 2 teaspoons active dry yeast

1. In bread machine pan, place all ingredients in the order suggested by manufacturer. Select the dough setting (check the dough after 5 minutes of mixing; add 1 to 2 tablespoons of water or flour if needed).

2. When the cycle is completed, turn dough onto a lightly floured surface. Divide into six portions; shape into balls. Roll each ball into a ¼-in. thick oval. Let rest for 5 minutes.

3. Brush the tops of dough with water. In a greased large skillet, cover and cook the dough, wet side down, over medium-high heat for 1 minute. Turn dough; cover and cook for 30 seconds longer or until golden brown. Repeat with remaining dough.
PER SERVING *1 naan equals 363 cal., 7 g fat (2 g sat. fat), 42 mg chol., 502 mg sodium, 64 g carb., 2 g fiber, 14 g pro.*

Chocolate Peppermint Scones

During the Christmas season, I decorate these chocolate-drizzled scones with a festive red-and-white peppermint candy topping. My holiday guests love them with cups of coffee and mint tea.
—**SHELLY PLATTEN** AMHERST, WI

PREP: 25 MIN. • **BAKE:** 20 MIN.
MAKES: 1 DOZEN

- 2 cups all-purpose flour
- ½ cup whole wheat pastry flour
- ½ cup baking cocoa
- ½ cup packed brown sugar
- 2 teaspoons baking powder
- 1 teaspoon baking soda
- ½ cup cold butter, cubed
- ¾ cup (6 ounces) vanilla yogurt
- ½ cup buttermilk
- 1 large egg
- 1 teaspoon peppermint extract
- 1 cup 60% cacao bittersweet chocolate baking chips
- 1 tablespoon coarse sugar
- 2 ounces bittersweet chocolate, melted
- ¼ cup crushed peppermint candies

1. In a large bowl, combine first six ingredients. Cut in butter until mixture resembles coarse crumbs. In a small bowl, whisk yogurt, buttermilk, egg and extract; add to the crumb mixture just until moistened. Stir in chips.

2. Turn dough onto a floured surface; knead 10 times. Divide dough in half; transfer each half to a greased baking sheet. Pat into a 6-in. circle. Cut into six wedges, but do not separate. Sprinkle with coarse sugar.

3. Bake at 400° for 18-20 minutes or until puffed and tops are cracked. Remove to wire racks; cool slightly. Drizzle with melted chocolate and sprinkle with peppermint candies. Serve warm.
PER SERVING *1 scone equals 328 cal., 15 g fat (9 g sat. fat), 39 mg chol., 257 mg sodium, 46 g carb., 3 g fiber, 6 g pro.*

CHOCOLATE PEPPERMINT SCONES

Honey-Squash Dinner Rolls

These puffy dinner rolls take on rich color when you add squash to the dough.

—MARCIA WHITNEY GAINESVILLE, FL

PREP: 40 MIN. + RISING • **BAKE:** 20 MIN.
MAKES: 2 DOZEN

- 2 packages (¼ ounce each) active dry yeast
- 2 teaspoons salt
- ¼ teaspoon ground nutmeg
- 6 to 6½ cups all-purpose flour
- 1¼ cups 2% milk
- ½ cup butter, cubed
- ½ cup honey
- 1 package (12 ounces) frozen mashed winter squash, thawed (about 1⅓ cups)
- 1 large egg, lightly beaten
  Poppy seeds, salted pumpkin seeds or pepitas, or sesame seeds

1. In a large bowl, mix the yeast, salt, nutmeg and 3 cups flour. In a small saucepan, heat milk, butter and honey to 120°-130°. Add to dry ingredients; beat on medium speed 2 minutes. Add squash; beat on high 2 minutes. Stir in enough remaining flour to form a soft dough (dough will be sticky).

2. Turn dough onto a floured surface; knead until smooth and elastic, about 6-8 minutes. Place in a greased bowl, turning once to grease the top. Cover with plastic wrap and let rise in a warm place until doubled, about 1 hour.

3. Punch down dough. Turn onto a lightly floured surface; divide and shape into 24 balls. Divide between two greased 9-in. round baking pans.

4. Cover with kitchen towels; let rise in a warm place until doubled, about 45 minutes. Preheat oven to 375°.

5. Brush tops with beaten egg; sprinkle with seeds. Bake 20-25 minutes or until dark golden brown. Cover top loosely with foil during the last 5-7 minutes if needed to prevent overbrowning. Remove from the pans to wire racks; serve warm.

PER SERVING *1 roll equals 186 cal., 5 g fat (3 g sat. fat), 19 mg chol., 238 mg sodium, 32 g carb., 1 g fiber, 4 g pro.* **Diabetic Exchanges:** *2 starch, 1 fat.*

A BIT NUTTY BOSTON BROWN BREAD

A Bit Nutty Boston Brown Bread

Big slices of this dense hazelnut loaf are good with just about anything, from soups to roasts.

—LORRAINE CALAND
SHUNIAH, ON

PREP: 30 MIN. • **BAKE:** 45 MIN. + COOLING
MAKES: 2 LOAVES (12 SLICES EACH)

- 3 cups whole wheat flour
- 1 cup all-purpose flour
- 2½ teaspoons baking soda
- 1 teaspoon salt
- 2½ cups buttermilk
- 1 cup molasses
- 1 cup golden raisins
- ¾ cup chopped hazelnuts

1. In a large bowl, combine the flours, baking soda and salt. In a small bowl, whisk the buttermilk and molasses. Stir into the dry ingredients just until moistened. Fold in the golden raisins and hazelnuts. Transfer to two greased 8x4-in. loaf pans.

2. Bake at 350° for 45-50 minutes or until a toothpick inserted near the center comes out clean. Cool for 10 minutes before removing from pans to wire racks.

NOTE *To toast nuts, bake in a shallow pan in a 350° oven for 5-10 minutes or cook in a skillet over low heat until lightly browned, stirring occasionally.*

PER SERVING *1 slice equals 159 cal., 3 g fat (trace sat. fat), 1 mg chol., 263 mg sodium, 31 g carb., 3 g fiber, 4 g pro.*

Strawberries 'n' Cream Scones

START TO FINISH: 30 MIN.
MAKES: 8 SCONES

- 2 cups all-purpose flour
- ⅓ cup plus 2 teaspoons sugar, divided
- 2¼ teaspoons baking powder
- 1 teaspoon grated lemon peel
- ¾ teaspoon salt
- ¼ teaspoon ground cinnamon
- ¼ cup cold butter, cubed
- ⅔ cup half-and-half cream
- ½ cup coarsely chopped fresh strawberries
- 1 large egg, lightly beaten

1. In a large bowl, combine the flour, ⅓ cup sugar, baking powder, lemon peel, salt and cinnamon. Cut in butter until the mixture resembles coarse crumbs. Stir in the cream just until moistened.

2. Turn onto a lightly floured surface; knead five times. Gently knead in the strawberries, about five times. Pat into an 8-in. circle; brush with the egg and sprinkle with the remaining sugar. Cut into eight wedges.

3. Separate the wedges and place 2 in. apart on a greased baking sheet. Bake at 425° for 9-12 minutes or until the scones are golden brown. Serve warm.

FREEZE OPTION *To freeze, wrap scones in foil; transfer to a resealable plastic freezer bag. May be frozen for up to 3 months. To use frozen scones, remove the foil. Thaw scones at room temperature. Warm if desired.*

PER SERVING *1 scone equals 233 cal., 8 g fat (5 g sat. fat), 33 mg chol., 387 mg sodium, 35 g carb., 1 g fiber, 4 g pro.*

Parker House Cornmeal Biscuits

Cornmeal gives these biscuits a lovely golden hue and subtle crunch.

—KATRINA RIVERA PITTSFIELD, MA

START TO FINISH: 30 MIN.
MAKES: 1 DOZEN

- 1⅓ cups all-purpose flour
- ½ cup yellow cornmeal
- 2 tablespoons sugar
- 1¾ teaspoons baking powder
- 1½ teaspoons salt
- 1 large egg, lightly beaten
- ¾ cup sour cream
  Melted butter

1. In a large bowl, combine the flour, cornmeal, sugar, baking powder and salt. Combine the egg and sour cream; stir into the dry ingredients just until moistened.

2. Turn dough onto a lightly floured surface; knead 6-8 times. Roll out to ½-in. thickness; cut with a floured 2½-in. biscuit cutter.

3. Place 1 in. apart on a greased baking sheet. Brush with butter; fold dough over and seal edges with a fork.

4. Bake at 400° for 12-15 minutes or until golden brown. Serve warm.

PER SERVING *1 each equals 136 cal., 5 g fat (3 g sat. fat), 31 mg chol., 380 mg sodium, 18 g carb., 1 g fiber, 3 g pro.*

PARKER HOUSE CORNMEAL BISCUITS

Sausage Cheese Crescents

Mom filled her crescents with everything from fruit and nuts to seafood and meats.
—**PAULA MARCHESI** LENHARTSVILLE, PA

PREP: 55 MIN. + RISING • **BAKE:** 15 MIN.
MAKES: 3 DOZEN

- 3¼ teaspoons active dry yeast
- 2 cups warm 2% milk (110° to 115°)
- 4 large eggs
- 1 cup mashed potato flakes
- 1 cup butter, softened
- ½ cup sugar
- 1 teaspoon salt
- 7 to 8 cups all-purpose flour
- 12 ounces bulk Italian sausage
- ¾ cup shredded cheddar cheese

FINISHING
- 1 large egg, beaten

1. In a large bowl, dissolve the yeast in the warm milk. Add eggs, potato flakes, butter, sugar, salt and 4 cups flour. Beat on medium speed for 3 minutes. Stir in enough remaining flour to form a soft dough (dough will be sticky).

2. Turn dough onto a floured surface; knead until smooth and elastic, about 6-8 minutes. Place in a greased bowl, turning once to grease top. Cover and let rise in a warm place until doubled, about 1 hour.

3. In a large skillet, cook the sausage over medium heat until no longer pink; drain and set aside to cool.

4. Punch down the dough. Turn onto a lightly floured surface; divide into thirds. Roll each portion of the dough into a 12-in. circle; sprinkle with 1 cup sausage and ¼ cup cheese. Cut each circle into 12 wedges.

5. Roll up wedges from the wide ends and place point side down 2 in. apart on greased baking sheets. Curve the ends to form crescents. Cover and let rise until doubled, about 30 minutes. Brush with egg.

6. Bake at 375° for 14-18 minutes or until golden brown. Serve warm.
PER SERVING *1 crescent equals 207 cal., 9 g fat (5 g sat. fat), 53 mg chol., 215 mg sodium, 24 g carb., 1 g fiber, 6 g pro.*

CRANBERRY ORANGE MUFFINS

EAT SMART
Cranberry Orange Muffins

We love the tangy cranberries and splash of orange flavor in these golden, tender muffins. They're surprisingly light, so my husband and I have one for breakfast almost every morning.
—**SARA EICHENLAUB** BURLINGTON, ON

PREP: 20 MIN. • **BAKE:** 15 MIN.
MAKES: 1 DOZEN

- 2 cups whole wheat flour
- ⅓ cup sugar
- 2 teaspoons baking powder
- ½ teaspoon baking soda
- ¼ teaspoon salt
- 1 large egg
- 1½ cups orange juice
- ¼ cup canola oil
- 1 cup fresh or frozen cranberries, halved

1. Preheat oven to 400°. In a large bowl, whisk the flour, sugar, baking powder, baking soda and salt. In another bowl, whisk egg, orange juice and oil until blended. Add to flour mixture; stir just until moistened. Fold in cranberries.

2. Coat muffin cups with cooking spray or use paper liners; fill three-fourths full. Bake 15-20 minutes or until a toothpick inserted in center comes out clean. Cool 5 minutes before removing from pan to a wire rack. Serve warm.
PER SERVING *1 muffin equals 153 cal., 5 g fat (1 g sat. fat), 18 mg chol., 175 mg sodium, 24 g carb., 3 g fiber, 3 g pro.* **Diabetic Exchanges:** *1½ starch, 1 fat.*

SAUSAGE CHEESE CRESCENTS

Pumpkin Egg Braid

In celebration of our two favorite holidays, Thanksgiving and Hanukkah, I created a spiced pumpkin braid. Use the leftovers for a yummy breakfast of French toast.

—**SARA MELLAS** HARTFORD, CT

PREP: 30 MIN. + RISING • **BAKE:** 20 MIN.
MAKES: 1 LOAF (12 SLICES)

- 1 **package (¼ ounce) active dry yeast**
- 3 **tablespoons warm water (110° to 115°)**
- ½ **cup canned pumpkin**
- 1 **large egg**
- 2 **tablespoons light brown sugar**
- 2 **tablespoons butter, softened**
- 1 **teaspoon pumpkin pie spice**
- ½ **teaspoon salt**
- 2 **to 2½ cups bread flour**

EGG WASH
- 1 **large egg**
- 1 **tablespoon water**

1. In a small bowl, dissolve yeast in the warm water. In a large bowl, combine pumpkin, egg, brown sugar, butter, pie spice, salt, yeast mixture and 1 cup flour; beat on medium speed until smooth. Stir in enough remaining flour to form a soft dough (dough will be sticky).

2. Turn dough onto a floured surface; knead until smooth and elastic, about 6-8 minutes. Place in a greased bowl, turning once to grease the top. Cover with plastic wrap and let rise in a warm place until doubled, about 1 hour.

3. Punch down the dough. Turn onto a lightly floured surface; divide into thirds. Roll each portion of the dough into a 16-in. rope. Place the ropes on a greased baking sheet and braid. Pinch the ends to seal; tuck under.

4. Cover with a kitchen towel; let rise in a warm place until almost doubled, about 45 minutes. Preheat oven to 350°.

5. For egg wash, in a small bowl, whisk the egg and water until blended; brush over loaf. Bake 20-25 minutes or until golden brown. Remove from pan to a wire rack to cool.

PER SERVING *1 slice equals 126 cal., 3 g fat (2 g sat. fat), 36 mg chol., 129 mg sodium, 20 g carb., 1 g fiber, 4 g pro.* ***Diabetic Exchanges:*** *1 starch, ½ fat.*

FAVORITE IRISH BREAD

Favorite Irish Bread

Serve this classic from the Emerald Isle with butter, jam and a hot cup of tea.

—**SADIE ROTONDO** ROCKLAND, MA

PREP: 10 MIN. • **BAKE:** 40 MIN. + COOLING
MAKES: 12 SERVINGS

- 3 **cups all-purpose flour**
- 1 **cup sugar**
- 3 **teaspoons baking powder**
- ¼ **teaspoon salt**
- 1 **large egg**
- 2 **cups 2% milk**
- ½ **cup butter, melted**
- 1½ **cups raisins**
- 2 **tablespoons caraway seeds, optional**

1. In a large bowl, combine the flour, sugar, baking powder and salt. In a small bowl, whisk the egg, milk and melted butter. Stir into the dry ingredients just until moistened. Fold in the raisins and, if desired, caraway seeds.

2. Transfer the batter to a 9-in.-square baking pan coated with cooking spray. Bake at 350° for 40-45 minutes or until a toothpick inserted near the center of bread comes out clean. Cool on a wire rack.

PER SERVING *1 piece equals 145 cal., 4 g fat (2 g sat. fat), 18 mg chol., 103 mg sodium, 25 g carb., 1 g fiber, 3 g pro.* ***Diabetic Exchanges:*** *1 starch, 1 fat, ½ fruit.*

CHEESY HERB MINI LOAVES

Cheesy Herb Mini Loaves

This savory recipe yields three mini loaves. If you like, try different herbs or cheeses.
—**KAREN PAUMEN** ANNANDALE, MN

PREP: 20 MIN. • **BAKE:** 25 MIN. + COOLING
MAKES: 3 MINI LOAVES (6 SLICES EACH)

- 2¼ cups all-purpose flour
- 2 ounces provolone cheese, shredded
- ½ cup grated Parmesan cheese
- ¼ cup minced fresh parsley
- 1 teaspoon baking powder
- 1 teaspoon sugar
- 1 teaspoon salt
- 1 teaspoon pepper
- ¾ teaspoon dried thyme
- ½ teaspoon baking soda
- ½ teaspoon dried savory
- 2 large eggs
- 1¼ cups buttermilk
- 3 tablespoons canola oil

1. In a large bowl, combine the first 11 ingredients. In a small bowl, whisk the eggs, buttermilk and oil. Stir into dry ingredients just until moistened.
2. Transfer mixture to three greased 5¾x3x2-in. loaf pans. Bake at 350° for 25-30 minutes or until a toothpick inserted near center comes out clean. Cool for 10 minutes before removing from pans to wire racks.
PER SERVING *1 slice equals 115 cal., 5 g fat (1 g sat. fat), 28 mg chol., 276 mg sodium, 13 g carb., 1 g fiber, 5 g pro. Diabetic Exchanges: 1 starch, 1 fat.*

Banana Eggnog Bread

PREP: 20 MIN. • **BAKE:** 50 MIN. + COOLING
MAKES: 1 LOAF (16 SLICES)

- ½ cup butter, softened
- 1½ cups sugar
- 2 large eggs
- 1 cup mashed ripe bananas (about 2 medium)
- ¼ cup eggnog
- 1 teaspoon vanilla extract
- 1¾ cups all-purpose flour
- 1 teaspoon baking powder
- ½ teaspoon ground nutmeg, divided
- ¼ teaspoon salt
- ⅛ teaspoon baking soda

1. Preheat oven to 350°. In a large bowl, cream the butter and sugar until light and fluffy. Add the eggs, one at a time, beating well after each addition. Beat in bananas, eggnog and vanilla. In another bowl, whisk flour, baking powder, ¼ teaspoon nutmeg, salt and baking soda; gradually beat into the banana mixture.
2. Transfer to a greased 9x5-in. loaf pan; sprinkle with the remaining nutmeg. Bake 50-60 minutes or until a toothpick inserted in center comes out clean. Cool in the pan 10 minutes before removing to a wire rack to cool.
NOTE *This recipe was tested with commercially prepared eggnog.*
PER SERVING *1 slice equals 200 cal., 7 g fat (4 g sat. fat), 41 mg chol., 134 mg sodium, 33 g carb., 1 g fiber, 3 g pro.*

Banana Eggnog Bread combines two of my favorite winter treats, banana bread and eggnog. Fresh from the oven, a big slice will warm you from head to toe.
—**KRISTIN STONE** LITTLE ELM, TX

BANANA EGGNOG BREAD

Caramelized Onion Flatbread

For a great side or snack, top pizza dough with caramelized onions and Parmesan.

—**DEIRDRE COX** KANSAS CITY, MO

PREP: 45 MIN. • **BAKE:** 15 MIN.
MAKES: 15 SERVINGS

- 3 large sweet onions, thinly sliced
- 2 tablespoons brown sugar
- 1 tablespoon Marsala wine or apple juice
- ¼ teaspoon salt
- ¼ teaspoon pepper
- 2 tablespoons butter
- 1 tube (13.8 ounces) refrigerated pizza crust
- 1 tablespoon olive oil
- ¼ cup shredded Parmesan cheese

1. In a large skillet, cook the onions, brown sugar, wine, salt and pepper in butter over medium-low heat for 30-40 minutes or until onions are caramelized, stirring frequently.
2. On a greased baking sheet, roll out crust into a 13x10-in. rectangle. Brush with oil. Top with onions and cheese.
3. Bake at 400° for 15-18 minutes or until lightly browned. Serve warm.
PER SERVING *1 piece equals 116 cal., 4 g fat (1 g sat. fat), 5 mg chol., 246 mg sodium, 17 g carb., 1 g fiber, 3 g pro. Diabetic Exchanges: 1 starch, ½ fat.*

Dutch Apple Pie Muffins

I love waking up my overnight guests with a batch of these spiced apple delights.

—**SUZANNE PAULEY** RENTON, WA

PREP: 25 MIN. • **BAKE:** 20 MIN.
MAKES: 1 DOZEN

- 2 cups finely chopped peeled tart apples
- 3 tablespoons sugar
- 3 tablespoons water
- 2 tablespoons brown sugar
- 1 tablespoon all-purpose flour
- 2 tablespoons butter
- 1 teaspoon lemon juice
- 1 teaspoon vanilla extract

TOPPING
- 3 tablespoons brown sugar
- 2 tablespoons all-purpose flour
- 2 tablespoons quick-cooking oats
- 2 tablespoons cold butter

DUTCH APPLE PIE MUFFINS

BATTER
- 1¾ cups all-purpose flour
- ½ cup sugar
- 2 teaspoons baking powder
- 1 teaspoon ground cinnamon
- ½ teaspoon salt
- 1 large egg
- ¾ cup 2% milk
- ¼ cup canola oil

GLAZE
- ¼ cup confectioners' sugar
- 1 to 2 teaspoons 2% milk

1. In a small saucepan, combine the apples, sugar, water and brown sugar. Bring to a boil over medium heat. Sprinkle with flour; cook and stir for 2 minutes or until thickened. Stir in butter and lemon juice. Remove from the heat; add vanilla. Set aside to cool.
2. For topping, combine the brown sugar, flour and oats. Cut in the butter until the mixture resembles coarse crumbs; set aside.
3. In a large bowl, combine the flour, sugar, baking powder, cinnamon and salt. In another bowl, beat egg, milk and oil. Stir into dry ingredients just until moistened. Fill greased or paper-lined muffin cups three-fourths full. Drop apple mixture by tablespoonfuls into the center of each muffin. Sprinkle with topping.
4. Bake at 400° for 20-24 minutes or until a toothpick inserted in muffin comes out clean. Cool for 5 minutes before removing from pan to a wire rack. Combine glaze ingredients; drizzle over muffins. Serve warm.
PER SERVING *1 muffin equals 251 cal., 9 g fat (3 g sat. fat), 29 mg chol., 208 mg sodium, 39 g carb., 1 g fiber, 3 g pro.*

TOP TIP

When baking muffins or cupcakes in paper liners, I spray the liners with nonstick cooking spray before pouring in the batter. The liners peel off neatly and easily, without leaving large crumbs or pieces behind.

—**PAMELA K.** MARTINSBURG, WV

CONFETTI CORN BREAD

Pumpkin Cheesecake Muffins

My mother-in-law combined a few of her all-time-favorite muffins and created new goodies. With wonderful pumpkin flavor, a sweet cream cheese filling and a crunchy praline topping, they're hard to resist.

—**LISA POWELSON** SCOTT CITY, KS

PREP: 25 MIN. • **BAKE:** 15 MIN.
MAKES: 2 DOZEN

- 3 cups all-purpose flour
- 2 cups sugar
- 2 teaspoons baking soda
- 2 teaspoons baking powder
- 1 teaspoon salt
- 1 teaspoon ground cinnamon
- 4 large eggs
- 1 can (15 ounces) solid-pack pumpkin
- 1½ cups canola oil

CREAM CHEESE FILLING
- 1 package (8 ounces) cream cheese, softened
- ½ cup sugar
- 1 large egg
- 1 tablespoon all-purpose flour

PRALINE TOPPING
- ⅔ cup chopped pecans
- ⅓ cup packed brown sugar
- 2 tablespoons sour cream

1. Preheat oven to 400°. In a large bowl, combine the first six ingredients. In another bowl, whisk eggs, pumpkin and oil. Stir into the dry ingredients just until moistened. Fill greased or paper-lined muffin cups one-third full.
2. For the filling, beat cream cheese, sugar, egg and flour until smooth. Drop by tablespoonfuls into center of each muffin. Top with remaining batter.
3. For the praline topping, in a small bowl, combine pecans, brown sugar and sour cream; spoon over muffin batter. Bake 15-18 minutes or until a toothpick inserted in muffin comes out clean. Cool 5 minutes before removing from pans to wire racks. Serve warm. Refrigerate leftovers.
PER SERVING *1 muffin equals 354 cal., 21 g fat (4 g sat. fat), 55 mg chol., 282 mg sodium, 38 g carb., 2 g fiber, 4 g pro.*

Confetti Corn Bread

Southwest corn bread was always on my grandmother Virginia's table. In her honor, I came up with a variation that requires a little less prep but never skimps on taste.

—**ANGIE PRICE** BRADFORD, TN

PREP: 20 MIN. • **BAKE:** 50 MIN.
MAKES: 12 SERVINGS

- 2 packages (8½ ounces each) corn bread/muffin mix
- ¼ teaspoon cayenne pepper
- 2 large eggs
- 1 can (14¾ ounces) cream-style corn
- ½ cup buttermilk
- ¼ cup plus 1½ teaspoons canola oil, divided
- 1 cup (4 ounces) shredded cheddar cheese
- 1 small onion, chopped
- 1 can (4 ounces) chopped green chilies
- 1 jar (2 ounces) pimiento strips, drained
- 1 jalapeno pepper, seeded and chopped

1. Preheat oven to 350°. In large bowl, combine muffin mixes and cayenne pepper. In another bowl, mix the eggs, corn, buttermilk and ¼ cup oil until blended. Add to dry ingredients; stir just until moistened. Fold in cheese, onion, chilies, pimientos and jalapeno.
2. Brush remaining oil onto bottom of a 13x9-in. baking pan; place in oven 4-5 minutes or until hot. Pour batter into hot pan. Bake 50-60 minutes or until edges are golden brown and a toothpick inserted in center comes out clean. Cool in pan on a wire rack. Serve warm.
PER SERVING *1 piece equals 299 cal., 14 g fat (4 g sat. fat), 42 mg chol., 547 mg sodium, 36 g carb., 3 g fiber, 7 g pro.*

Sun-Dried Tomato & Olive Loaf

I can't get enough of this rich, savory treat that starts in my bread machine. I tear off big chunks, dip them into a bowl of extra virgin olive oil and eat. Delicious!

—**CAROLE HOLT** MENDOTA HEIGHTS, MN

PREP: 20 MIN. + RISING • **BAKE:** 20 MIN.
MAKES: 1 LOAF (16 SLICES)

- 1 **cup warm tomato juice (70° to 80°)**
- 2 **tablespoons olive oil, divided**
- ½ **teaspoon salt**
- 2 **teaspoons brown sugar**
- 1 **tablespoon minced fresh rosemary or 1 teaspoon dried rosemary, crushed**
- 2¾ **cups bread flour**
- 1 **package (¼ ounce) quick-rise yeast**
- ½ **cup chopped oil-packed sun-dried tomatoes, well-drained**
- ½ **cup chopped pitted Greek olives, well-drained**

1. In bread machine pan, place the tomato juice, 1 tablespoon oil, salt, brown sugar, rosemary, flour and yeast in order suggested by manufacturer. Select the dough setting. Check the dough after 5 minutes of mixing; add 1-2 tablespoons water or flour if needed. Just before the final kneading (your machine may audibly signal this), add tomatoes and olives.

2. When cycle is completed, turn bread dough onto a lightly floured surface. Roll into a 15x10-in. oval. Roll up jelly-roll style, starting with a long side; pinch the seam to seal and tuck the ends under. Place on a greased baking sheet, seam side down. Cover with a kitchen towel; let rise in a warm place until doubled, about 45 minutes. Preheat oven to 400°.

3. Brush the loaf with the remaining oil. With a sharp knife, make five deep slashes across the top of the loaf. Bake 20-25 minutes or until golden brown. Remove from pan to a wire rack to cool.

PER SERVING *1 slice equals 126 cal., 4 g fat (1 g sat. fat), 0 chol., 194 mg sodium, 20 g carb., 1 g fiber, 3 g pro.*

EAT SMART
Honey Whole Wheat Bread

Why buy fast-food lunches for work when you can pack something tastier—and less costly? This recipe turns out two golden loaves that make the perfect starting point for a week's worth of sandwiches.

—**ROBYN LINDBERG** KECHI, KS

PREP: 20 MIN. + RISING
BAKE: 35 MIN. + COOLING
MAKES: 2 LOAVES (16 SLICES EACH)

- 2 **packages (¼ ounce each) active dry yeast**
- 3 **cups warm water (110° to 115°)**
- ½ **cup nonfat dry milk powder**
- ½ **cup honey**
- ⅓ **cup wheat bran**
- ⅓ **cup toasted wheat germ**
- ¼ **cup ground flaxseed**
- 2 **tablespoons canola oil**
- 2 **teaspoons salt**
- 4 **cups whole wheat flour**
- 3½ **to 4 cups all-purpose flour**

1. In a large bowl, dissolve yeast in warm water. Add the milk powder, honey, wheat bran, wheat germ, flax, oil, salt, whole wheat flour and 3 cups all-purpose flour. Beat until smooth. Stir in enough remaining flour to form a soft dough (dough will be sticky).

2. Turn onto a lightly floured surface; knead until smooth and elastic, about 6-8 minutes. Place in a bowl coated with cooking spray, turning once to coat the top. Cover; let rise in a warm place until doubled, about 1 hour.

3. Punch the dough down and turn onto a floured surface; shape into two loaves. Place in two 9x5-in. loaf pans coated with cooking spay. Cover and let rise until doubled, about 30 minutes.

4. Bake at 350° for 35-40 minutes or until golden brown. Remove from pans to wire rack to cool.

PER SERVING *1 slice equals 139 cal., 2 g fat (trace sat. fat), trace chol., 155 mg sodium, 28 g carb., 3 g fiber, 5 g pro. Diabetic Exchange: 2 starch.*

HONEY WHOLE WHEAT BREAD

**LAURIE CORNETT'S CRANBERRY
COOKIES WITH BROWNED
BUTTER GLAZE** *PAGE 103*

Cookies, Bars & Candies

Sweeten any occasion with brownies, cutouts, truffles and more. Whether you're hosting a holiday party or contributing to a bake sale, you'll have crowd-pleasing treats **well in hand.**

TERRYANN MOORE'S CRANBERRY ORANGE TRUFFLES *PAGE 96*

ANNE MULLEN'S CHERRY COCONUT TREATS *PAGE 103*

PAULA MARCHESI'S SALTED CASHEW & CARAMEL CHEWS *PAGE 102*

Fig & Almond Cookies

In our family, Christmastime treats—like these cute little filled logs—are a big deal. I'm proud to pass this traditional Italian recipe on to my two sons.

—ANGELA LEMOINE HOWELL, NJ

PREP: 50 MIN. + CHILLING
BAKE: 10 MIN./BATCH + COOLING
MAKES: ABOUT 6½ DOZEN

- 2 large eggs
- 1 tablespoon cold water
- 2 teaspoons vanilla extract
- 2¾ cups all-purpose flour
- 1½ cups confectioners' sugar
- 3 teaspoons baking powder
- ¼ teaspoon salt
- 6 tablespoons cold butter, cubed

FILLING
- 8 ounces dried figs (about 1⅓ cups)
- 3 tablespoons unblanched almonds
- 2 tablespoons apricot preserves
- 4 teaspoons orange juice

GLAZE
- 1 cup confectioners' sugar
- 2 tablespoons 2% milk
- ½ teaspoon vanilla extract

1. In a small bowl, whisk the eggs, cold water and vanilla until blended. Place the flour, confectioners' sugar, baking powder and salt in a food processor; pulse until blended. Add cold butter; pulse until crumbly. While pulsing, add egg mixture just until combined.
2. Divide dough in half. Shape each half into a disk; wrap in plastic wrap. Refrigerate 1 hour or until firm enough to roll.
3. Wipe food processor clean. Add figs and almonds; pulse until chopped. Add the apricot preserves and juice; pulse until combined.
4. Preheat oven to 350°. On a lightly floured surface, roll each half of dough into a 10x8-in. rectangle; cut each lengthwise into four 2-in.-wide strips.
5. Spread about 2 tablespoons filling down center of each strip. Fold dough over filling; pinch edges to seal. Roll each gently to shape into a log; cut crosswise into 1-in. pieces.
6. Place 1 in. apart on parchment paper-lined baking sheets. Bake 10-12 minutes or until light brown. Remove from the pans to wire racks to cool completely.

CRANBERRY ORANGE TRUFFLES

7. In a small bowl, mix the glaze ingredients until smooth. Drizzle over cookies. Let stand until set.
PER SERVING *1 cookie equals 51 cal., 1 g fat (1 g sat. fat), 7 mg chol., 33 mg sodium, 9 g carb., trace fiber, 1 g pro.*

Cranberry Orange Truffles

Homemade truffles are an indulgence we look forward to every year during the holiday season. We love the contrasting flavors of bittersweet chocolate, orange and cranberry—all in one decadent bite.

—TERRYANN MOORE VINELAND, NJ

PREP: 1 HOUR + CHILLING
MAKES: ABOUT 3 DOZEN

- 12 ounces bittersweet chocolate, chopped
- ½ cup unsalted butter, cubed
- 4 large egg yolks, beaten
- 1 cup dried cranberries, chopped
- 3 tablespoons thawed orange juice concentrate
- 1 teaspoon almond extract

COATING
- 12 ounces white candy coating, chopped
- 1 ounce bittersweet chocolate, melted

1. In a double boiler or metal bowl over simmering water, heat bittersweet chocolate and butter until melted, stirring frequently. Whisk a small amount of the mixture into the egg yolks. Return all to the heat, whisking constantly. Cook and stir until mixture reaches at least 160° and coats the back of a metal spoon.
2. Remove from the heat; stir in the cranberries, juice concentrate and extract. Cool to room temperature, stirring occasionally. Refrigerate for 1 hour or until easy to handle. Shape into 1-in. balls.
3. In a microwave, melt the white candy coating. Dip the truffles in the coating; allow excess to drip off. Place on waxed paper-lined baking sheets and drizzle with bittersweet chocolate. Refrigerate for 2 hours or until firm. Store in an airtight container in the refrigerator.
PER SERVING *1 truffle equals 136 cal., 10 g fat (6 g sat. fat), 27 mg chol., 11 mg sodium, 14 g carb., 1 g fiber, 1 g pro.*

DID YOU KNOW?

Also known as confectionery coating, candy coating is tempered, is ready for melting and sets up quickly at room temperature. Candy coating is sold in blocks or discs in stores and is available in white, milk and dark chocolate and butterscotch flavors.

Raspberry Almonettes

My sandwich cookies have a surprisingly rich center of sweetened cream cheese and raspberry preserves. They're fun to make and even more fun to eat!

—ANGELA SHERIDAN OPDYKE, IL

PREP: 55 MIN.
BAKE: 10 MIN./BATCH + COOLING
MAKES: ABOUT 3½ DOZEN

- 1 **cup butter, softened**
- 2 **cups sugar**
- 2 **large eggs**
- 1 **cup canola oil**
- 2 **tablespoons almond extract**
- 4½ **cups all-purpose flour**
- 1 **teaspoon salt**
- 1 **teaspoon baking powder**
- ¾ **cup sliced almonds, finely chopped**

FILLING

- 1 **package (8 ounces) cream cheese, softened**
- ½ **cup confectioners' sugar**
- 1 **tablespoon almond extract**
- ¼ **cup red raspberry preserves**

1. Preheat oven to 350°. In a large bowl, cream the butter and sugar until light and fluffy. Add the eggs, one at a time, beating well after each addition. Gradually beat in the oil and extract. In another bowl, whisk flour, salt and baking powder; gradually beat into creamed mixture.

2. Shape dough into 1-in. balls; press one side into almonds. Place 2 in. apart on ungreased baking sheets, almond side up. Flatten to ¼-in. thickness with the bottom of a glass.

3. Bake 8-10 minutes or until the edges are light brown. Cool on pans 5 minutes; remove to wire racks to cool completely.

4. For filling, in a small bowl, beat the cream cheese, confectioners' sugar and almond extract until smooth. Place rounded teaspoonfuls of the filling on the bottoms of half of the cookies. Make an indentation in the center of each; fill with ¼ teaspoon preserves. Cover with the remaining cookies. Store in an airtight container in the refrigerator.

PER SERVING *1 sandwich cookie equals 216 cal., 13 g fat (4 g sat. fat), 26 mg chol., 125 mg sodium, 23 g carb., 1 g fiber, 2 g pro.*

Ginger & Maple Macadamia Nut Cookies

With plenty of ginger, these nicely spiced goodies remind me of German lebkuchen.

—THOMAS FAGLON SOMERSET, NJ

PREP: 45 MIN. + CHILLING
BAKE: 10 MIN./BATCH + COOLING
MAKES: ABOUT 7 DOZEN

- 1½ **cups butter, softened**
- ½ **cup sugar**
- ¾ **cup maple syrup**
- 4 **cups all-purpose flour**
- 3 **teaspoons ground ginger**
- 3 **teaspoons ground cinnamon**
- 1 **teaspoon ground allspice**
- ½ **teaspoon ground cloves**
- 1½ **teaspoons salt**
- 1½ **teaspoons baking soda**
- 1½ **cups finely chopped macadamia nuts**
- 24 **ounces dark chocolate candy coating, melted**
- ⅓ **cup finely chopped crystallized ginger**

1. In a large bowl, cream butter and sugar until light and fluffy. Gradually beat in syrup. In another bowl, whisk flour, spices, salt and baking soda; gradually beat into creamed mixture. Stir in nuts.

2. Divide cookie dough in half; shape each portion into a 12-in.-long roll. Wrap in plastic wrap; refrigerate 2 hours or until firm.

3. Preheat oven to 350°. Unwrap and cut dough crosswise into ¼-in. slices. Place 1 in. apart on ungreased baking sheets. Bake 8-10 minutes or until set. Cool on the pans 2 minutes. Remove to wire racks to cool completely.

4. Dip each cookie halfway into the melted dark chocolate candy coating; allow excess to drip off. Place on waxed paper-lined baking sheets; sprinkle with chopped crystallized ginger. Refrigerate until set.

PER SERVING *1 cookie equals 126 cal., 8 g fat (4 g sat. fat), 9 mg chol., 103 mg sodium, 14 g carb., 1 g fiber, 1 g pro.*

GINGER & MAPLE MACADAMIA NUT COOKIES

GINGERSNAP
COCONUT CREAMS

Frosted Butter Cutout Cookies

Holiday cutouts always bring back fond memories of making them with my mom.

—**SANDY NACE** GREENSBURG, KS

PREP: 1 HOUR + CHILLING
BAKE: 10 MIN./BATCH + COOLING
MAKES: ABOUT 8 DOZEN

- 1 **cup butter, softened**
- 2 **cups sugar**
- 1 **teaspoon vanilla extract**
- ½ **teaspoon almond extract**
- 2 **large eggs**
- 1 **cup buttermilk**
- 5 **cups all-purpose flour**
- 2 **teaspoons baking powder**
- 1 **teaspoon baking soda**
- ¼ **teaspoon salt**
- **FROSTING**
- ¼ **cup butter, softened**
- 2 **cups confectioners' sugar**
- ½ **teaspoon almond extract**
- 2 **to 3 tablespoons heavy whipping cream**
  Green or red food coloring, optional
  Coarse sugar

1. In a large bowl, beat the butter, sugar and extracts until blended. Beat in the eggs, one at a time. Gradually beat in the buttermilk. In another bowl, whisk the flour, baking powder, baking soda and salt; gradually beat into creamed mixture (dough will be soft). Refrigerate, covered, overnight.
2. Preheat oven to 350°. Divide dough in half. On a floured surface, roll each portion of dough to ¼-in. thickness. Cut with a floured 2½-in. or other cookie cutter. Place 1 in. apart on greased baking sheets.
3. Bake 6-8 minutes or until light brown. Remove to wire racks to cool completely.
4. For the frosting, in a bowl, beat the butter, confectioners' sugar, extract and enough whipping cream to reach a spreading consistency. If desired, tint the frosting with food coloring. Spread over cookies; sprinkle with coarse sugar. Let stand until set.
PER SERVING *1 cookie (calculated without coarse sugar) equals 75 cal., 3 g fat (2 g sat. fat), 11 mg chol., 53 mg sodium, 12 g carb., trace fiber, 1 g pro.*

When the Christmas season is around the corner, we start to crave gingerbread and macaroons. Nibbling on Gingersnap Coconut Creams is like enjoying two favorites in one.

—**DARLENE BRENDEN** SALEM, OR

Gingersnap Coconut Creams

PREP: 35 MIN.
BAKE: 10 MIN./BATCH + COOLING
MAKES: 4 DOZEN

- ⅓ **cup butter, softened**
- ⅓ **cup packed brown sugar**
- 1 **large egg**
- ⅓ **cup molasses**
- 1½ **cups all-purpose flour**
- 1 **teaspoon baking soda**
- ½ **teaspoon ground ginger**
- ½ **teaspoon ground cinnamon**
- ¼ **teaspoon ground cloves**
- **FILLING**
- ¼ **cup butter, softened**
- ¾ **cup confectioners' sugar**
- ½ **teaspoon orange extract**
- ¼ **cup flaked coconut**

1. Preheat oven to 375°. In a large bowl, cream butter and brown sugar until light and fluffy. Beat in egg and molasses. In another bowl, whisk flour, baking soda and spices; gradually beat into creamed mixture.
2. Drop dough by level teaspoonfuls 1 in. apart onto parchment paper-lined baking sheets. Bake 6-8 minutes or just until the edges begin to brown. Remove from the pans to wire racks to cool completely.
3. For the filling, in a small bowl, mix the butter, confectioners' sugar and extract until blended; stir in coconut. Spread on the bottoms of half of the cookies; cover with remaining cookies.
PER SERVING *1 sandwich cookie equals 58 cal., 3 g fat (2 g sat. fat), 10 mg chol., 50 mg sodium, 8 g carb., trace fiber, 1 g pro.*

Red Star Cookies

These starry treats spread with red icing are fun for the Fourth of July. Create any shapes you like to suit any occasion.

—TASTE OF HOME TEST KITCHEN

PREP: 55 MIN. + CHILLING
BAKE: 10 MIN./BATCH + STANDING
MAKES: ABOUT 3½ DOZEN

- 1½ cups butter, softened
- ½ cup shortening
- 1 cup sugar
- 1 cup packed brown sugar
- 2 large eggs
- ¼ cup thawed orange juice concentrate
- 1 teaspoon vanilla extract
- 5 cups all-purpose flour
- 1 teaspoon baking soda
- 1 teaspoon salt

ICING

- 3 cups confectioners' sugar
- ⅓ cup warm water
- 2 tablespoons plus 2 teaspoons meringue powder
- ¼ teaspoon cream of tartar
  Red paste food coloring
- 2 tablespoons red colored sugar

1. In a large bowl, cream the butter, shortening and sugars until light and fluffy. Beat in eggs, one at a time. Beat in the orange juice concentrate and vanilla. In another bowl, whisk flour, baking soda and salt; gradually beat into creamed mixture.

2. Divide cookie dough in half. Shape each half into a disk; wrap in plastic wrap. Refrigerate 2 hours or until firm enough to roll.

3. Preheat oven to 350°. On a lightly floured surface, roll each half of dough to ¼-in. thickness. Cut with a floured 4-in. star-shaped cookie cutter. Place 1 in. apart on ungreased baking sheets.

4. Bake 8-10 minutes or until edges are light brown. Cool on pans 5 minutes. Remove to wire racks; cool completely.

5. For icing, in a small bowl, combine the confectioners' sugar, warm water, meringue powder and cream of tartar; beat on low speed just until blended. Beat on high 4-5 minutes or until stiff peaks form. Tint red with food coloring. Keep unused icing covered with a damp cloth at all times. If necessary, beat again on high speed to restore texture.

6. Spread the icing on the cookies; immediately sprinkle with colored sugar. Let stand until set.

PER SERVING *1 cookie equals 215 cal., 9 g fat (5 g sat. fat), 26 mg chol., 154 mg sodium, 31 g carb., trace fiber, 2 g pro.*

Orange-Cranberry Nut Tarts

I tweaked a recipe for tart-shaped cookies. Friends and family request them often.

—NANCY BRUCE BIG TIMBER, MT

PREP: 50 MIN. + CHILLING
BAKE: 10 MIN./BATCH + COOLING
MAKES: 4 DOZEN

- ½ cup butter, softened
- 1 cup sugar
- 1 large egg
- 4 teaspoons grated orange peel
- ¼ cup orange juice
- 2 tablespoons evaporated milk or 2% milk
- 3 cups all-purpose flour
- 3 teaspoons baking powder
- ¼ teaspoon salt

FILLING

- 1 can (14 ounces) whole-berry cranberry sauce
- ½ cup sugar
- 2 tablespoons orange juice
- 1 cup chopped walnuts
- 4 ounces white baking chocolate, melted

1. In a large bowl, cream the butter and sugar until light and fluffy. Beat in the egg until blended. Beat in the orange peel, orange juice and milk. In another bowl, whisk flour, baking powder and salt; gradually beat into creamed mixture.

2. Divide dough into three portions. On a lightly floured surface, shape each into a 10-in.-long roll. Wrap in plastic wrap; refrigerate overnight or until firm.

3. For the filling, in a small saucepan, combine the cranberry sauce, sugar and orange juice. Bring to a boil; cook and stir 2 minutes. Remove from the heat. Cool completely; stir in the chopped walnuts.

4. Preheat oven to 375°. Unwrap each portion of dough; cut crosswise into 16 slices. Press onto the bottoms and up the sides of greased mini-muffin cups. Fill each with 2 teaspoons cranberry mixture.

5. Bake 8-10 minutes or until the edges are light golden. Cool in pans 10 minutes. Remove to wire racks to cool completely.

6. Drizzle the cooled tarts with the melted white baking chocolate; let stand until set.

PER SERVING *1 tart equals 113 cal., 4 g fat (2 g sat. fat), 9 mg chol., 60 mg sodium, 18 g carb., 1 g fiber, 2 g pro.*

ORANGE-CRANBERRY NUT TARTS

Brownie Bonanza

Stir up a bowlful of batter, pour it into a pan and bake the **chocolaty bars** no one can resist. Then watch them disappear **square by square!**

Banana-Split Brownies

This recipe mixes the toppings of a classic ice cream sundae into scrumptious brownies. It just doesn't get much better than that!

—**CONNEE SHECKLER** CHESTERTOWN, MD

PREP: 45 MIN. • **BAKE:** 40 MIN. + COOLING • **MAKES:** 2 DOZEN

- 8 **ounces unsweetened chocolate, chopped**
- ¾ **cup butter, cubed**
- 3 **large eggs**
- 2 **cups sugar**
- 1 **teaspoon vanilla extract**
- 1 **cup plus 2 tablespoons all-purpose flour**
- 1 **cup maraschino cherries, chopped**

TOPPING
- 1 **package (8 ounces) cream cheese, softened**
- ½ **cup mashed ripe banana (about 1 medium)**
- ⅓ **cup strawberry preserves**
- 1 **large egg, lightly beaten**
- ¼ **cup chopped salted peanuts**
  Sliced bananas and additional chopped maraschino cherries, optional

1. Preheat oven to 350°. In a microwave, melt chocolate and butter; stir until smooth.

2. In a large bowl, beat the eggs and sugar on high speed 10 minutes. Stir in vanilla and chocolate mixture. Gradually stir in the flour. Fold in the maraschino cherries. Spread into a greased 13x9-in. baking pan.

3. In a small bowl, beat cream cheese until smooth. Beat in mashed banana and preserves. Add egg; beat on low speed just until blended. Spread over batter; sprinkle with nuts.

4. Bake 40-45 minutes or until the topping is set and a toothpick inserted in brownie portion comes out mostly clean. Cool completely on a wire rack.

5. Cut into bars. If desired, serve bars topped with sliced bananas and additional maraschino cherries. Store in an airtight container in the refrigerator.

PER SERVING *1 brownie equals 262 cal., 16 g fat (9 g sat. fat), 57 mg chol., 101 mg sodium, 31 g carb., 2 g fiber, 4 g pro.*

BANANA-SPLIT
BROWNIES

CHOCOLATE FUDGE BROWNIES

Chocolate Fudge Brownies

Here are rich, fudgy treats everyone loves. For an extra-special touch, sprinkle on confectioners' sugar or try the ideas below.

—**HAZEL FRITCHIE** PALESTINE, IL

PREP: 15 MIN. • **BAKE:** 35 MIN. + COOLING • **MAKES:** 16 SERVINGS

- 1 cup butter, cubed
- 6 ounces unsweetened chocolate, chopped
- 4 large eggs
- 2 cups sugar
- 1 teaspoon vanilla extract
- ½ teaspoon salt
- 1 cup all-purpose flour
- 2 cups chopped walnuts
  Confectioners' sugar, optional

1. Preheat oven to 350°. In a small saucepan, melt butter and chocolate over low heat. Cool slightly.
2. In a large bowl, beat eggs, sugar, vanilla and salt until blended. Stir in chocolate mixture. Add flour, mixing well. Stir in nuts. Spread into a greased 9-in.-square baking pan.
3. Bake 35-40 minutes or until a toothpick inserted in the center comes out with moist crumbs (do not overbake).
4. Cool completely in pan on a wire rack. If desired, dust with confectioners' sugar. Cut into bars.

PER SERVING *1 brownie equals 395 cal., 28 g fat (12 g sat. fat), 77 mg chol., 196 mg sodium, 36 g carb., 3 g fiber, 6 g pro.*

BUILD-YOUR-OWN BROWNIE

Start with the Chocolate Fudge Brownies recipe (top right). Then have fun dressing them up with any of these yummy ideas!

Raspberry Brownies

Mash ¼ cup fresh raspberries and stir into the batter. Add a few more berries on top.

—**MICHELLE GUILMETTE** TUCSON, AZ

M&M Brownie Explosion

Mix Peanut Butter M&M's into the batter, bake, then spread on a fudgy frosting. Finish off your treats with a generous sprinkling of M&M's.

—**BRODI JEAN PATRICIA TALLMAN** EDMONTON, AB

Awesome Rocky Road Brownies

I pile on mini marshmallows and toasted pecans during the last five minutes of baking. A drizzle of chocolate sauce adds the awesome!

—**JANYTH PASHIN** STILLWATER, OK

RASPBERRY BROWNIES

CHOCOLATE FUDGE BROWNIES

M&M BROWNIE EXPLOSION

AWESOME ROCKY ROAD BROWNIES

SALTED CASHEW & CARAMEL CHEWS

Salted Cashew & Caramel Chews

Sweet and salty in one recipe—what a blissful combination! Caramel ice cream topping is the luscious secret in the batter. I add melted semisweet chocolate and chopped pecans for good measure.

—PAULA MARCHESI LENHARTSVILLE, PA

PREP: 25 MIN.
BAKE: 10 MIN./BATCH + COOLING
MAKES: ABOUT 3 DOZEN

- ¾ cup unsalted butter, softened
- 1½ cups packed brown sugar
- 2 large eggs
- ¼ cup hot caramel ice cream topping
- 1 teaspoon vanilla extract
- 2½ cups all-purpose flour
- ¾ teaspoon baking soda
- ¼ teaspoon salt
- 2 cups (12 ounces) semisweet chocolate chips, divided
- ¾ cup plus ½ cup lightly salted cashew pieces, divided

1. Preheat oven to 350°. In a large bowl, cream the butter and brown sugar until light and fluffy. Gradually beat in the eggs, caramel ice cream topping and vanilla. In another bowl, whisk the flour, baking soda and salt; gradually beat into creamed mixture. Stir in 1⅓ cups semisweet chocolate chips and ¾ cup cashews.

2. Drop the cookie dough by rounded tablespoonfuls 2 in. apart onto parchment paper-lined baking sheets. Bake 10-12 minutes or until edges are firm. Cool on pans 5 minutes. Remove to wire racks; cool completely.

3. In a microwave, melt remaining chocolate chips; stir until smooth. Drizzle over cookies; sprinkle with remaining cashews. Let stand until set.

PER SERVING *1 cookie equals 184 cal., 9 g fat (5 g sat. fat), 21 mg chol., 68 mg sodium, 24 g carb., 1 g fiber, 3 g pro.*

Aunt Myrtle's Coconut Oat Cookies

These are the stuff of happy memories. Store them in your best cookie jar!

—CATHERINE CASSIDY MILWAUKEE, WI

PREP: 30 MIN. • **BAKE:** 10 MIN./BATCH
MAKES: ABOUT 5 DOZEN

- 1 cup butter, softened
- 1 cup packed brown sugar
- 2 large eggs
- 2 teaspoons vanilla extract
- 2⅓ cups all-purpose flour
- 1 teaspoon salt
- 1 teaspoon baking soda
- ¾ teaspoon baking powder
- 2 cups flaked coconut
- 1 cup old-fashioned or quick-cooking oats
- ¾ cup chopped walnuts, toasted

1. Preheat oven to 375°. In a large bowl, cream butter and brown sugar until light and fluffy. Beat in eggs and vanilla. In another bowl, whisk the flour, salt, baking soda and baking powder; gradually beat into creamed mixture. Stir in the coconut, oats and toasted walnuts.

2. Drop the dough by tablespoonfuls 2 in. apart onto ungreased baking sheets. Bake 8-10 minutes or until light brown. Remove from the pans to wire racks to cool.

NOTE *To toast nuts, bake in a shallow pan in a 350° oven for 5-10 minutes or cook in a skillet over low heat until lightly browned, stirring occasionally.*
PER SERVING *1 cookie equals 86 cal., 5 g fat (3 g sat. fat), 13 mg chol., 95 mg sodium, 9 g carb., trace fiber, 1 g pro.*

Crisp Lemon Shortbread

Buttery, crispy shortbread squares get a tangy twist of citrus when you mix in lemon juice and zest. For a bit of sparkle, sprinkle on coarse sugar.

—MARCIA WHITNEY GAINESVILLE, FL

PREP: 20 MIN. • **BAKE:** 20 MIN.
MAKES: 2 DOZEN

- ¾ cup butter, softened
- ½ cup confectioners' sugar
- 1 teaspoon grated lemon peel
- 1 tablespoon lemon juice
- 1½ cups all-purpose flour
- 2 teaspoons coarse sugar

1. Preheat oven to 325°. In a bowl, beat the butter, confectioners' sugar and lemon peel until blended. Beat in the lemon juice. Gradually beat in the flour.

2. Divide dough into four portions. On a lightly floured surface, roll each portion into a 5x3½-in. rectangle. Transfer to ungreased baking sheets. Cut each rectangle into six squares, but do not separate. Prick tops with a fork. Sprinkle with sugar.

3. Bake 20-25 minutes or until light brown. Cool on the pans 10 minutes. Transfer the shortbread to a cutting board; recut into squares. Cool on a wire rack.

PER SERVING *1 cookie equals 91 cal., 6 g fat (4 g sat. fat), 15 mg chol., 46 mg sodium, 9 g carb., trace fiber, 1 g pro.*

Cranberry Cookies with Browned Butter Glaze

PREP: 40 MIN.
BAKE: 10 MIN./BATCH + COOLING
MAKES: ABOUT 4½ DOZEN

- ½ **cup butter, softened**
- 1 **cup sugar**
- ¾ **cup packed brown sugar**
- 1 **large egg**
- 2 **tablespoons orange juice**
- 3 **cups all-purpose flour**
- 1 **teaspoon baking powder**
- ½ **teaspoon salt**
- ¼ **teaspoon baking soda**
- ¼ **cup 2% milk**
- 2½ **cups coarsely chopped fresh cranberries**
- 1 **cup white baking chips**
- 1 **cup chopped pecans or walnuts**

GLAZE
- ⅓ **cup butter, cubed**
- 2 **cups confectioners' sugar**
- 1½ **teaspoons vanilla extract**
- 3 **to 4 tablespoons water**

1. Preheat oven to 375°. In a large bowl, cream butter and sugars until light and fluffy. Beat in the egg and orange juice. In another bowl, whisk flour, baking powder, salt and baking soda; add to the creamed mixture alternately with the milk. Stir in the cranberries, white baking chips and chopped pecans.

2. Drop the cookie dough by level tablespoonfuls 1 in. apart onto greased baking sheets. Bake 10-12 minutes or until light brown. Remove from pans to wire racks to cool completely.

3. For the glaze, in a small heavy saucepan, melt butter over medium heat. Heat 5-7 minutes or until golden brown, stirring constantly. Remove from heat. Stir in confectioners' sugar, vanilla and enough water to reach a drizzling consistency. Drizzle over the cookies. Let stand until set.

PER SERVING *1 cookie equals 130 cal., 5 g fat (3 g sat. fat), 12 mg chol., 66 mg sodium, 19 g carb., 1 g fiber, 1 g pro.*

Cherry Coconut Treats

My great-grandmother first baked her coconut bars more than a century ago. Through the years, they've appeared at countless gatherings. At Christmastime, use both red and green cherries for an extra-festive presentation.

—**ANNE MULLEN** WINDSOR, ON

PREP: 15 MIN. • **BAKE:** 35 MIN. + CHILLING
MAKES: 2 DOZEN

- 1½ **cups all-purpose flour**
- 1 **cup graham cracker crumbs**
- ⅔ **cup packed brown sugar**
- 1 **teaspoon baking powder**
- ½ **teaspoon salt**
- 1 **cup butter, melted**

FILLING
- 4 **cups finely shredded unsweetened coconut**
- 2 **cans (14 ounces each) sweetened condensed milk**
- 2 **jars (10 ounces each) maraschino cherries, drained and chopped**
- 2 **teaspoons vanilla extract**
- 1 **teaspoon almond extract**

1. Preheat oven to 325°. In a small bowl, mix the first five ingredients; stir in melted butter. Press onto bottom of a greased 13x9-in. baking pan.

2. In another bowl, mix the filling ingredients; pour over the crust. Bake 35-40 minutes or until the edges are lightly browned. Cool on a wire rack 1 hour. Refrigerate, covered, 4 hours before cutting. Store in an airtight container in the refrigerator.

NOTE *Look for unsweetened coconut in the baking or health food section of your grocery store.*

PER SERVING *1 bar equals 362 cal., 20 g fat (14 g sat. fat), 32 mg chol., 202 mg sodium, 45 g carb., 3 g fiber, 5 g pro.*

Peanut Butter Cups

The popular blend of peanut butter and chocolate is one my children, grandkids and great-grandkids can't get enough of. They snatch up these quick and easy candy cups as soon as I have them.

—**DORIS PRICE** SAINT JOHN, NB

PREP: 20 MIN. + CHILLING
MAKES: 3 DOZEN

- 1½ **cups confectioners' sugar**
- 1 **cup creamy peanut butter**
- ½ **cup packed brown sugar**
- 2 **tablespoons butter, softened**
- 1 **teaspoon vanilla extract**
- 2 **cups (12 ounces) semisweet chocolate chips**
- ¼ **cup shortening**

1. In a small bowl, combine the confectioners' sugar, peanut butter, brown sugar, butter and vanilla; cover and set aside.

2. In a microwave, melt the semisweet chocolate chips and shortening; stir until smooth. Pour teaspoonfuls into paper-lined muffin cups.

3. Drop a rounded teaspoonful of peanut butter mixture into each cup; top with another teaspoonful of the chocolate mixture. Refrigerate until set. Store in an airtight container.

PER SERVING *1 serving equals 182 cal., 11 g fat (5 g sat. fat), 2 mg chol., 41 mg sodium, 21 g carb., 2 g fiber, 3 g pro.*

PEANUT BUTTER CUPS

EAT SMART
Red, White & Blue Cheesecake Bars

After trying light cheesecake recipes with mixed results, I decided to create my own. I think it tastes like the real deal.
—**KATIE FARRELL** BRIGHTON, MI

PREP: 20 MIN. • **BAKE:** 25 MIN. + CHILLING
MAKES: 1 DOZEN

- **1** graham cracker crust (9 inches)
- **¾** cup 2% cottage cheese
- **1** package (8 ounces) reduced-fat cream cheese
  Sugar substitute blend equivalent to 1 cup sugar
- **1** teaspoon grated lemon peel
- **2** tablespoons lemon juice
- **1** teaspoon vanilla extract
- **2** large egg whites
- **1** large egg
- **⅓** cup reduced-sugar strawberry preserves
- **½** cup fresh blueberries

1. Preheat oven to 375°. Line an 8-in.-square baking pan with foil, letting ends extend up sides; coat foil with cooking spray. Remove pie crust from foil pan; break into fine crumbs into prepared pan. Press crumbs onto bottom of pan.

2. Place the cottage cheese in a small food processor; process until smooth. Transfer to a bowl. Add cream cheese, sugar blend, lemon peel, lemon juice and vanilla; beat until smooth. In a small bowl, lightly beat egg whites and egg; add to the cottage cheese mixture. Beat on low speed just until blended. Pour over crust.

3. Drop the preserves by teaspoonfuls over filling. Cut through cheesecake with a knife to swirl. Sprinkle with blueberries.

4. Bake 25-30 minutes or until the center of the cheesecake is almost set. Cool 1 hour on a wire rack. Refrigerate 2 hours or until cold.

5. Lifting with the foil, remove the cheesecake from pan. Cut into bars.
NOTE *This recipe was tested with Truvia baking blend.*
PER SERVING *1 bar equals 193 cal., 8 g fat (4 g sat. fat), 31 mg chol., 226 mg sodium, 31 g carb., trace fiber, 5 g pro.*
***Diabetic Exchanges:** 2 starch, 1 fat.*

Cherry Almond Snowdrops

PREP: 25 MIN. • **BAKE:** 10 MIN./BATCH
MAKES: ABOUT 3 DOZEN

- **2** cups plus 2 tablespoons cake flour
- **¾** cup plus ½ cup confectioners' sugar, divided
- **¼** teaspoon salt
- **1** cup cold butter, cubed
- **2** teaspoons vanilla extract
- **½** teaspoon almond extract
- **½** cup dried cherries, chopped
- **¼** cup finely chopped almonds, toasted

1. Preheat oven to 350°. Place cake flour, ¾ cup confectioner's sugar and salt in a food processor; pulse until blended. Add the butter and extracts; pulse until butter is the size of peas. Add cherries and almonds; pulse until combined (dough will be crumbly).

2. Shape the dough into 1-in. balls, pressing firmly to adhere; place 1 in. apart on ungreased baking sheets. Bake 10-12 minutes or until lightly browned.

3. Cool on pans 10 minutes. Roll warm cookies in remaining confectioners' sugar. Cool on wire racks.

NOTE *To toast nuts, place in a dry skillet and heat over low heat until lightly browned, stirring occasionally.*
PER SERVING *1 cookie equals 113 cal., 6 g fat (4 g sat. fat), 15 mg chol., 59 mg sodium, 13 g carb., trace fiber, 1 g pro.*

> As soon as I was old enough, I helped make Cherry Almond Snowdrops for the holidays. Now I freeze the dough to save time during the busy Christmas season.
> —**TRISHA KRUSE** EAGLE, ID

CHERRY ALMOND SNOWDROPS

Peanut Bars

With peanut butter in both the batter and frosting, plus chopped nuts sprinkled on top, these treats have triple the goodness.

—REN REED TAVARES, FL

PREP: 20 MIN. • **BAKE:** 20 MIN. + COOLING
MAKES: 2 CAKES (20 PIECES EACH)

- 1 cup butter, softened
- 2 cups sugar
- 1 cup creamy peanut butter
- 2 large eggs
- 1 teaspoon vanilla extract
- 2 cups all-purpose flour
- 1 teaspoon baking powder
- 1 cup water
- ½ cup 2% milk

FROSTING
- ¾ cup creamy peanut butter
- ¼ cup butter, softened
- 3¾ cups confectioners' sugar
- 5 to 6 tablespoons 2% milk
- 1 cup chopped unsalted peanuts

1. Preheat oven to 350°. Grease two 13x9-in. baking pans.
2. In a large bowl, cream the butter, sugar and peanut butter until blended. Add the eggs, one at a time, beating well after each addition. Beat in the vanilla. In another bowl, whisk flour and baking powder; add to creamed mixture alternately with water and milk, beating well after each addition.
3. Transfer to the prepared baking pans. Bake 20-25 minutes or until a toothpick inserted in the center comes out clean. Meanwhile, for the frosting, in a large bowl, beat the peanut butter and butter until blended. Beat in the confectioners' sugar alternately with enough milk to reach a spreading consistency.
4. Remove the cakes from the oven; place on wire racks. Spread frosting over the warm cakes; sprinkle with peanuts. Cool completely.
PER SERVING *1 piece equals 250 cal., 14 g fat (5 g sat. fat), 25 mg chol., 114 mg sodium, 29 g carb., 1 g fiber, 5 g pro.*

LEMONY COCONUT BARS

Lemony Coconut Bars

Want something different to include on your cookie tray? These citrusy, chewy bars are refreshing and especially popular with lemon lovers. For a zingy twist, use the juice and zest of a lime instead.

—NANCY ZIMMERMAN
CAPE MAY COURT HOUSE, NJ

PREP: 25 MIN. • **BAKE:** 25 MIN. + COOLING
MAKES: 2 DOZEN

- ½ cup butter, softened
- ½ cup packed light brown sugar
- 1½ cups all-purpose flour

FILLING
- 2 large eggs
- 1 cup packed light brown sugar
- ½ teaspoon grated lemon peel
- ½ teaspoon vanilla extract
- ¼ teaspoon lemon extract
- 2 tablespoons all-purpose flour
- ½ teaspoon baking powder
- ¼ teaspoon salt
- 1½ cups flaked coconut
- 1 cup chopped pecans or walnuts

GLAZE
- 1 cup confectioners' sugar
- 1 tablespoon butter, melted
- ½ teaspoon grated lemon peel
- 3 tablespoons lemon juice

1. Preheat oven to 350°. In a bowl, cream butter and sugar until light and fluffy; gradually beat in flour, mixing well. Press onto bottom of a greased 13x9-in. baking pan. Bake 8-10 minutes or until edges are golden brown. Cool on a wire rack.
2. For the filling, in a large bowl, beat the eggs, brown sugar, lemon peel and extracts until blended. In a small bowl, mix the flour, baking powder and salt; stir into the egg mixture. Stir in the coconut and pecans. Spread over crust.
3. Bake 17-20 minutes longer or until golden brown. Cool 10 minutes on a wire rack. Meanwhile, in a small bowl, mix glaze ingredients until smooth; drizzle over the warm filling. Cool completely. Cut into bars.
PER SERVING *1 bar equals 208 cal., 10 g fat (5 g sat. fat), 27 mg chol., 96 mg sodium, 29 g carb., 1 g fiber, 2 g pro.*

**BERNICE JANOWSKI'S
PUMPKIN MOUSSE PIE WITH
GINGERSNAP CRUST** *PAGE 110*

Cakes & Pies

From frosted layer cakes to lattice-topped pies, the recipes here are a **marvelous mix** of beloved classics and creative twists. Enjoy your family's favorites and try something **delightfully new!**

LISA POTTER'S GRANDMA PIETZ'S CRANBERRY CAKE PUDDING *PAGE 108*

JENNIFER BRUCE'S MAMAW EMILY'S STRAWBERRY CAKE *PAGE 113*

BARBARA MOYER'S BUTTERSCOTCH PEACH PIE *PAGE 114*

Yellow Cupcakes

Want a sure way to brighten someone's day? Homemade cupcakes! Start with a buttery yellow base that works with just about any frosting you care to spread on. Then have fun dressing them up with lots of sprinkles or other decorations.

—TASTE OF HOME TEST KITCHEN

PREP: 20 MIN. • **BAKE:** 15 MIN. + COOLING
MAKES: ABOUT 2 DOZEN

- ⅔ cup butter, softened
- 1¾ cups sugar
- 2 large eggs
- 1½ teaspoons vanilla extract
- 2½ cups all-purpose flour
- 2½ teaspoons baking powder
- ½ teaspoon salt
- 1¼ cups 2% milk
  Frosting of your choice

1. Preheat the oven to 350°. Line 22-24 muffin cups with paper liners.
2. In a large bowl, cream butter and sugar until light and fluffy. Add eggs, one at a time, beating well after each addition. Beat in vanilla. In another bowl, whisk the flour, baking powder and salt; add to the creamed mixture alternately with milk, beating well after each addition.
3. Fill prepared cups three-fourths full. Bake 15-20 minutes or until a toothpick inserted in the center comes out clean. Cool in the pans 10 minutes before removing to wire racks to cool completely. Spread with frosting.
PER SERVING *1 cupcake (calculated without frosting) equals 163 cal., 6 g fat (4 g sat. fat), 32 mg chol., 138 mg sodium, 25 g carb., trace fiber, 2 g pro.*

TOP TIP

Do you find filling muffin cups with cupcake or muffin batter to be a difficult, messy process? The pros in the *Taste of Home* Test Kitchen prefer to use a dry measuring cup if the batter is thin and a spring-loaded ice cream scoop for thicker batters. These are easy ways to fill the muffin cups and will assure that the batter is divided evenly. You'll end up with cupcakes or muffins of uniform size.

GRANDMA PIETZ'S CRANBERRY CAKE PUDDING

Grandma Pietz's Cranberry Cake Pudding

Our relatives have been passing down this simple, comforting recipe for generations.

—LISA POTTER CAMP DOUGLAS, WI

PREP: 30 MIN. • **BAKE:** 20 MIN.
MAKES: 15 SERVINGS (2 CUPS SAUCE)

- 3 tablespoons butter, softened
- 1 cup sugar
- 1 large egg
- 2 cups all-purpose flour
- 2 teaspoons baking powder
  Dash salt
- 1 cup 2% milk
- 2 cups fresh or frozen cranberries, thawed

SAUCE
- 2 cups packed brown sugar
- 1 cup water
- ½ cup sugar
- 3 tablespoons butter
- ¼ teaspoon vanilla extract

1. Preheat oven to 350°. Grease a 13x9-in. baking pan.
2. In a large bowl, beat butter and sugar until crumbly. Beat in the egg. In another bowl, whisk flour, baking powder and salt; add to butter mixture alternately with the milk, beating well after each addition. If desired, coarsely chop cranberries. Fold cranberries into batter.
3. Transfer to prepared pan. Bake 20-25 minutes or until a toothpick inserted in center comes out clean.
4. In a large saucepan, combine the brown sugar, water, sugar and butter; bring to a boil over medium heat, stirring constantly to dissolve sugar. Cook and stir until slightly thickened; stir in vanilla. Serve warm with cake.
PER SERVING *1 piece with 2 tablespoons sauce equals 311 cal., 5 g fat (3 g sat. fat), 26 mg chol., 125 mg sodium, 64 g carb., 1 g fiber, 3 g pro.*

Chocolate-Peanut Butter Sheet Cake

I'm a fan of peanut butter and chocolate, so I think this dessert is doubly divine.

—LISA VARNER EL PASO, TX

PREP: 25 MIN. • **BAKE:** 25 MIN. + COOLING
MAKES: 15 SERVINGS

- 2 cups all-purpose flour
- 2 cups sugar
- 1 teaspoon baking soda
- ½ teaspoon salt
- 1 cup water
- ½ cup butter, cubed
- ½ cup creamy peanut butter
- ¼ cup baking cocoa
- 3 large eggs
- ½ cup sour cream
- 2 teaspoons vanilla extract

FROSTING

- 3 cups confectioners' sugar
- ½ cup creamy peanut butter
- ½ cup 2% milk
- ½ teaspoon vanilla extract
- ½ cup chopped salted or unsalted peanuts

1. Preheat oven to 350°. Grease a 13x9-in. baking pan.
2. In a large bowl, whisk the flour, sugar, baking soda and salt. In a small saucepan, combine the water, butter, peanut butter and cocoa; bring just to a boil, stirring occasionally. Add to flour mixture, stirring just until moistened.
3. In a small bowl, whisk eggs, sour cream and vanilla until blended; add to flour mixture, whisking constantly. Transfer to the prepared pan. Bake 25-30 minutes or until a toothpick inserted in center comes out clean.
4. Prepare the frosting while cake is baking. In a large bowl, beat the confectioners' sugar, peanut butter, milk and vanilla until smooth.
5. Remove the cake from oven; place on a wire rack. Immediately spread with frosting; sprinkle with peanuts. Cool completely.
PER SERVING *1 piece equals 482 cal., 20 g fat (7 g sat. fat), 59 mg chol., 337 mg sodium, 70 g carb., 2 g fiber, 9 g pro.*

Aunt Lou's Fresh Apple Cake

One of my Great-Aunt Lou's signature specialties was a scrumptious cake she made with fresh apples. It was so good, it became a family tradition. My mother bakes one for our annual beach trip.

—CRISTY KING SCOTT DEPOT, WV

PREP: 15 MIN. • **BAKE:** 50 MIN. + COOLING
MAKES: 12 SERVINGS

- 2 cups sugar
- 1 cup canola oil
- 3 large eggs
- 2 teaspoons vanilla extract
- 3 cups all-purpose flour
- 1 teaspoon salt
- 1 teaspoon baking powder
- 3 cups chopped peeled apples (about 3 medium)
  Confectioners' sugar, optional

1. Preheat oven to 350°. Grease and flour a 10-in. fluted tube pan.
2. In a large bowl, beat the sugar, oil, eggs and vanilla until well blended. In another bowl, whisk flour, salt and baking powder; gradually beat into oil mixture. Stir in apples. Transfer batter to prepared pan.
3. Bake 50-60 minutes or until a toothpick inserted in center comes out clean. Cool in the pan 10 minutes. Run a knife around sides and center tube of pan. Remove the cake to a wire rack to cool. Dust with confectioners' sugar if desired.
NOTE *To remove cakes easily, use solid shortening to grease plain and fluted tube pans.*
PER SERVING *1 slice equals 445 cal., 20 g fat (2 g sat. fat), 47 mg chol., 249 mg sodium, 62 g carb., 2 g fiber, 5 g pro.*

AUNT LOU'S FRESH APPLE CAKE

BLACKBERRY-ORANGE CAKE

Pumpkin Mousse Pie with Gingersnap Crust

Gingersnaps and pumpkin pair so well. This is a must for our Thanksgiving dinner.
—**BERNICE JANOWSKI** STEVENS POINT, WI

PREP: 45 MIN. + CHILLING
MAKES: 8 SERVINGS

- 1½ cups finely crushed gingersnap cookies (about 30 cookies)
- 1 cup finely chopped pecans, toasted
- ⅓ cup butter, melted
- 1 envelope unflavored gelatin
- ¼ cup cold water
- ½ cup packed brown sugar
- ½ cup half-and-half cream
- 3 large egg yolks
- 1 can (15 ounces) solid-pack pumpkin
- 2 teaspoons pumpkin pie spice
- 2 cups whipped topping
- ¼ cup butterscotch-caramel ice cream topping
- ½ cup chopped pecans, toasted

1. Preheat oven to 350°. In a small bowl, mix the crushed cookies and chopped pecans; stir in the butter. Press onto bottom and up sides of an ungreased 9-in. deep-dish pie plate. Bake 10-12 minutes or until lightly browned. Cool on a wire rack.
2. In a microwave-safe bowl, sprinkle unflavored gelatin over the cold water; let stand 1 minute. Microwave on high for 30-40 seconds. Stir and let stand 1 minute or until gelatin is completely dissolved.
3. In a large saucepan, whisk brown sugar, cream and egg yolks until blended. Cook over low heat until a thermometer reads at least 160°, stirring constantly. (Do not allow to boil.) Remove from the heat; stir in the pumpkin, pie spice and gelatin mixture. Cool completely.
4. Fold in whipped topping. Pour into crust; refrigerate until set. Drizzle with ice cream topping; sprinkle with nuts.
NOTE *To toast nuts, bake in a shallow pan in a 350° oven for 5-10 minutes or cook in a skillet over low heat until lightly browned, stirring occasionally.*
PER SERVING *1 piece equals 516 cal., 32 g fat (12 g sat. fat), 98 mg chol., 227 mg sodium, 53 g carb., 4 g fiber, 7 g pro.*

Grandma prepared all kinds of treats using the berries from her garden. I decided to follow her lead and came up with Blackberry-Orange Cake. With lots of fruity flavor, it's a refreshing finale for a summer dinner.
—**LISA VARNER** EL PASO, TX

Blackberry-Orange Cake

PREP: 20 MIN. • **BAKE:** 40 MIN. + COOLING
MAKES: 10 SERVINGS

- ½ cup butter, softened
- 1 cup sugar, divided
- 1 egg
- 1 teaspoon grated orange peel
- 1½ cups plus 1 tablespoon all-purpose flour, divided
- ½ teaspoon baking soda
- ⅛ teaspoon salt
- ½ cup sour cream or plain yogurt
- 2 cups fresh blackberries
  Confectioners' sugar, optional

1. Preheat oven to 350°. Grease and flour a 9-in. springform pan.
2. In a large bowl, cream butter and ¾ cup sugar until light and fluffy. Beat in the egg and orange peel. In another bowl, whisk 1½ cups flour, baking soda and salt; add to the creamed mixture alternately with sour cream, beating well after each addition. Transfer to prepared pan.
3. In a bowl, toss blackberries with remaining flour; arrange over batter. Sprinkle with remaining sugar. Bake 40-45 minutes or until a toothpick inserted in the center of cake portion comes out clean.
4. Loosen the sides from pan with a knife; remove rim from pan. Cool on a wire rack; serve warm or at room temperature. If desired, dust with confectioners' sugar before serving.
PER SERVING *1 slice equals 274 cal., 12 g fat (7 g sat. fat), 51 mg chol., 177 mg sodium, 38 g carb., 2 g fiber, 4 g pro.*

Pineapple Pie with Coconut Cream

Here in Hawaii, pineapples and coconuts are everywhere. We put them to luscious use in a cool and creamy pie.

—**KAREN NAIHE** KAMUELA, HI

PREP: 35 MIN. + COOLING
BAKE: 35 MIN. + CHILLING
MAKES: 8 SERVINGS
(⅔ CUP COCONUT CREAM)

- 1½ cups chopped fresh pineapple or canned pineapple tidbits
- 2 tablespoons plus 1 cup sugar, divided
- 1 package (5¼ ounces) coconut cookies
- ¼ cup butter, melted
- 12 ounces cream cheese, softened
- 1 cup plain Greek yogurt
- ½ cup ground almonds
- 1 teaspoon vanilla extract
- 3 eggs, lightly beaten

COCONUT CREAM
- 1 can (13.66 ounces) coconut milk
- 2 tablespoons confectioners' sugar
- ¼ teaspoon vanilla extract

1. In a small saucepan, combine pineapple and 2 tablespoons sugar. Bring to a boil; cook 6-8 minutes or until the liquid is almost evaporated, stirring occasionally. Cool completely.
2. Preheat oven to 350°. Place cookies in a food processor; pulse until fine crumbs form. Add butter; pulse just until blended. Press onto bottom and up sides of a 9-in. deep-dish pie plate.
3. In a large bowl, beat cream cheese and remaining sugar until smooth. Beat in yogurt, almonds and vanilla. Add eggs; beat on low speed just until blended. Fold in pineapple mixture. Pour into crust. Bake 35-40 minutes or until center is almost set. Cool on a wire rack 1 hour. Refrigerate pie and can of coconut milk at least 4 hours or until cold.
4. Place a mixer bowl and whisk attachment in the freezer until cold, about 15 minutes. Turn chilled can of coconut milk upside down; open can. Pour off and discard the liquid portion. Transfer solid portion remaining in can to chilled bowl. Add confectioners' sugar and vanilla; beat until stiff peaks form. Serve with pie.

NOTE *Light coconut milk is not recommended for this recipe.*
PER SERVING *1 piece with about 1 tablespoon coconut cream equals 601 cal., 41 g fat (24 g sat. fat), 139 mg chol., 320 mg sodium, 53 g carb., 1 g fiber, 10 g pro.*

Cranberry Walnut Pie

With ruby red color and a golden lattice crust, this holiday-special dessert looks just as good as it tastes.

—**DIANE EVERETT** DUNKIRK, NY

PREP: 20 MIN. • **BAKE:** 50 MIN. + COOLING
MAKES: 8 SERVINGS

- 1 package (12 ounces) fresh or frozen cranberries, thawed
- 1½ cups packed brown sugar
- 1 cup chopped walnuts
- ¼ cup butter, melted
- 4½ teaspoons all-purpose flour
- 2 teaspoons grated orange peel
  Dash salt
  Pastry for double-crust pie (9 inches)

1. Preheat oven to 375°. Place the cranberries in a food processor; cover and process until finely chopped.

Transfer to a large bowl; stir in brown sugar, nuts, butter, flour, peel and salt.
2. On a lightly floured surface, roll one half of pastry dough to a ⅛-in.-thick circle; transfer to a 9-in. pie plate. Trim pastry to ½ in. beyond the rim of plate. Add filling.
3. Roll the remaining dough into a ⅛-in.-thick circle; cut into ½-in.-wide strips. Arrange over filling in a lattice pattern. Trim and seal strips to edge of bottom pastry; flute edge. Cover edges loosely with foil.
4. Bake 30 minutes. Remove foil; bake 20-25 minutes or until crust is golden brown and filling is bubbly. Cool on a wire rack.

PASTRY FOR DOUBLE-CRUST PIE (9 INCHES) *Combine 2½ cups of all-purpose flour and ½ teaspoon salt; cut in 1 cup cold butter until crumbly. Gradually add ⅓ to ⅔ cup ice water, tossing with a fork until dough holds together when pressed. Divide dough in half and shape into disks; wrap in plastic wrap and refrigerate 1 hour.*
PER SERVING *1 piece equals 550 cal., 28 g fat (10 g sat. fat), 25 mg chol., 273 mg sodium, 74 g carb., 3 g fiber, 4 g pro.*

CRANBERRY WALNUT PIE

White Chocolate Fluffy Cake

A former co-worker shared her recipe for a white chocolate cake topped with a fluffy frosting. It's my go-to treat whenever I'm craving something decadent.
—**MARILYN MOHR** TOLEDO, OH

PREP: 1 HOUR + STANDING
BAKE: 20 MIN. + COOLING
MAKES: 16 SERVINGS

- 4 large eggs, separated
- 4 ounces white baking chocolate, chopped
- ½ cup boiling water
- 1 cup butter, softened
- 2 cups sugar
- 1 teaspoon vanilla extract
- 2½ cups cake flour
- 1 teaspoon baking soda
- ½ teaspoon salt
- 1 cup buttermilk

FROSTING
- 16 ounces white baking chocolate, chopped
- ½ cup boiling water
- ½ cup butter, softened
- 1 teaspoon vanilla extract
- ⅛ teaspoon salt
- 3 cups confectioners' sugar

1. Place egg whites in a bowl; let stand at room temperature 30 minutes. Line bottoms of three greased 9-in. round baking pans with parchment paper; grease paper well.
2. Preheat oven to 350°. Place the white baking chocolate in a small bowl. Pour the boiling water over the white baking chocolate; stir with a whisk until smooth. Cool slightly.
3. In a large bowl, cream butter and sugar until light and fluffy. Add egg yolks, one at a time, beating well after each addition. Beat in the vanilla and chocolate mixture. In another bowl, whisk the flour, baking soda and salt; add to chocolate mixture alternately with buttermilk, beating well after each addition.
4. With clean beaters, beat the egg whites on medium speed until stiff peaks form. Fold into batter. Transfer to prepared pans.

5. Bake 20-25 minutes or until a toothpick inserted in center comes out clean. Cool in pans 10 minutes before removing to wire racks; carefully remove paper. Cool completely.
6. For frosting, place white chocolate in a small bowl. Pour the boiling water over chocolate; stir with a whisk until smooth. Cool to room temperature, stirring occasionally.
7. In a large bowl, beat the butter, vanilla and salt until creamy. Beat in confectioners' sugar alternately with chocolate mixture until smooth. Spread frosting between layers and over top and sides of cake.
PER SERVING *1 slice equals 618 cal., 29 g fat (19 g sat. fat), 93 mg chol., 383 mg sodium, 88 g carb., trace fiber, 7 g pro.*

OLD-FASHIONED PEANUT BUTTER PIE

Old-Fashioned Peanut Butter Pie

My mother baked a chewy, gooey peanut butter pie I adored as a kid. Now I continue her tradition for a new generation.
—**BRIANNA DEBLAKE** FREMONT, MI

PREP: 20 MIN. • **BAKE:** 1 HOUR
MAKES: 8 SERVINGS

- Pastry for single-crust pie (9 inches)
- 1½ cups light corn syrup
- ½ cup sugar
- ½ cup creamy peanut butter
- ¼ teaspoon salt
- 4 large eggs
- ½ teaspoon vanilla extract
- Optional toppings: broken Nutter Butter cookies, chopped peanuts and whipped topping

1. Preheat oven to 350°. On a lightly floured surface, roll pastry dough to a ⅛-in.-thick circle; transfer to a 9-in. pie plate. Trim pastry to ½ in. beyond rim of plate; flute edge.
2. In a large bowl, beat corn syrup, sugar, peanut butter and salt until blended. Beat in eggs and vanilla until smooth. Pour into pastry-lined pie plate. Bake 60-70 minutes or until top is puffed and center is almost set; cover top loosely with foil during the last 30 minutes to prevent overbrowning.
3. Remove foil. Cool on a wire rack. (Top may sink and crack slightly upon cooling.) Serve or refrigerate within 2 hours. Top as desired.
PASTRY FOR SINGLE-CRUST PIE (9 INCHES) *Combine 1¼ cups of all-purpose flour and ¼ teaspoon salt; cut in ½ cup cold butter until crumbly. Gradually add 3-5 tablespoons ice water, tossing with a fork until dough holds together when pressed. Wrap in plastic wrap and refrigerate 1 hour.*
PER SERVING *1 piece (calculated without optional toppings) equals 538 cal., 22 g fat (10 g sat. fat), 123 mg chol., 379 mg sodium, 82 g carb., 1 g fiber, 9 g pro.*

Scrumptious Sweet Potato Pie

I've tried many good variations of classic sweet potato desserts, but none quite like this. It skips the milk and has both a splash of whiskey and a hint of lemon.

—**SUZANNE SMITH** MAUMEE, OH

PREP: 1 HOUR + CHILLING
BAKE: 40 MIN. + COOLING
MAKES: 8 SERVINGS

- Pastry for single-crust pie (9 inches)
- 1½ pounds sweet potatoes (about 2 medium), cubed
- ⅓ cup butter, softened
- ⅔ cup sugar
- ¼ teaspoon ground cinnamon
- ⅛ teaspoon ground nutmeg
- ⅛ teaspoon baking powder
- 2 large eggs, lightly beaten
- 1 teaspoon vanilla extract
- ¼ teaspoon lemon extract
- 1 to 2 tablespoons whiskey or apple juice

1. On a lightly floured surface, roll pastry dough to a ⅛-in.-thick circle; transfer to a 9-in. pie plate. Trim the pastry to ½ in. beyond rim of plate; flute edge. Refrigerate 30 minutes. Preheat oven to 425°.

2. Meanwhile, place sweet potatoes in a large saucepan; add water to cover. Bring to a boil. Reduce the heat; cook, uncovered, 15-18 minutes or until tender. Drain well; return to the pot. Mash sweet potatoes until smooth (you should have 2 cups).

3. Line unpricked pastry with a double thickness of foil. Fill with pie weights, dried beans or uncooked rice. Bake on a lower oven rack 15-20 minutes or until edges are light golden brown. Remove the foil and weights; bake 3-6 minutes longer or until bottom is golden brown. Cool on a wire rack. Reduce oven setting to 350°.

4. In a large bowl, beat butter, sugar, cinnamon, nutmeg and baking powder until blended. Beat in the eggs, sweet potatoes and extracts until smooth. Stir in whiskey.

5. Add the filling to the crust. Bake on a middle oven rack 40-45 minutes or until center is set. Cool on a wire rack; serve or refrigerate within 2 hours.

PASTRY FOR SINGLE-CRUST PIE (9 INCHES) *Combine 1¼ cups of all-purpose flour and ¼ teaspoon salt; cut in ½ cup cold butter until crumbly. Gradually add 3-5 tablespoons ice water, tossing with a fork until dough holds together when pressed. Wrap in plastic wrap and refrigerate 1 hour.*
PER SERVING *1 piece equals 413 cal., 21 g fat (13 g sat. fat), 97 mg chol., 248 mg sodium, 53 g carb., 3 g fiber, 5 g pro.*

Mamaw Emily's Strawberry Cake

My husband loved his Mamaw's strawberry specialty. I like to surprise him with it.

—**JENNIFER BRUCE** MANITOU, KY

PREP: 15 MIN. • **BAKE:** 25 MIN. + COOLING
MAKES: 12 SERVINGS

- 1 package white cake mix (regular size)
- 1 package (3 ounces) strawberry gelatin
- 3 tablespoons sugar
- 3 tablespoons all-purpose flour
- 1 cup water
- ½ cup canola oil
- 2 large eggs
- 1 cup finely chopped strawberries

FROSTING
- ½ cup butter, softened
- ½ cup crushed strawberries
- 4½ to 5 cups confectioners' sugar

1. Preheat oven to 350°. Line the bottoms of two greased 8-in. round baking pans with parchment paper; grease paper.

2. In a large bowl, combine cake mix, strawberry gelatin, sugar and flour. Add water, oil and eggs; beat on low speed 30 seconds. Beat on medium 2 minutes. Fold in chopped berries. Transfer to prepared pans.

3. Bake 25-30 minutes or until a toothpick inserted in center comes out clean. Cool in pans 10 minutes before removing to wire racks; remove paper. Cool completely.

4. For the frosting, in a small bowl, beat the butter until creamy. Beat in the crushed strawberries. Gradually beat in enough confectioners' sugar to reach desired consistency. Spread the frosting between layers and over top and sides of cake.

PER SERVING *1 slice equals 532 cal., 21 g fat (7 g sat. fat), 51 mg chol., 340 mg sodium, 85 g carb., 1 g fiber, 4 g pro.*

MAMAW EMILY'S STRAWBERRY CAKE

Butterscotch Peach Pie

During peach season, this old-fashioned favorite is sure to be on our table.

—BARBARA MOYER TIFFIN, OH

PREP: 30 MIN. + CHILLING
BAKE: 45 MIN. + COOLING
MAKES: 8 SERVINGS

- 2 cups all-purpose flour
- 1 teaspoon salt
- ¾ cup shortening
- 4 to 5 tablespoons cold water

FILLING
- ¾ cup packed brown sugar
- 2 tablespoons all-purpose flour
- ⅓ cup light corn syrup
- 3 tablespoons butter, melted
- 2 tablespoons lemon juice
- ¼ teaspoon almond extract
- 8 medium peaches, peeled and sliced

1. In a large bowl, combine flour and salt; cut in shortening until crumbly. Gradually add cold water, tossing with a fork until dough forms a ball. Cover and refrigerate for 30 minutes or until easy to handle.

2. For the filling, in a small saucepan, combine brown sugar and flour. Stir in the light corn syrup and butter until blended. Bring to a boil; cook and stir for 2 minutes or until thickened.

Remove from heat; stir in lemon juice and extract. Place peaches in a large bowl; add syrup mixture. Toss to coat.

3. Divide the dough in half so one ball is slightly larger than the other. Roll out larger ball to fit a 9-in. pie plate. Transfer to pie plate; trim pastry to ½ in. beyond rim of plate. Add filling. Roll out the remaining pastry; make a lattice crust. Trim, seal and flute edges. Cover edges loosely with foil.

4. Bake at 375° for 25 minutes. Uncover; bake 20-25 minutes longer or until crust is golden brown and filling is bubbly. Cool on a wire rack.

PER SERVING *1 piece equals 480 cal., 23 g fat (7 g sat. fat), 11 mg chol., 342 mg sodium, 66 g carb., 2 g fiber, 4 g pro.*

Dar's Coconut Cream Pie

As soon as I whip up a toasted coconut cream pie, my family makes it vanish.

—DARLENE BARTOS SHOREVIEW, MN

PREP: 1 HOUR + CHILLING
COOK: 20 MIN. + CHILLING
MAKES: 10 SERVINGS

- **Pastry for single-crust pie (9 inches)**
- 4 large egg yolks
- 2 cups coconut milk
- 1½ cups half-and-half cream
- 1 cup sugar
- ⅓ cup cornstarch
- ¼ teaspoon salt
- 2 teaspoons vanilla extract
- 1½ cups flaked coconut, toasted, divided
- 2 cups heavy whipping cream
- ¼ cup confectioners' sugar
- ½ teaspoon vanilla extract

1. On a lightly floured surface, roll pastry dough to a ⅛-in.-thick circle; transfer to a 9-in. pie plate. Trim the pastry to ½ in. beyond rim of plate; flute edge. Refrigerate 30 minutes. Preheat oven to 425°.

2. Line pastry with a double thickness of foil. Fill with pie weights, dried beans or uncooked rice. Bake on a lower oven rack 20-25 minutes or until edges are golden brown. Remove foil and weights; bake 3-6 minutes longer or until the bottom is golden brown. Cool completely on a wire rack.

3. In a large heavy saucepan, whisk egg yolks, coconut milk, cream, sugar, cornstarch and salt until blended. Bring to a gentle boil over medium heat, whisking constantly. Reduce heat to medium-low; cook 2 minutes longer, whisking vigorously. Remove from heat; stir in vanilla and 1 cup coconut. Immediately transfer to crust.

4. Press plastic wrap onto surface of filling. Refrigerate 2 hours or until cold.

5. In a large bowl, beat cream until it begins to thicken. Add confectioners' sugar and vanilla; beat until soft peaks form. Spread over pie. Sprinkle with remaining coconut.

PASTRY FOR SINGLE-CRUST PIE (9 INCHES) *Combine 1¼ cups of all-purpose flour and ¼ teaspoon salt; cut in ½ cup cold butter until crumbly. Gradually add 3-5 tablespoons ice water, tossing with a fork until dough holds together when pressed. Wrap in plastic wrap and refrigerate 1 hour.*

NOTE *To toast coconut, spread in a 15x10x1-in. baking pan. Bake at 350° for 5-10 minutes or until lightly browned, stirring frequently.*

PER SERVING *1 piece equals 641 cal., 47 g fat (33 g sat. fat), 182 mg chol., 265 mg sodium, 50 g carb., 1 g fiber, 6 g pro.*

BUTTERSCOTCH PEACH PIE

Brownie Cheesecake Snickers Pie

What do you get when you mix brownies, cheesecake and candy bars? Pure bliss!

—**GENISE KRAUSE** STURGEON BAY, WI

PREP: 45 MIN. • **BAKE:** 20 MIN. + COOLING
MAKES: 10 SERVINGS

- ⅓ cup butter, cubed
- 1 cup sugar
- 2 tablespoons water
- 6 ounces semisweet chocolate, chopped
- 1 teaspoon vanilla extract
- 2 large eggs
- ¾ cup all-purpose flour
- ¼ teaspoon baking soda
- ⅛ teaspoon salt

CREAM CHEESE LAYER
- 10 ounces cream cheese, softened
- ⅓ cup sugar
- 1 large egg, beaten
- 1 teaspoon vanilla extract
- 4 Snickers candy bars (2.07 ounces each), cut into ½-inch pieces

GLAZE
- ½ cup heavy whipping cream
- 4 ounces semisweet chocolate, chopped

1. Preheat oven to 325°. In a heavy saucepan, bring butter, sugar and water to a boil, stirring constantly. Remove from the heat. Stir in chocolate until melted; cool slightly. Stir in vanilla.
2. In a large bowl, beat the eggs until lightly beaten. Gradually add chocolate mixture; mix well. Combine flour, baking soda and salt; gradually add to the egg mixture. Spread into a greased 9-in. deep-dish pie plate. Bake 20 minutes. Cool on a wire rack 10 minutes.
3. Meanwhile, in a large bowl, beat cream cheese, sugar, egg and vanilla just until blended. Arrange candy bar pieces over the brownie layer; spread cream cheese mixture over top. Bake 18-20 minutes or until top is set and edges are lightly browned. Cool on a wire rack for 1 hour.
4. For glaze, bring cream to a simmer; remove from heat. Add the chocolate and stir until smooth. Cool 15 minutes; pour over pie. Refrigerate until serving.
TO MAKE AHEAD *Pie can be made a day in advance. Cover and refrigerate.*

7UP POUND CAKE

> My grandmother gave me my 7UP Pound Cake recipe—and her grandmother gave it to her. For me, this dessert represents tradition, connection and love.
>
> —MARSHA DAVIS DESERT HOT SPRINGS, CA

PER SERVING *1 piece equals 510 cal., 30 g fat (17 g sat. fat), 102 mg chol., 246 mg sodium, 55 g carb., 2 g fiber, 7 g pro.*

7UP Pound Cake

PREP: 25 MIN. • **BAKE:** 65 MIN. + COOLING
MAKES: 16 SERVINGS

- 1½ cups butter, softened
- 3 cups sugar
- 5 large eggs
- 2 tablespoons lemon juice
- 1 teaspoon vanilla extract
- 3 cups all-purpose flour
- ¾ cup 7UP soda

GLAZE
- 1½ cups confectioners' sugar
- 1 tablespoon lemon or lime juice
- 1 to 2 tablespoons 7UP soda
- ½ teaspoon grated lemon or lime peel, optional

1. Preheat oven to 350°. Grease and flour a 10-in. fluted or plain tube pan.
2. In a large bowl, cream butter and sugar until light and fluffy. Add eggs, one at a time, beating well after each addition. Beat in the lemon juice and vanilla. Add flour alternately with 7UP, beating well after each addition.
3. Transfer the batter to the prepared pan. Bake 65-75 minutes or until a toothpick inserted in center comes out clean. Cool in pan 20 minutes before removing to a wire rack to cool.
4. In a small bowl, mix confectioners' sugar, lemon juice and enough 7UP to reach desired consistency. If desired, stir in peel. Drizzle glaze over cake.
NOTE *To remove cakes easily, use solid shortening to grease tube pans.*
PER SERVING *1 slice equals 457 cal., 19 g fat (11 g sat. fat), 104 mg chol., 177 mg sodium, 69 g carb., 1 g fiber, 5 g pro.*

TOP TIP

To easily make grated lemon or lime peel for recipes, I slice off big pieces of the peel and grind them for just a few seconds in my food processor.
—**LARUE H.** SAFFORD, AZ

CHARLOTTE'S GREEN TOMATO PIE

Charlotte's Green Tomato Pie

Green tomato pie is not only delicious, but also tends to become a topic of conversation when I take it to a potluck, party or other event.

—**CHARLOTTE MCDANIEL** JACKSONVILLE, AL

PREP: 30 MIN. • **BAKE:** 50 MIN. + COOLING
MAKES: 8 SERVINGS

- 1 cup packed light brown sugar
- ⅓ cup all-purpose flour
- 2 tablespoons lemon juice
- ½ teaspoon ground nutmeg
- ½ teaspoon ground cinnamon
- ¼ teaspoon salt
- 3 medium green tomatoes (about 1¾ pounds), cored and cut into thin wedges
  Pastry for double-crust pie (9 inches)

1. Preheat oven to 425°. In a large bowl, mix the first six ingredients until blended. Add the tomatoes; toss gently to combine.

2. On a lightly floured surface, roll one half of pastry dough to a ⅛-in.-thick circle; transfer to a 9-in. pie plate. Trim pastry even with rim. Add filling.

3. Roll the remaining pastry dough to a ⅛-in.-thick circle. Place over the filling. Trim, seal and flute edge. Cut slits in top.

4. Bake 15 minutes. Reduce oven setting to 350°. Bake 35-45 minutes longer or until the crust is golden brown and the filling is bubbly. Cool on a wire rack.

PASTRY FOR DOUBLE-CRUST PIE (9 INCHES) *Combine 2¼ cups of all-purpose flour and ¾ teaspoon salt;* cut in ¾ cup shortening until crumbly. *Gradually add 4-6 tablespoons 2% milk, tossing with a fork until dough holds together when pressed. Divide dough in half. Shape each half into a disk; wrap in plastic wrap. Refrigerate 1 hour or overnight.*
PER SERVING *1 slice equals 434 cal., 19 g fat (5 g sat. fat), 1 mg chol., 314 mg sodium, 61 g carb., 2 g fiber, 5 g pro.*

Salted Caramel Cupcakes

A creamy salted frosting complements the sweetness of these brown sugar cupcakes. It's the best of both worlds!

—***TASTE OF HOME*** TEST KITCHEN

PREP: 25 MIN. + CHILLING
BAKE: 20 MIN. + COOLING
MAKES: 10 CUPCAKES

- ½ cup butter, softened
- 1 cup packed dark brown sugar
- ½ cup sugar
- 2 large eggs
- 1 teaspoon vanilla extract
- 1¼ cups all-purpose flour
- ¾ teaspoon baking powder
- ¼ teaspoon salt
- ½ cup 2% milk
  FROSTING
- ⅓ cup sugar
- 4 teaspoons water
- ⅛ teaspoon salt
- 1⅓ cups heavy whipping cream

1. Preheat oven to 350°. In a large bowl, cream butter and sugars until light and fluffy. Add eggs, one at a time, beating well after each addition. Beat in the vanilla. Combine flour, baking powder and salt; add to the creamed mixture alternately with milk, beating well after each addition.

2. Fill 10 paper-lined muffin cups three-fourths full. Bake 18-22 minutes or until a toothpick inserted in center comes out clean. Cool 10 minutes before removing from pan to a wire rack to cool completely.

3. In a large heavy saucepan, combine the sugar, water and salt. Cook over medium-low heat until sugar begins to melt. Gently pull melted sugar to center of pan until sugar melts evenly. Cook, without stirring, until mixture turns an amber color.

4. Remove from heat; gradually stir in cream until smooth. Transfer to a small bowl; cover and refrigerate for 4 hours. Beat until stiff peaks form. Frost cupcakes.

PER SERVING *1 cupcake equals 416 cal., 22 g fat (14 g sat. fat), 111 mg chol., 224 mg sodium, 52 g carb., trace fiber, 4 g pro.*

SALTED CARAMEL CUPCAKES

Black Forest Dump Cake

I love classic German Black Forest cake but wanted to cut the prep work. My solution? Dump everything into a baking dish and pop it into the oven! For a topping, reserve two tablespoons of juice from the canned cherries and stir it into whipped cream.
—**MEGHAN MCDERMOTT** SPRINGFIELD, MO

PREP: 10 MIN. • **BAKE:** 40 MIN.
MAKES: 12 SERVINGS

- 1 **can (21 ounces) cherry pie filling**
- 1 **can (15 ounces) pitted dark sweet cherries, undrained**
- 1 **chocolate cake mix (regular size)**
- ½ **cup sliced almonds**
- ¾ **cup butter, cubed**

1. Preheat the oven to 375°. Spread the cherry pie filling into a greased 13x9-in. baking dish; top with the undrained sweet cherries. Sprinkle with chocolate cake mix and almonds. Top with cubed butter.

2. Bake 40-50 minutes or until the topping is set. Serve warm or at room temperature.

PER SERVING *1 serving equals 347 cal., 16 g fat (8 g sat. fat), 31 mg chol., 346 mg sodium, 49 g carb., 2 g fiber, 3 g pro.*

Rich Buttercream Frosting

Here's a recipe you'll want to keep close at hand. A few basic ingredients make a luscious finish for a variety of desserts.
—**TASTE OF HOME** TEST KITCHEN

START TO FINISH: 10 MIN.
MAKES: 5 CUPS

- 1 **cup butter, softened**
- 8 **cups confectioners' sugar**
- 6 **tablespoons 2% milk**
- 2 **teaspoons vanilla extract**
  Food coloring, optional

In a large bowl, combine the butter, confectioners' sugar, milk and vanilla; beat until smooth (the frosting will be thick). If desired, tint frosting with food coloring.

PER SERVING *2 tablespoons equals 136 cal., 5 g fat (3 g sat. fat), 12 mg chol., 38 mg sodium, 24 g carb., 0 fiber, trace pro.*

UPSIDE-DOWN PEAR GINGERBREAD CAKE

Upside-Down Pear Gingerbread Cake

The aroma of baking gingerbread always stirs up warm holiday memories.
—**NANCY BECKMAN** HELENA, MT

PREP: 25 MIN. • **BAKE:** 25 MIN. + COOLING
MAKES: 8 SERVINGS

- 3 **tablespoons butter**
- ⅓ **cup packed dark brown sugar**
- 2 **medium Bosc pears, peeled and thinly sliced**

CAKE
- ½ **cup 2% milk**
- 1 **tablespoon cider vinegar**
- 1 **large egg**
- ½ **cup packed dark brown sugar**
- ⅓ **cup molasses**
- ¼ **cup butter, melted**
- 1¼ **cups all-purpose flour**
- 2 **teaspoons ground cinnamon**
- 1 **teaspoon baking soda**
- 1 **teaspoon ground ginger**
- ¼ **teaspoon salt**
- ¼ **teaspoon ground cloves**
  Whipped cream, optional

1. Preheat the oven to 350°. In a small saucepan, melt butter over medium heat; stir in the brown sugar. Spread over bottom of a greased 9-in. round baking pan. Arrange the sliced pears over the top.

2. For the cake, mix the milk and cider vinegar; let stand 5 minutes. In a large bowl, beat egg, brown sugar, molasses, melted butter and milk mixture until well blended. In another bowl, whisk flour, cinnamon, baking soda, ginger, salt and cloves; gradually beat into molasses mixture. Spoon carefully over pears.

3. Bake 25-30 minutes or until a toothpick inserted in center comes out clean. Cool 10 minutes before inverting onto a serving plate. Serve warm or at room temperature with whipped cream if desired.

PER SERVING *1 slice (calculated without whipped cream) equals 331 cal., 11 g fat (7 g sat. fat), 51 mg chol., 348 mg sodium, 56 g carb., 2 g fiber, 4 g pro.*

NUTELLA HAND PIES

FAST FIX
Nutella Hand Pies

For even more of a yum factor, drizzle these with warmed Nutella in addition to the citrusy confectioners' sugar glaze.
—**TASTE OF HOME** TEST KITCHEN

START TO FINISH: 30 MIN.
MAKES: 9 SERVINGS

- 1 large egg
- 1 tablespoon water
- 1 sheet frozen puff pastry, thawed
- 3 tablespoons Nutella
- 1 to 2 teaspoons grated orange peel

ICING
- ⅓ cup confectioners' sugar
- ½ teaspoon orange juice
- ⅛ teaspoon grated orange peel
  Additional Nutella, optional

1. Preheat oven to 400°. In a small bowl, whisk egg with water.
2. Unfold puff pastry; cut into nine squares. Place 1 teaspoon Nutella in center of each; sprinkle with orange peel. Brush edges of pastry with egg mixture. Fold one corner over filling to form a triangle; press edges to seal. Transfer to an ungreased baking sheet.
3. Bake 17-20 minutes or until golden brown. Cool slightly.

4. In a small bowl, mix confectioners' sugar, orange juice and orange peel; drizzle over the pies. If desired, warm additional Nutella in a microwave and drizzle over tops.
PER SERVING *1 hand pie equals 190 cal., 10 g fat (2 g sat. fat), 21 mg chol., 100 mg sodium, 24 g carb., 2 g fiber, 3 g pro.*

Best Ever Fresh Strawberry Pie

When you have a bounty of fresh-picked strawberries, try my recipe. It adds a layer of richness with lemony cream cheese. To save time, use a premade shell.
—**JANET LEACH** GRANGER, WA

PREP: 1 HOUR + CHILLING
COOK: 10 MIN. + CHILLING
MAKES: 8 SERVINGS

- 2 cups all-purpose flour
- 2 teaspoons sugar
- ½ teaspoon salt
- ⅔ cup shortening
- 1 tablespoon white vinegar
- 4 to 5 tablespoons 2% milk

FILLING
- 1 package (8 ounces) cream cheese, softened
- ¾ cup confectioners' sugar

- 2 teaspoons grated lemon peel
- ½ teaspoon lemon extract

TOPPING
- 6 cups fresh strawberries, hulled (about 2 pounds)
- ¾ cup sugar
- 1 tablespoon cornstarch
- ¼ teaspoon salt
- 1 cup water
- 1 package (3 ounces) strawberry gelatin
- 1 teaspoon butter

1. In a large bowl, mix the flour, sugar and salt; cut in the shortening until crumbly. Gradually add the vinegar and milk, tossing with a fork until dough holds together when pressed. Shape into a disk; wrap in plastic wrap. Refrigerate 1 hour or overnight.
2. On a lightly floured surface, roll dough to a ⅛-in.-thick circle; transfer to a 9-in. deep-dish pie plate. Trim pastry to ½ in. beyond rim of plate; flute edge. Refrigerate 30 minutes. Preheat oven to 425°.
3. Line pastry with a double thickness of foil. Fill with pie weights, dried beans or uncooked rice. Bake on a lower oven rack 20-25 minutes or until the edges are golden brown. Remove the foil and weights; bake 3-6 minutes longer or until bottom is golden brown. Cool completely on a wire rack.
4. In a bowl, beat the cream cheese, confectioners' sugar, lemon peel and extract until blended. Spread carefully onto the bottom of crust. Refrigerate while preparing topping.
5. Place the strawberries in a large bowl. In a small saucepan, mix the sugar, cornstarch, salt and water until blended; bring to a boil over medium heat, stirring constantly. Cook and stir 1-2 minutes longer or until thickened and clear. Remove from the heat; stir in the gelatin until dissolved. Stir in butter. Pour over the berries, tossing gently to coat. Arrange over filling. Refrigerate 4 hours or until set.
NOTE *Let pie weights cool before storing. Beans and rice may be reused for pie weights, but not for cooking.*
PER SERVING *1 piece equals 564 cal., 27 g fat (10 g sat. fat), 33 mg chol., 359 mg sodium, 75 g carb., 3 g fiber, 7 g pro.*

Coconut Italian Cream Cake

PREP: 50 MIN. • **BAKE:** 20 MIN. + COOLING
MAKES: 16 SERVINGS

- 5 large eggs, separated
- 1 cup butter, softened
- 1⅔ cups sugar
- 1½ teaspoons vanilla extract
- 2 cups all-purpose flour
- ¾ teaspoon baking soda
- ½ teaspoon salt
- 1 cup buttermilk
- 1⅓ cups flaked coconut
- 1 cup chopped pecans, toasted

FROSTING

- 12 ounces cream cheese, softened
- 6 tablespoons butter, softened
- 2¼ teaspoons vanilla extract
- 5⅔ cups confectioners' sugar
- 3 to 4 tablespoons heavy whipping cream
- ½ cup chopped pecans, toasted
- ¼ cup toasted flaked coconut, optional

1. Place egg whites in a small bowl; let stand at room temperature 30 minutes.
2. Preheat oven to 350°. Line bottoms of three greased 9-in. round baking pans with parchment paper; grease the paper.
3. In a large bowl, cream the butter and sugar until light and fluffy. Add egg yolks, one at a time, beating well after each addition. Beat in vanilla. In another bowl, whisk flour, baking soda and salt; add to creamed mixture alternately with buttermilk, beating well after each addition. Fold in the coconut and pecans.

4. With clean beaters, beat the egg whites on medium speed until stiff peaks form. Gradually fold into batter. Transfer to the prepared pans. Bake 20-25 minutes or until a toothpick inserted in center comes out clean. Cool in the pans 10 minutes before removing to wire racks; remove paper. Cool completely.
5. For frosting, in a large bowl, beat cream cheese and butter until smooth. Beat in the vanilla. Gradually beat in the confectioners' sugar and enough cream to reach spreading consistency. Spread frosting between layers and over top and sides of cake. Sprinkle with pecans and, if desired, coconut. Refrigerate leftovers.
NOTE *To toast pecans and coconut, spread each, one at a time, in a 15x10x1-in. baking pan. Bake at 350° for 5-10 minutes or until lightly browned, stirring occasionally.*
PER SERVING *1 slice equals 667 cal., 36 g fat (18 g sat. fat), 128 mg chol., 402 mg sodium, 82 g carb., 2 g fiber, 7 g pro.*

Apple Cranberry Slab Pie

My husband is a huge pie fan. To change things up, I put cranberries, apples and raspberries in the filling. I'm not sure who liked it more—my husband or grandkids!
—BRENDA SMITH CURRAN, MI

PREP: 45 MIN. • **BAKE:** 40 MIN. + COOLING
MAKES: 15 SERVINGS

- Pastry for two double-crust pies (9 inches)
- 1½ cups sugar
- ¼ cup all-purpose flour
- 4 medium tart apples, peeled and sliced (about 4½ cups)
- 4 cups frozen or fresh raspberries
- 2 cups fresh or frozen cranberries
- 2 teaspoons grated orange peel
- ½ cup orange juice
- 1 teaspoon ground nutmeg
- 1 teaspoon ground cinnamon
  Additional orange juice and sugar, optional

1. Divide the pastry dough into two portions so that one is slightly larger than the other; wrap each in plastic wrap. Refrigerate 1 hour or overnight.

2. In a Dutch oven, mix sugar and flour; stir in the fruit, orange peel, orange juice and spices. Bring to a boil. Reduce the heat; simmer, uncovered, 10-12 minutes or until the apples are tender and juices are thickened, stirring occasionally. Cool slightly.
3. Preheat oven to 375°. Between waxed paper, roll larger portion of pastry dough into a 16x12-in. rectangle. Remove the top piece of waxed paper; place a 13x9-in. baking pan upside down over pastry. Lifting with waxed paper, carefully invert pastry into pan. Remove the waxed paper; press pastry onto the bottom and up the sides of the pan. Add filling.
4. On a well-floured surface, roll the remaining dough into a 14x10-in. rectangle; cut into ¾-in.-wide strips. Arrange strips over filling, sealing ends to bottom pastry. If desired, brush the pastry with additional orange juice and sprinkle with additional sugar.
5. Bake 40-50 minutes or until crust is golden brown and filling is bubbly. Cool on a wire rack.
PASTRY FOR TWO DOUBLE-CRUST PIES (9 INCHES) *In a large bowl, combine 4½ cups all-purpose flour, 1 tablespoon sugar and 2 teaspoons salt; cut in 1¾ cups of shortening until crumbly. Whisk 1 large egg, 1 tablespoon white vinegar and ½ cup ice water; gradually add to the flour mixture, tossing with a fork until dough holds together when pressed.*
PER SERVING *1 piece equals 478 cal., 23 g fat (6 g sat. fat), 12 mg chol., 322 mg sodium, 62 g carb., 3 g fiber, 5 g pro.*

APPLE CRANBERRY SLAB PIE

BECKY MCCLAFLIN'S
MARBLED CAPPUCCINO
FUDGE CHEESECAKE *PAGE 131*

Just Desserts

Surprise your family with a golden fruit crisp, creamy cheesecake, cozy bread pudding or any of the other **decadent delights** here. These sweet recipes **make it easy** to indulge.

CARMELL CHILDS' STRAWBERRY-ROSEMARY YOGURT POPS *PAGE 127*

ANGELA BENEDICT'S PEACH CREAM PUFFS *PAGE 130*

JUDY SCHUT'S RHUBARB-PINEAPPLE CRISP *PAGE 137*

CRANBERRY CREME BRULEE

Cranberry Creme Brulee

Love traditional creme brulee? Dress it up for the Christmas season or anytime with ruby red cranberries in a sweet-tart sauce. As both the bottom layer and topping, it complements the rich custard.

—*TASTE OF HOME* TEST KITCHEN

PREP: 35 MIN. • **BAKE:** 35 MIN. + CHILLING
MAKES: 8 SERVINGS

- 1 **package (12 ounces) fresh or frozen cranberries**
- 1 **cup granulated sugar**
- ¼ **cup water**
- ⅛ **teaspoon salt**

CUSTARD

- 2½ **cups heavy whipping cream, divided**
- 1 **teaspoon vanilla extract**
- 10 **large egg yolks**
- ⅔ **cup granulated sugar**
- 8 **teaspoons superfine sugar**

1. Preheat oven to 325°. In a large saucepan, combine the cranberries, granulated sugar, water and salt. Cook over medium heat 12-15 minutes or until the cranberries pop, stirring frequently. Remove from the heat. Spoon 2 tablespoons sauce into each of eight 6-oz. broiler-safe ramekins or custard cups; refrigerate 10 minutes. Cover and refrigerate remaining sauce until serving.

2. For custard, in a small saucepan, heat 1 cup cream over medium heat until bubbles form around sides of pan; remove from heat. In a large bowl, whisk egg yolks and granulated sugar until smooth. Slowly stir in hot cream. Stir in vanilla and remaining cream.

3. Place the prepared ramekins in a baking pan large enough to hold them without touching. Spoon custard over cranberry sauce. Place the pan on oven rack; add 1 in. of very hot water to the pan. Bake 35-40 minutes or until set (centers will still be soft). Immediately remove ramekins from water bath to a wire rack; cool 10 minutes. Refrigerate at least 8 hours or until cold.

4. To caramelize the topping with a kitchen torch, gently blot surface of custard with a paper towel to remove any moisture. Sprinkle the tops with superfine sugar. Hold the torch flame 2 in. above the custard surface and rotate it slowly until the sugar is evenly caramelized.

5. To caramelize the topping in a broiler, place ramekins on a baking sheet; let stand at room temperature 15 minutes. Preheat broiler. Gently blot the surface of the custard with a paper towel to remove any moisture. Sprinkle tops with superfine sugar. Broil 3-4 in. from heat 1-2 minutes or until sugar is caramelized.

6. Serve custards with remaining cranberry sauce.

PER SERVING *1 serving equals 530 cal., 34 g fat (19 g sat. fat), 368 mg chol., 75 mg sodium, 54 g carb., 2 g fiber, 5 g pro.*

FAST FIX ▶

Rum Banana Sauce

Plain vanilla ice cream becomes amazing thanks to this delectable recipe.

—**KATHERINE DESROSIERS** TRAIL, BC

START TO FINISH: 15 MIN.
MAKES: 4 SERVINGS

- ¾ **cup packed brown sugar**
- ¼ **cup butter, cubed**
- ¼ **cup heavy whipping cream**
- 2 **tablespoons maple syrup**
- 2 **large bananas, cut into ½-inch slices**
- ½ **teaspoon rum extract**
  Vanilla ice cream

In a small saucepan, combine the brown sugar, butter, cream and maple syrup. Cook and stir over medium heat for 4-5 minutes or until the sauce is smooth. Stir in bananas; heat through. Remove from the heat; stir in extract. Serve with ice cream.

PER SERVING *½ cup equals 397 cal., 17 g fat (11 g sat. fat), 50 mg chol., 104 mg sodium, 63 g carb., 2 g fiber, 1 g pro.*

RUM BANANA SAUCE

Croissant Pudding with Chocolate Kahlua Sauce

These decadent custards puff up slightly during baking, forming golden crowns. Kahlua lends a mild coffee flavor to the heavenly chocolate sauce.

—CHERYL TUCKER HOUSTON, TX

PREP: 25 MIN. • **BAKE:** 40 MIN.
MAKES: 9 SERVINGS

- 6 **croissants, torn into pieces**
- 4 **large egg yolks**
- 2 **large eggs**
- 3 **cups heavy whipping cream**
- 2¼ **cups sugar**
- 1½ **cups half-and-half cream**
- 4½ **teaspoons vanilla extract**
- 1½ **teaspoons salt**

SAUCE

- 2 **ounces unsweetened chocolate, coarsely chopped**
- 2 **tablespoons butter**
- 1 **cup sugar**
- ½ **cup evaporated milk**
    Dash salt
- 3 **tablespoons Kahlua (coffee liqueur)**

1. Divide croissant pieces among nine greased 10-oz. ramekins or custard cups. Place on baking sheets.

2. In a large bowl, combine the yolks, eggs, heavy cream, sugar, half-and-half, vanilla and salt. Pour over croissant pieces; let stand for 15 minutes or until the croissant pieces are softened. Bake at 325° for 40-45 minutes or until a knife inserted near the center comes out clean.

3. For the sauce, in a small saucepan, melt the chocolate and butter over medium-low heat. Add the sugar, evaporated milk and salt; cook and stir for 3-4 minutes or until thickened. Remove from the heat; stir in Kahlua. Serve with warm pudding.

PER SERVING *1 serving with about 2 tablespoons sauce equals 894 cal., 51 g fat (31 g sat. fat), 303 mg chol., 795 mg sodium, 99 g carb., 2 g fiber, 10 g pro.*

EASY MINI CARAMEL APPLE CHEESECAKES

Easy Mini Caramel Apple Cheesecakes

Cheesecake is the ultimate indulgence, but a whole slice is sometimes too much. Miniature ones are bite-size bliss!

—BRANDIE CRANSHAW RAPID CITY, SD

PREP: 30 MIN. • **BAKE:** 15 MIN. + COOLING
MAKES: 1 DOZEN

- 1 **cup graham cracker crumbs**
- 2 **tablespoons sugar**
- ¼ **teaspoon ground cinnamon**
- 3 **tablespoons butter, melted**

CHEESECAKE

- 2 **packages (8 ounces each) cream cheese, softened**
- ½ **cup sugar**
- 1 **teaspoon vanilla extract**
- 2 **large eggs, lightly beaten**

TOPPING

- 1 **tablespoon butter**
- 1 **large apple, peeled and finely chopped**
- 1 **tablespoon sugar**
- ¼ **teaspoon ground cinnamon**
    Dash ground cloves
- ½ **cup butterscotch-caramel ice cream topping**

1. Preheat oven to 350°. Line 12 muffin cups with paper liners.

2. In a small bowl, mix the cracker crumbs, sugar and cinnamon; stir in the melted butter. Spoon 1 rounded tablespoon crumb mixture into each muffin cup; press down with a narrow glass or spoon.

3. In a large bowl, beat cream cheese and sugar until smooth. Beat in vanilla. Add eggs; beat on low speed just until blended. Pour over crusts.

4. Bake 15-18 minutes or until the centers are set (do not overbake). Cool in the pan on a wire rack 30 minutes. Serve within 2 hours or refrigerate and serve cold.

5. In a small skillet, heat the butter over medium heat. Add apple, sugar, cinnamon and cloves; cook and stir 4-5 minutes or until apple is tender. Stir in the caramel topping. Serve over cheesecakes.

PER SERVING *1 cheesecake with about 1 tablespoon topping equals 307 cal., 19 g fat (10 g sat. fat), 84 mg chol., 244 mg sodium, 31 g carb., trace fiber, 4 g pro.*

Buttermilk Peach Ice Cream

My mother's family owned peach orchards in Missouri. This wonderful homemade ice cream reminds me of my heritage.

—KIM HIGGINBOTHAM KNOXVILLE, TN

PREP: 15 MIN. + CHILLING
PROCESS: 30 MIN./BATCH + FREEZING
MAKES: 2 QUARTS

- 2 pounds ripe peaches (about 7 medium), peeled and quartered
- ½ cup sugar
- ½ cup packed brown sugar
- 1 tablespoon lemon juice
- 1 teaspoon vanilla extract
  Pinch salt
- 2 cups buttermilk
- 1 cup heavy whipping cream

1. Place peaches in a food processor; process until smooth. Add the sugars, lemon juice, vanilla and salt; process until blended.

2. In a large bowl, mix the buttermilk and heavy whipping cream. Stir in the peach mixture. Refrigerate, covered, 1 hour or until cold.

3. Fill the cylinder of ice cream maker no more than two-thirds full. Freeze according to manufacturer's directions, refrigerating any remaining mixture to process later. Transfer ice cream to freezer containers, allowing headspace for expansion. Freeze 2-4 hours or until firm. Let ice cream stand at room temperature 10 minutes before serving.
PER SERVING *½ cup equals 137 cal., 6 g fat (4 g sat. fat), 22 mg chol., 75 mg sodium, 20 g carb., 1 g fiber, 2 g pro.*

BUTTERMILK PEACH ICE CREAM

Key Lime Marshmallow Meringue Tarts

When my husband and I visited Key West, we became obsessed with Key lime pie. Here's my downsized version of one of the best variations we sampled there.

—BARBARA HAHN PARK HILLS, MO

PREP: 30 MIN. • **BAKE:** 15 MIN. + CHILLING
MAKES: 8 TARTS

- 1¼ cups graham cracker crumbs
- ½ cup almond paste
- ⅓ cup unsalted butter, melted
- 2 tablespoons brown sugar
FILLING
- 2 cans (14 ounces each) sweetened condensed milk
- ¾ cup plus 2 tablespoons Key lime juice
MERINGUE
- 2 large egg whites
- ¼ teaspoon cream of tartar
- 1 jar (7 ounces) marshmallow creme

1. In a large bowl, combine graham cracker crumbs, almond paste, butter and sugar; press onto bottom and up sides of eight ungreased 4-in. fluted tart pans with removable bottoms. Place on baking sheets. Bake at 350° for 7-9 minutes or until lightly browned. Cool on wire racks.

2. In large bowl, whisk milk and lime juice. Pour into crusts. In a large bowl with clean beaters, beat egg whites and cream of tartar on medium speed until soft peaks form. Add the marshmallow creme, a tablespoon at a time, beating on high until stiff peaks form. Spread the meringue over the filling. Return to baking sheets.

3. Bake at 325° for 15-20 minutes or until meringue is lightly browned. Cool completely on wire racks. Refrigerate for at least 4 hours before serving.
PER SERVING *1 tart equals 624 cal., 22 g fat (11 g sat. fat), 54 mg chol., 239 mg sodium, 99 g carb., 1 g fiber, 11 g pro.*

Saying goodbye to seasonal summer desserts is easier when you have a cozy fall treat to look forward to. For me, that's Autumn Harvest Cobbler.

—**NANCY FOUST** STONEBORO, PA

Autumn Harvest Cobbler

PREP: 35 MIN. • **BAKE:** 15 MIN.
MAKES: 12 SERVINGS

- ½ cup sugar
- 1 teaspoon ground cinnamon
- ½ teaspoon salt
- ½ teaspoon ground nutmeg
- 2 cups cold water, divided
- 6 large tart apples, peeled and thinly sliced
- 1 cup golden raisins
- 1 cup dried apricots, halved
- 1 tablespoon lemon juice
- 2 tablespoons cornstarch

TOPPING

- 2 cups biscuit/baking mix
- ¾ cup 2% milk
- 1 tablespoon coarse sugar
- 2 teaspoons grated lemon peel
  Whipped cream

1. In a large saucepan combine the sugar, cinnamon, salt, nutmeg and 1¾ cups water. Bring to a boil. Stir in the apples, raisins, apricots and lemon juice. Return to a boil. Reduce heat; simmer, uncovered, for 10 minutes, stirring occasionally.
2. Combine cornstarch and remaining water until smooth. Stir into pan. Bring to a boil; cook and stir for 2 minutes or until thickened. Transfer to a greased 13x9-in. baking dish.
3. In a small bowl combine the biscuit mix and milk just until blended. Drop by tablespoonfuls onto the hot apple mixture. Sprinkle with coarse sugar and lemon peel.
4. Bake at 400° for 15-20 minutes or until topping is golden brown. Serve warm with whipped cream.

PER SERVING *1 serving (calculated without whipped cream) equals 245 cal., 4 g fat (1 g sat. fat), 1 mg chol., 359 mg sodium, 53 g carb., 3 g fiber, 3 g pro.*

Easy Cherry Strudels

My original strudel recipe called for phyllo dough and was rather time-consuming to prepare. One day I bought puff pastry by mistake—and found it was much faster!

—**SUSAN DANCY** TALLAHASSEE, FL

PREP: 15 MIN. • **BAKE:** 20 MIN.
MAKES: 2 STRUDELS (5 SLICES EACH)

- 1 can (14½ ounces) pitted tart cherries
- 1 cup sugar
- ½ cup dried cranberries or raisins
- 1 tablespoon butter
- 3 tablespoons cornstarch
- 1½ cups chopped walnuts
- 1 package (17.3 ounces) frozen puff pastry, thawed
- 1 large egg, lightly beaten

1. Drain cherries, reserving ⅓ cup juice. In a large saucepan, combine the cherries, sugar, cranberries and butter. Cook and stir over medium heat until heated through. Combine cornstarch and reserved cherry juice and add to the pan. Bring to a boil. Cook and stir 1-2 minutes longer or until thickened. Remove from the heat; stir in walnuts.
2. Unfold one pastry sheet and cut in half. Mound half of the cherry mixture on one pastry half to within ½ in. of the edges. Top with remaining pastry half; pinch edges to seal. Repeat with remaining pastry and filling.
3. Place on a greased foil-lined baking sheet. With a sharp knife, cut diagonal slits into tops of strudels; brush with egg. Bake at 400° for 20-25 minutes or until golden brown.

PER SERVING *1 slice equals 506 cal., 25 g fat (5 g sat. fat), 24 mg chol., 180 mg sodium, 65 g carb., 5 g fiber, 9 g pro.*

EASY CHERRY STRUDELS

Strawberry Sweetness

Back from the patch with those **little red gems?** Head straight for the kitchen and whip up any of the **berry good delights** featured here!

WHITE CHOCOLATE-STRAWBERRY TIRAMISU

SLOW COOKER

Slow-Cooked Strawberry Rhubarb Sauce

I put fresh-picked summer fruit into a tongue-tingling sauce that gets raves when I serve it over ice cream or pound cake.
—**JUDITH WASMAN** HARKERS ISLAND, NC

PREP: 10 MIN. • **COOK:** 6 HOURS • **MAKES:** 10 SERVINGS

- 6 **cups chopped rhubarb (½-inch pieces)**
- 1 **cup sugar**
- ½ **teaspoon grated orange peel**
- ½ **teaspoon ground ginger**
- 1 **cinnamon stick (3 inches)**
- ½ **cup white grape juice**
- 2 **cups halved unsweetened strawberries**
  Angel food cake, pound cake or vanilla ice cream

1. Place rhubarb in a 3-qt. slow cooker. Combine sugar, peel and ginger; sprinkle over rhubarb. Add cinnamon and juice. Cover; cook on low for 5-6 hours or until rhubarb is tender.
2. Stir in the berries; cook 1 hour longer. Discard cinnamon stick. Serve with cake or ice cream.
PER SERVING *One ½-cup serving (calculated without cake or ice cream) equals 115 cal., trace fat (0 sat. fat), 0 chol., 4 mg sodium, 29 g carb., 0 fiber, 1 g pro.* **Diabetic Exchange: 2 fruit.**

SLOW-COOKED STRAWBERRY RHUBARB SAUCE

FAST FIX

White Chocolate-Strawberry Tiramisu

Here's a refreshing variation of traditional Italian tiramisu that my husband and I love. Keeping an eye on fat and calories? I've had good results with ingredients like reduced-fat cream cheese and light non-dairy whipped topping.
—**ANNA GINSBERG** AUSTIN, TX

START TO FINISH: 30 MIN. • **MAKES:** 15 SERVINGS

- 2 **cups heavy whipping cream**
- 1 **package (8 ounces) cream cheese, softened**
- ½ **cup (4 ounces) mascarpone cheese**
- 9 **ounces white baking chocolate, melted and cooled**
- 1 **cup confectioners' sugar, divided**
- 1 **teaspoon vanilla extract**
- 2 **packages (3 ounces each) ladyfingers, split**
- ⅔ **cup orange juice**
- 4 **cups sliced fresh strawberries**
  Chocolate syrup, optional

1. In a large bowl, beat the cream until soft peaks form. In another bowl, beat cheeses until light and fluffy. Beat in the cooled chocolate, ½ cup confectioners' sugar and vanilla. Fold in 2 cups of the whipped cream.
2. Brush half of the ladyfingers with half of the orange juice; arrange in a 13x9-in. dish. Spread with 2 cups cream cheese mixture; top with half of the strawberries. Brush remaining ladyfingers with remaining orange juice; arrange over the strawberries.
3. Gently stir the remaining confectioners' sugar into the remaining cream cheese mixture; fold in the remaining whipped cream. Spread over the ladyfingers. Top with the remaining strawberries. Refrigerate until serving. If desired, drizzle with chocolate syrup before serving.
PER SERVING *1 piece (calculated without syrup) equals 404 cal., 30 g fat (18 g sat. fat), 103 mg chol., 169 mg sodium, 33 g carb., 1 g fiber, 5 g pro.*

EAT SMART

Strawberry-Rosemary Yogurt Pops

PREP: 20 MIN. + FREEZING • **MAKES:** 6 POPS

- 1   cup chopped fresh strawberries
- 2   tablespoons balsamic vinegar
- 2   tablespoons strawberry preserves
- 2   fresh rosemary sprigs
- 1½ cups (12 ounces) vanilla yogurt
- 6   freezer pop molds or paper cups (3 ounces each) and wooden pop or lollipop sticks

1. In a small bowl, mix strawberries, vinegar, preserves and rosemary. Let stand 30 minutes; discard rosemary.
2. Spoon 2 tablespoons yogurt and 1 tablespoon strawberry mixture into each mold or cup. Repeat layers. Top the molds with the holders. If using cups, top with foil and insert sticks through foil. Freeze until firm.
PER SERVING *1 pop equals 81 cal., 1 g fat (trace sat. fat), 3 mg chol., 42 mg sodium, 16 g carb., 1 g fiber, 3 g pro. **Diabetic Exchange:** 1 starch.*

STRAWBERRY-ROSEMARY YOGURT POPS

STRAWBERRY CHEESECAKE MOUSSE

Strawberry Cheesecake Mousse

In just 20 minutes, this smooth mousse goes into the refrigerator to chill. All that's left to do is indulge! The taste reminds me of a no-bake cheesecake without the crust.
—VIRGINIA ANTHONY JACKSONVILLE, FL

PREP: 20 MIN. + CHILLING • **MAKES:** 6 SERVINGS

- ½   teaspoon unflavored gelatin
- ¼   cup cold water
- 1   quart fresh strawberries, halved
- 2   tablespoons reduced-sugar strawberry preserves
- 1   package (8 ounces) reduced-fat cream cheese
- ½   cup sugar, divided
- ¼   cup reduced-fat sour cream, divided
- ½   cup heavy whipping cream

1. Sprinkle unflavored gelatin over cold water; let stand for 1 minute. Microwave on high for 20 seconds. Stir and let stand for 1 minute or until gelatin is completely dissolved. Meanwhile, combine strawberries and preserves; set aside.
2. In a large bowl, beat the cream cheese, ¼ cup sugar and 2 tablespoons sour cream until blended; set aside.
3. In another bowl, beat the heavy whipping cream and remaining sour cream until it begins to thicken. Add the gelatin mixture and remaining sugar; beat until stiff peaks form. Fold into cream cheese mixture.
4. In each of six dessert dishes, layer ½ cup strawberry mixture and ⅓ cup cream cheese mixture. Refrigerate desserts until chilled.
PER SERVING *1 serving equals 279 cal., 16 g fat (10 g sat. fat), 57 mg chol., 176 mg sodium, 29 g carb., 2 g fiber, 6 g pro.*

PANNA COTTA WITH PAPAYA COULIS

Creamy
Raspberry Dessert

Here's a favorite for family celebrations. The fruity cream cheese filling contrasts wonderfully with the chocolate crust.

—KAREN WIRTH TAVISTOCK, ON

PREP: 25 MIN. + FREEZING
MAKES: 10 SERVINGS

- 1 **cup chocolate wafer crumbs**
- 2 **tablespoons butter, melted**
- 1 **can (11½ ounces) frozen white grape-raspberry juice concentrate, thawed**
- 1 **package (8 ounces) cream cheese, cubed**
- 2 **tablespoons confectioners' sugar**
- 4 **cups whipped topping**
  Chocolate curls or grated chocolate, optional

1. In a small bowl, combine the chocolate wafer crumbs and butter. Press onto the bottom of a greased 9-in. springform pan. Refrigerate for 30 minutes.
2. Meanwhile, in a food processor, combine the juice concentrate, cream cheese and sugar. Cover and process until smooth; pour into a large bowl and fold in the whipped topping. Pour over the crust. Cover and freeze for 4 hours or until firm.
3. Remove from freezer 10 minutes before slicing. Garnish with chocolate curls if desired.
PER SERVING *1 slice (calculated without chocolate) equals 292 cal., 17 g fat (12 g sat. fat), 31 mg chol., 151 mg sodium, 31 g carb., trace fiber, 3 g pro.*

CREAMY RASPBERRY DESSERT

Panna Cotta
with Papaya Coulis

Panna Cotta is an Italian dessert that means "cooked cream." My friend and I came up with a tropical version that features papaya. For special events, add a garnish of mint and berries.

—SHAUNA HAVEY ROY, UT

PREP: 15 MIN. + CHILLING
COOK: 5 MIN. + CHILLING
MAKES: 4 SERVINGS

- 2½ **teaspoons unflavored gelatin**
- ¼ **cup 2% milk**
- 2 **cups heavy whipping cream**
- ¼ **cup sugar**
- 1 **teaspoon vanilla extract**

PAPAYA COULIS

- 2 **cups coarsely chopped papaya**
- 2 **to 3 tablespoons lime juice**
- 1 **tablespoon sugar**
  Fresh raspberries and fresh mint leaves

1. In a small bowl, sprinkle gelatin over the milk; let stand 5 minutes. Meanwhile, in a small saucepan, combine the heavy whipping cream and sugar; cook and stir over medium heat until the sugar is dissolved. Add gelatin mixture and vanilla, stirring until gelatin is completely dissolved.
2. Divide mixture among four dessert dishes. Refrigerate, covered, 2 hours or until set.
3. For the coulis, place papaya, lime juice and sugar in a food processor; process until smooth, scraping down the sides of bowl as needed. Transfer to a small bowl. Refrigerate, covered, until cold.
4. To serve, spoon coulis over panna cotta. Top with berries and mint.
PER SERVING *1 serving equals 524 cal., 45 g fat (28 g sat. fat), 166 mg chol., 62 mg sodium, 28 g carb., 1 g fiber, 5 g pro.*

Mint Ice Cream Torte

It's every busy cook's dream—having an amazing dessert just waiting in the freezer for company. This cool favorite is perfect for both hot summer nights and get-togethers at Christmas.
—*TASTE OF HOME* TEST KITCHEN

PREP: 20 MIN. + FREEZING
MAKES: 12 SERVINGS

 20 **Oreo cookies, crushed**
 ¼ **cup butter, melted**
 10 **mint Andes candies, melted**
 ½ **gallon mint chocolate chip ice cream, divided**
 1 **jar (11¾ ounces) hot fudge ice cream topping**

1. In a small bowl, combine crumbs and butter. Press half of the mixture into a greased 9-in. springform pan. Spread the melted candies over crust. Top with half of the mint chocolate chip ice cream.
2. Place ¼ cup hot fudge ice cream topping in a small bowl; cover and refrigerate until serving. In another bowl, combine remaining hot fudge topping and crumb mixture; spread over the ice cream. Cover and freeze for 2 hours or until firm.
3. Top with the remaining ice cream. Cover; freeze for 8 hours or overnight until firm. Remove from the freezer 5 minutes before serving. Warm the reserved fudge topping and use to garnish torte.
PER SERVING *1 serving (1 slice) equals 462 cal., 24 g fat (13 g sat. fat), 44 mg chol., 245 mg sodium, 55 g carb., 1 g fiber, 5 g pro.*

Parmesan Crisp Baked Apples

A little Parmesan adds a deliciously savory touch to sweet and tangy baked apples. They're even better with a drizzle of honey.
—**SUSAN STETZEL** GAINESVILLE, NY

START TO FINISH: 25 MIN.
MAKES: 2 SERVINGS

 2 **small Braeburn or Gala apples**
 ¼ **cup grated Parmesan cheese**
 3 **tablespoons quick-cooking oats**
 2 **tablespoons all-purpose flour**
 2 **tablespoons brown sugar**
   Dash ground nutmeg
 1 **tablespoon butter, melted**
   Honey, optional

1. Preheat the oven to 350°. Cut a ¼-in. slice off the top of each apple. Core apples, leaving bottoms intact; place in a microwave-safe 8-in.-square baking dish. Microwave, covered, 3-4 minutes or until tender.
2. In a small bowl, mix cheese, oats, flour, brown sugar and nutmeg; stir in melted butter until crumbly. Carefully fill the apples with oat mixture. Bake, uncovered, 12-15 minutes or until the topping is golden brown. If desired, drizzle with honey.
PER SERVING *1 stuffed apple (calculated without honey) equals 255 cal., 9 g fat (6 g sat. fat), 24 mg chol., 204 mg sodium, 39 g carb., 3 g fiber, 6 g pro.*

PARMESAN CRISP BAKED APPLES

Lemonade Dessert

Planning a backyard barbecue? Look no further than this frosty lemon treat.

—MARGARET LINDER QUINCY, WA

PREP: 30 MIN. + FREEZING
MAKES: 12-15 SERVINGS

- 1½ cups all-purpose flour
- ¾ cup packed brown sugar
- ¾ cup cold butter, cubed
- ¾ cup chopped pecans
- ½ gallon vanilla ice cream, softened
- 1 can (12 ounces) frozen lemonade concentrate, thawed

1. Preheat oven to 375°. In a small bowl, combine flour and brown sugar; cut in butter until crumbly. Stir in the pecans. Spread in a single layer into a greased 15x10x1-in. baking pan.

2. Bake 9-12 minutes or until golden brown, stirring once. Cool on a wire rack 10 minutes.

3. In a large bowl, beat ice cream and lemonade until blended. Sprinkle half of crumbles into a greased 13x9-in. dish. Spread with ice cream mixture; sprinkle with the remaining crumbles. Cover; freeze overnight. Remove from the freezer 15 minutes before serving.

PER SERVING *1 serving (1 piece) equals 391 cal., 21 g fat (11 g sat. fat), 56 mg chol., 154 mg sodium, 48 g carb., 1 g fiber, 4 g pro.*

Peach Cream Puffs

Here's a summertime delight—airy puffs stuffed with fresh peaches and cream.

—ANGELA BENEDICT DUNBAR, WV

PREP: 55 MIN. + COOLING
BAKE: 25 MIN. + COOLING
MAKES: 16 SERVINGS

- 1 cup water
- ½ cup butter, cubed
- ⅛ teaspoon salt
- 1 cup all-purpose flour
- 4 large eggs

FILLING

- 4 medium peaches, peeled and cubed (about 3 cups)
- ½ cup sugar
- ½ cup water
- ½ cup peach schnapps liqueur or peach nectar
- ½ teaspoon ground cinnamon
- ¼ teaspoon ground nutmeg

WHIPPED CREAM

- 2 cups heavy whipping cream
- ½ cup confectioners' sugar
- 3 tablespoons peach schnapps liqueur, optional
  Additional confectioners' sugar

1. Preheat oven to 400°. In a large saucepan, bring water, butter and salt to a rolling boil. Add flour all at once and beat until blended. Cook over medium heat, stirring vigorously until mixture pulls away from the sides of pan and forms a ball. Transfer dough to a large bowl; let stand 5 minutes.

2. Add the eggs, one at a time, beating well after each addition until smooth. Continue beating until the mixture is smooth and shiny.

3. Cut a ½-in. hole in tip of a pastry bag or in a corner of a food-safe plastic bag. Transfer the dough to bag; pipe sixteen 2-in. mounds 3 in. apart onto parchment paper-lined baking sheets.

4. Bake on a lower oven rack 25-30 minutes or until puffed, very firm and golden brown. Pierce side of each puff with tip of a knife to allow steam to escape. Cool completely on wire racks.

5. Meanwhile, in a large saucepan, combine filling ingredients; bring to a boil, stirring occasionally. Reduce heat; simmer, uncovered, 25-30 minutes or until slightly thickened and peaches are tender. Cool completely.

6. In a bowl, beat cream until it begins to thicken. Add confectioners' sugar and, if desired, peach schnapps; beat until soft peaks form.

7. Cut top third off each cream puff. Pull out and discard soft dough from inside tops and bottoms.

8. To serve, spoon 2 tablespoons whipped cream into each bottom; top with 2 tablespoons filling and 2 tablespoons additional whipped cream. Replace the tops. Dust with additional confectioners' sugar.

PER SERVING *1 cream puff with ¼ cup whipped cream and 2 tablespoons filling equals 256 cal., 18 g fat (11 g sat. fat), 103 mg chol., 94 mg sodium, 21 g carb., 1 g fiber, 3 g pro.*

PEACH CREAM PUFFS

Marbled Cappuccino Fudge Cheesecake

This is like having my favorite coffeeshop frozen cappuccino in cheesecake form. Don't skip the topping—it's the best part!

—BECKY MCCLAFLIN BLANCHARD, OK

PREP: 45 MIN. • **BAKE:** 70 MIN. + CHILLING
MAKES: 12 SERVINGS

- 1½ cups chocolate graham cracker crumbs (about 8 whole crackers)
- 3 tablespoons sugar
- ¼ cup butter, melted

FILLING

- 4 packages (8 ounces each) cream cheese, softened
- 1¼ cups sugar
- ¼ cup heavy whipping cream
- 3 tablespoons double mocha cappuccino mix
- 2 tablespoons all-purpose flour
- 1½ teaspoons vanilla extract
- 3 large eggs, lightly beaten
- ⅔ cup hot fudge ice cream topping, warmed

CAPPUCCINO CREAM TOPPING

- 1 cup heavy whipping cream
- 2 tablespoons double mocha cappuccino mix
- 1 tablespoon confectioners' sugar
  Chocolate curls, optional

1. Place a greased 9-in. springform pan on a double thickness of heavy-duty foil (about 18 in. square). Securely wrap foil around pan.
2. In a small bowl, combine graham cracker crumbs, sugar and butter. Press onto bottom and 2 in. up sides of prepared pan. Place pan on a baking sheet. Bake at 325° for 7-9 minutes. Cool on a wire rack.
3. In a large bowl, beat cream cheese and sugar until smooth. Beat in the cream, cappuccino mix, flour and vanilla. Add eggs; beat on low speed just until combined. Pour half of batter into crust. Drizzle with ⅓ cup fudge topping. Repeat layers. Cut through batter with a knife to swirl the fudge topping. Place the springform pan in a large baking pan; add 1 in. of hot water to larger pan.
4. Bake at 325° for 70-80 minutes or until center is just set and top appears dull. Remove the springform pan from the water bath. Cool on a wire rack for

10 minutes. Carefully run a knife around edge of pan to loosen; cool 1 hour longer. Refrigerate overnight. Remove sides of pan.
5. For topping, in a small bowl, beat cream until it begins to thicken. Add cappuccino mix and confectioners' sugar; beat until soft peaks form. Spread over the cheesecake. Garnish with chocolate curls if desired.

PER SERVING *1 slice equals 625 cal., 43 g fat (26 g sat. fat), 180 mg chol., 382 mg sodium, 51 g carb., 1 g fiber, 10 g pro.*

Peach Melba Trifle

I think my trifle tastes even better on busy days because I can make it ahead of time.

—CHRISTINA MOORE CASAR, NC

PREP: 20 MIN. + CHILLING
MAKES: 12 SERVINGS

- 2 packages (12 ounces each) frozen unsweetened raspberries, thawed
- 1 tablespoon cornstarch
- 1½ cups (12 ounces) fat-free peach yogurt
- ⅛ teaspoon almond extract
- 1 carton (8 ounces) frozen reduced-fat whipped topping, thawed
- 2 prepared angel food cakes (8 to 10 ounces each), cut into 1-inch cubes (about 8 cups)
- 4 small peaches, peeled and sliced (about 2 cups)

1. In a large saucepan, mix berries and cornstarch until blended. Bring to a boil; cook and stir 1-2 minutes or until thickened. Strain seeds; cover and refrigerate.
2. In a large bowl, mix the yogurt and extract; fold in whipped topping. In a 4-qt. bowl, layer half of cake, yogurt mixture and peaches. Repeat layers. Refrigerate, covered, at least 3 hours before serving. Serve with sauce.

PER SERVING *⅔ cup equals 201 cal., 3 g fat (2 g sat. fat), 1 mg chol., 298 mg sodium, 41 g carb., 3 g fiber, 4 g pro.*

PEACH MELBA TRIFLE

SLOW COOKER
Slow Cooker Cherry Buckle

While my cherry buckle cooks, the aroma attracts everyone in the house.
—**SHERRI MELOTIK** OAK CREEK, WI

PREP: 10 MIN. • **COOK:** 3 HOURS
MAKES: 6 SERVINGS

- 2 **cans (15 ounces each) sliced pears, drained**
- 1 **can (21 ounces) cherry pie filling**
- ¼ **teaspoon almond extract**
- 1 **package yellow cake mix (regular size)**
- ¼ **cup old-fashioned oats**
- ¼ **cup sliced almonds**
- 1 **tablespoon brown sugar**
- ½ **cup butter, melted**
   Vanilla ice cream, optional

1. In a greased 5-qt. slow cooker, combine pears and pie filling; stir in extract. In a bowl, combine cake mix, oats, almonds and brown sugar; stir in melted butter. Sprinkle over fruit.
2. Cook, covered, on low 3-4 hours or until the topping is golden brown. If desired, serve with ice cream.
PER SERVING *½ cup (calculated without ice cream) equals 651 cal., 20 g fat (11 g sat. fat), 40 mg chol., 657 mg sodium, 116 g carb., 2 g fiber, 5 g pro.*

Elegant Orange Blossom Cheesecake

Candied orange slices beautifully decorate this citrusy white chocolate cheesecake.
—**SHARON DELANEY-CHRONIS**
SOUTH MILWAUKEE, WI

PREP: 40 MIN. • **BAKE:** 70 MIN. + CHILLING
MAKES: 16 SERVINGS

- 3 **cups crushed gingersnap cookies (about 60 cookies)**
- 2 **teaspoons plus 2 tablespoons grated orange peel, divided**
- ⅓ **cup butter, melted**
- 1½ **cups orange juice**
- ⅓ **cup sliced fresh gingerroot**
- 4 **packages (8 ounces each) cream cheese, softened**
- ⅔ **cup sugar**
- 6 **ounces white baking chocolate, melted**
- 1 **tablespoon vanilla extract**
- 4 **large eggs, lightly beaten**

CANDIED ORANGE SLICES
- 3 **cups water**
- 1½ **cups sugar**
- 2 **small navel oranges, thinly sliced**

1. Place a greased 9-in. springform pan on a double thickness of heavy-duty foil (about 18 in. square). Securely wrap foil around pan.
2. In a large bowl, combine crumbs, 2 teaspoons orange peel and butter. Press onto bottom and 2-in. up sides of prepared pan.
3. In a large saucepan, combine the orange juice and ginger; bring to a boil. Reduce the heat; simmer, stirring occasionally, until syrupy and reduced to about 3 tablespoons. Strain and discard ginger.
4. In a large bowl, beat cream cheese and sugar until smooth. Beat in ginger syrup, chocolate, vanilla and remaining peel. Add eggs; beat on low speed just until combined. Pour into crust. Place springform pan in a large baking pan; add 1 in. of hot water to larger pan.
5. Bake at 325° for 70-80 minutes or until the center is just set and the top appears dull. Remove the springform pan from the water bath; remove foil. Cool on a wire rack for 10 minutes. Carefully run a knife around the edge of pan to loosen; cool 1 hour longer. Refrigerate overnight.
6. For candied orange slices, in a large skillet, combine the water and sugar. Cook and stir over medium heat until the sugar is completely dissolved. Add orange slices. Bring to a boil. Reduce heat; simmer for 45 minutes or until translucent. Drain oranges on a wire rack; arrange in a single layer on waxed paper to dry.
7. Remove sides of springform pan. Top cheesecake with candied orange slices. Refrigerate leftovers.
PER SERVING *1 slice equals 752 cal., 35 g fat (18 g sat. fat), 119 mg chol., 660 mg sodium, 101 g carb., 2 g fiber, 10 g pro.*

ELEGANT ORANGE BLOSSOM CHEESECAKE

Caramel-Mocha Ice Cream Dessert

Feel free to substitute different ice creams for the coffee and dulce de leche flavors in this cool freezer recipe. The yummy possibilities are endless!

—**SCARLETT ELROD** NEWNAN, GA

PREP: 45 MIN. + FREEZING
MAKES: 20 SERVINGS

- 10 **whole graham crackers**
- 1 **cup butter, cubed**
- 1 **cup packed brown sugar**
- 1 **cup chopped pecans**

FILLING

- 1 **quart dulce de leche ice cream, softened**
- 1 **jar (16 ounces) hot fudge ice cream topping, warmed**
- 1 **quart coffee ice cream, softened**
- 1½ **cups heavy whipping cream**
- ⅓ **cup coffee liqueur**
  Chocolate curls

1. Preheat the oven to 350°. Arrange the graham crackers in a single layer in a greased 15x10x1-in. baking pan. In a large saucepan, melt butter over medium heat. Stir in brown sugar. Bring to a gentle boil; cook and stir for 2 minutes. Remove from heat and stir in pecans. Pour over graham crackers; spread to cover crackers.

2. Bake 8-10 minutes or until bubbly. Cool completely on a wire rack.

3. Crush graham cracker mixture into coarse crumbs; sprinkle half into an ungreased 13x9-in. dish. Spread with dulce de leche ice cream. Cover and freeze for 1 hour or until firm.

4. Drizzle with ice cream topping and sprinkle with the remaining crumb mixture. Cover and freeze 30 minutes or until ice cream topping is set.

5. Spread with the coffee ice cream; freeze. In a small bowl, beat the cream until stiff peaks form. Fold in coffee liqueur. Spread over the top of dessert. Cover and freeze 4 hours or until firm.

6. Remove the dessert from freezer 15 minutes before serving. Garnish with chocolate curls.

PER SERVING *1 piece (calculated without chocolate curls) equals 520 cal., 33 g fat (17 g sat. fat), 99 mg chol., 205 mg sodium, 51 g carb., 1 g fiber, 6 g pro.*

HAZELNUT POTS DE CREME

Hazelnut Pots de Creme

Guests will rave over silky hazelnut custard served in personal-size ramekins. Garnish them with elegant chocolate curls.

—**ELISE LALOR** ISSAQUAH, WA

PREP: 30 MIN. • **BAKE:** 25 MIN. + CHILLING
MAKES: 6 SERVINGS

- 2 **cups heavy whipping cream**
- 1 **cup ground hazelnuts, toasted**
- 4 **ounces white baking chocolate, chopped**
- 6 **large egg yolks**
- ⅓ **cup sugar**
- 2 **tablespoons hazelnut liqueur, optional**
  Chocolate curls

1. Preheat oven to 325°. In a small saucepan, heat cream, hazelnuts and chocolate until bubbles form around sides of pan and chocolate is melted, stirring occasionally.

2. In a small bowl, whisk yolks and sugar. Remove cream mixture from heat; stir a small amount of hot cream mixture into egg mixture. Return all to pan, stirring constantly. Stir in liqueur if desired. Strain, discarding hazelnuts.

3. Transfer to six 6-oz. ramekins. Place ramekins in a baking pan; add 1 in. of boiling water to pan. Bake, uncovered, 25-30 minutes or until the centers are just set (mixture will jiggle). Remove the ramekins from water bath; cool 10 minutes. Cover and refrigerate at least 2 hours. Garnish servings with chocolate curls.

PER SERVING *1 serving (calculated without chocolate curls) equals 555 cal., 48 g fat (24 g sat. fat), 318 mg chol., 58 mg sodium, 27 g carb., 1 g fiber, 7 g pro.*

Maple Dumplings

On cold evenings, finish your dinner with something warm, cozy and comforting. These tender homemade dumplings in a rich syrup are best fresh from the oven.
—**DENISE BOUTIN** GRAND ISLE, VERMONT

PREP: 15 MIN. • **BAKE:** 25 MIN.
MAKES: 8 SERVINGS

- 2 **cups all-purpose flour**
- 3 **teaspoons baking powder**
- ¼ **cup shortening**
- ¾ **cup 2% milk**
- 2 **cups maple syrup**
- ½ **cup water**
  Optional toppings: vanilla ice cream or whipped cream

1. In a large bowl, combine the flour and baking powder. Cut in shortening until crumbly. Gradually add the milk, tossing with a fork until dough forms a ball; set aside.
2. In a small saucepan, bring syrup and water to a boil. Carefully pour into an 11x7-in. baking dish. Drop dough by tablespoonfuls into syrup mixture.
3. Bake, uncovered, at 400° for 22-28 minutes or until a toothpick inserted in a dumpling comes out clean. Serve warm with ice cream or whipped cream if desired.
PER SERVING *1 serving (calculated without optional toppings) equals 389 cal., 7 g fat (2 g sat. fat), 2 mg chol., 169 mg sodium, 79 g carb., 1 g fiber, 4 g pro.*

GRILLED HONEY BALSAMIC-GLAZED FRUIT

EAT SMART **FAST FIX**
Grilled Honey Balsamic-Glazed Fruit

One summer, my mother-in-law made us grilled peaches basted with a sweet, tangy sauce. Now I make them myself—and I'm always tempted to eat the whole batch!
—**KRISTIN VAN DYKEN** KENNEWICK, WA

START TO FINISH: 25 MIN.
MAKES: 6 SERVINGS (½ CUP GLAZE)

- ½ **cup balsamic vinegar**
- ½ **cup honey**
  Dash salt
- 6 **medium peaches or nectarines, halved and pitted**
  Vanilla ice cream, optional

1. In a small saucepan, combine the vinegar, honey and salt; cook and stir over low heat 2-3 minutes or until blended. Reserve ⅓ cup mixture for brushing peaches.
2. Bring the remaining mixture to a boil over medium heat; cook and stir 4-6 minutes or just until the mixture begins to thicken slightly (do not overcook). Remove from heat.
3. Moisten a paper towel with cooking oil; using long-handled tongs, rub on the grill rack to coat lightly. Brush the peaches with some of the reserved balsamic mixture.
4. Grill the peaches, covered, over medium heat 6-8 minutes on each side or until caramelized, brushing peaches occasionally with remaining reserved balsamic mixture. Serve with glaze and, if desired, ice cream.
PER SERVING *1 serving (calculated without ice cream) equals 164 cal., trace fat (trace sat. fat), 0 chol., 26 mg sodium, 43 g carb., 2 g fiber, 1 g pro.*

TOP TIP

Store ripe peaches in a plastic bag in the refrigerator for up to 5 days. To ripen, keep them in a brown paper bag at room temperature for about 2 days. To remove the pit, cut the fruit from stem to stem all the way around, twist the peach halves in opposite directions and lift out the pit.

MAPLE DUMPLINGS

Peter Peter Pumpkin Whoopies

Who can resist a whoopie pie? I bake these cakelike sandwiches every fall. Cinnamon and nutmeg spice up the cream-cheese filling, and canned pumpkin keeps the big cookies nice and tender.

—**DAWN CONTE** SICKLERVILLE, NJ

PREP: 35 MIN. + COOLING
BAKE: 10 MIN./BATCH
MAKES: 10 WHOOPIE PIES

- 1 **package spice cake mix (regular size)**
- 1¼ **cups canned pumpkin**
- 2 **large eggs**
- ½ **cup 2% milk**
- ⅓ **cup butter, softened**

FILLING

- 2 **packages (3 ounces each) cream cheese, softened**
- ½ **cup marshmallow creme**
- ⅓ **cup butter, softened**
- 1½ **cups confectioners' sugar**
- ¾ **teaspoon vanilla extract**
- ½ **teaspoon ground cinnamon**
- ⅛ **teaspoon ground nutmeg**

1. Preheat the oven to 375°. In a large bowl, combine the first five ingredients; beat until well blended. Drop dough by ¼ cupfuls 3 in. apart onto lightly greased baking sheets. Bake 7-10 minutes or until set and edges are lightly browned. Remove to wire racks to cool completely.
2. For the filling, in a small bowl, beat the cream cheese, marshmallow creme and butter. Beat in remaining ingredients. Spread on the bottoms of half of the cookies; top with remaining cookies. Store in the refrigerator.
PER SERVING *1 whoopie pie equals 504 cal., 26 g fat (14 g sat. fat), 107 mg chol., 557 mg sodium, 64 g carb., 2 g fiber, 7 g pro.*

Toffee-Pear Crisp Bread Pudding

My son loves pear crisp and asked for it one night when I was already preparing bread pudding. To compromise, I tried combining the two into a new dessert. We've been enjoying it ever since!

—**KURT WAIT** REDWOOD CITY, CA

PREP: 20 MIN. + STANDING
BAKE: 40 MIN. + COOLING
MAKES: 12 SERVINGS

- 1¾ **cups 2% milk**
- 1 **cup butterscotch-caramel ice cream topping**
- ¼ **cup butter, cubed**
- 1 **teaspoon ground cinnamon**
- ½ **teaspoon ground ginger**
- 2 **large eggs**
- 4 **cups cubed day-old French bread**
- 2 **cups sliced peeled fresh pears (about 2 medium)**

TOPPING

- ½ **cup all-purpose flour**
- ½ **cup packed brown sugar**
- ⅓ **cup cold butter**
- ⅓ **cup English toffee bits**

1. Preheat oven to 350°. In a small saucepan, combine the milk, caramel topping, butter, cinnamon and ginger. Cook and stir over medium-low heat until the butter is melted. Remove from the heat.
2. Whisk the eggs in a large bowl; gradually whisk in a third of the milk mixture. Stir in the remaining milk mixture. Add bread; stir to coat. Let stand 10 minutes. Gently stir in pears; transfer to a greased 11x7-in. baking dish. Bake, uncovered, 20 minutes.
3. Meanwhile, for topping, in a small bowl, combine flour and brown sugar; cut in butter until crumbly. Stir in the toffee; sprinkle over the pudding. Bake, uncovered, 20-25 minutes longer or until puffed, golden and a knife inserted near center comes out clean. Let stand 10 minutes before serving. Serve warm. Refrigerate leftovers.
PER SERVING *1 piece equals 331 cal., 14 g fat (8 g sat. fat), 67 mg chol., 260 mg sodium, 48 g carb., 1 g fiber, 5 g pro.*

PETER PETER PUMPKIN WHOOPIES

Chocolate Peanut Butter Dessert

When I really want to splurge, I whip up a frozen, chocolate-glazed loaf of mousse. The taste reminds me of a peanut butter cup, and even a thin slice satisfies.

—CHRISTINE MONTALVO
WINDSOR HEIGHTS, IA

PREP: 40 MIN. + FREEZING
MAKES: 10-12 SERVINGS

- 1¼ cups packed dark brown sugar
- 1 cup heavy whipping cream, divided
- 3 large egg yolks
- 1¼ cups creamy peanut butter
- 6 tablespoons butter, softened

GLAZE

- 1½ cups heavy whipping cream
- 2 tablespoons butter
- 4 teaspoons dark corn syrup
- 12 ounces bittersweet chocolate, chopped
- ¼ cup coarsely chopped dry roasted peanuts

1. In a small saucepan, combine the brown sugar, ½ cup cream and egg yolks. Cook and stir over medium heat until mixture reaches 160° and is thick enough to coat the back of a metal spoon. Cover and refrigerate for 3 hours or until thickened.

2. Line an 8x4-in. loaf pan with plastic wrap; set aside. In a large bowl, cream peanut butter and butter until light and fluffy. Add brown sugar mixture; beat until smooth. In small bowl, beat the remaining cream until stiff peaks form. Fold into peanut butter mixture. Spoon into the prepared pan. Cover and refrigerate.

3. For the glaze, in a large heavy saucepan, bring the heavy whipping cream, butter and dark corn syrup to a boil, stirring frequently. Remove from the heat. Add the bittersweet chocolate; whisk until smooth. Set aside ⅓ cup glaze to cool. Place the remaining glaze in a microwave-safe bowl; cover and refrigerate overnight. Spread cooled glaze over loaf; cover and freeze overnight.

4. Using the plastic wrap, lift the loaf out of pan. Place chocolate side down in a 15x10x1-in. pan; place on a wire rack. Discard plastic wrap.

5. In microwave, warm refrigerated glaze; stir until smooth. Pour over the loaf; spread with a metal spatula to completely cover the top and sides. Sprinkle with peanuts. Freeze for 1 hour or until glaze is set.

PER SERVING *1 slice equals 533 cal., 43 g fat (20 g sat. fat), 142 mg chol., 259 mg sodium, 32 g carb., 2 g fiber, 9 g pro.*

Over-the-Top Blueberry Bread Pudding

Whether warm or at room temperature, this bread pudding truly is over the top!

—MARILYN HAYNES SYLACAUGA, AL

PREP: 15 MIN. + STANDING • **BAKE:** 50 MIN.
MAKES: 12 SERVINGS

- 3 large eggs
- 4 cups heavy whipping cream
- 2 cups sugar
- 3 teaspoons vanilla extract
- 2 cups fresh or frozen blueberries
- 1 package (10 to 12 ounces) white baking chips
- 1 loaf (1 pound) French bread, cut into 1-inch cubes

SAUCE

- 1 package (10 to 12 ounces) white baking chips
- 1 cup heavy whipping cream

1. Preheat oven to 350°. In a large bowl, combine eggs, heavy whipping cream, sugar and vanilla. Stir in the blueberries and baking chips. Stir in the bread cubes; let stand 15 minutes or until bread is softened.

2. Transfer the mixture to a greased 13x9-in. baking dish. Bake, uncovered, 50-60 minutes or until a knife inserted near center comes out clean. Let stand 5 minutes before serving.

3. For sauce, place the baking chips in a small bowl. In a small saucepan, bring heavy whipping cream just to a boil. Pour over baking chips; whisk until smooth. Serve with pudding.

OVER-THE-TOP RASPBERRY BREAD PUDDING *Substitute raspberries for the blueberries.*

PER SERVING *1 piece with about 2 tablespoons sauce equals 869 cal., 54 g fat (33 g sat. fat), 195 mg chol., 344 mg sodium, 89 g carb., 1 g fiber, 11 g pro.*

CHOCOLATE PEANUT BUTTER DESSERT

Pizzelle Cannoli

Mama Mia! We brought two classic Italian desserts together by wrapping beautiful pizzelle cookies, made with a pizzelle iron, around a rich cannoli filling. Enjoy them after your big pasta feast.

—TASTE OF HOME TEST KITCHEN

PREP: 45 MIN. + COOLING
COOK: 5 MIN./BATCH
MAKES: 12 FILLED PIZZELLE

- 1 large egg
- ¼ cup sugar
- ¼ cup butter, melted
- ½ teaspoon vanilla extract
- ¼ teaspoon grated lemon peel
- ⅛ teaspoon almond extract
- ½ cup all-purpose flour
- ¼ teaspoon baking powder

FILLING

- ¾ cup sugar
- 3 tablespoons cornstarch
- 1 cup milk
- 1⅛ teaspoons vanilla extract
- 1 drop cinnamon oil, optional
- 1¾ cups ricotta cheese
- 1 milk chocolate candy bar with almonds (4¼ ounces), chopped
- ½ cup chopped pistachios

1. In a large bowl, beat the egg, sugar, butter, vanilla, lemon peel and almond extract until blended. Combine flour and baking powder; stir into the egg mixture and mix well.

2. Bake in a preheated pizzelle iron according to manufacturer's directions until golden brown. Remove cookies and immediately shape into tubes. Place on wire racks to cool.

3. In a small saucepan, combine sugar and cornstarch. Stir in the milk until smooth. Bring to a boil; cook and stir for 2 minutes or until thickened. Stir in vanilla and cinnamon oil if desired. Cool completely.

4. In a large bowl, beat the ricotta cheese until smooth. Gradually beat in the custard mixture. Fold in the chopped candy bar pieces. Spoon or pipe into the pizzelle shells. Dip each side in pistachios. Serve immediately. Refrigerate leftovers.

PER SERVING *1 filled pizzelle equals 289 cal., 15 g fat (8 g sat. fat), 47 mg chol., 124 mg sodium, 33 g carb., 1 g fiber, 8 g pro.*

RHUBARB-PINEAPPLE CRISP

Rhubarb-Pineapple Crisp

We grow our own rhubarb, and I enjoy using it in new recipes. When I first tried this fruity crisp years ago, I thought the tangy pineapple would be too much. I was pleasantly surprised!

—JUDY SCHUT GRAND RAPIDS, MI

PREP: 15 MIN. • **BAKE:** 30 MIN.
MAKES: 6 SERVINGS

- 2 cups sliced fresh or frozen rhubarb, thawed and drained
- 1 can (20 ounces) unsweetened pineapple tidbits, drained
- ½ cup sugar, divided
- 2 tablespoons plus ⅓ cup all-purpose flour, divided
- ⅓ cup quick-cooking oats
- ¾ teaspoon ground cinnamon
- ⅛ teaspoon salt
- ¼ cup cold butter
    Whipped cream, optional

1. In a large bowl, combine rhubarb, pineapple tidbits, ¼ cup sugar and 2 tablespoons flour. Transfer to a 9-in. deep-dish pie plate coated with cooking spray.

2. In a small bowl, combine the oats, cinnamon, salt and remaining sugar and flour. Cut in butter until crumbly. Sprinkle over fruit. Bake, uncovered, at 350° for 30-35 minutes or until the filling is bubbly and topping is golden brown. Cool for 5 minutes; serve with whipped cream if desired.

NOTE *If using frozen rhubarb, measure rhubarb while still frozen, then thaw completely. Drain in a colander, but do not press liquid out.*

PER SERVING *1 serving (calculated without whipped cream) equals 232 cal., 8 g fat (5 g sat. fat), 20 mg chol., 106 mg sodium, 39 g carb., 2 g fiber, 2 g pro.*

DID YOU KNOW?

Pizzelles are traditional Italian waffle cookies created with a pizzelle iron, which is similar to a standard waffle iron. A pizzelle iron forms an intricate snowflake or other design on each cookie. Look for this appliance in housewares stores or online.

MINDY BAUKNECHT'S FLUFFY PUMPKIN PANCAKES *PAGE 145*

Breakfast & Brunch

Start your day with this chapter for any kind of morning menu you need. From baked French toast and hearty egg casseroles to homemade waffles and coffee cakes, **they're all here!**

**DAWN JARVIS'
FRUIT-FILLED FRENCH
TOAST WRAPS** *PAGE 142*

**JOAN HALLFORD'S
EASY CHEESY LOADED GRITS**
PAGE 147

**CAROL GAUS'
RICOTTA-RAISIN COFFEE CAKE**
PAGE 153

Prosciutto Breadsticks

Here's a delicious accompaniment not just for eggs, but also for saucy pasta.
—**MARIA REGAKIS** SAUGUS, MA

START TO FINISH: 30 MIN.
MAKES: 1 DOZEN

- 6 **thin slices prosciutto or deli ham**
- 1 **tube (11 ounces) refrigerated breadsticks**
- 1 **large egg, lightly beaten**
- ¼ **teaspoon fennel seed, crushed**
- ¼ **teaspoon pepper**

1. Preheat oven to 375°. Cut each slice of prosciutto into four thin strips. Unroll dough; separate into breadsticks. Top each with two strips prosciutto, pressing gently to adhere. Twist each breadstick; place on an ungreased baking sheet, pressing ends down firmly. Brush with beaten egg.
2. Combine the fennel and pepper; sprinkle over the breadsticks. Bake 10-13 minutes or until golden brown.
PER SERVING *1 breadstick equals 86 cal., 2 g fat (1 g sat. fat), 8 mg chol., 323 mg sodium, 13 g carb., trace fiber, 4 g pro.* **Diabetic Exchange:** *1 starch.*

Cheesy Zucchini Quiche

If you like to have breakfast for dinner, keep this freezer-friendly quiche in mind. I take out a frozen one in the morning, let it thaw in the refrigerator during the day and put it in the oven when I get home.
—**KAREN HOWARD** LAKEVILLE, MA

PREP: 25 MIN. • **BAKE:** 35 MIN. + STANDING
MAKES: 8 SERVINGS

- **Pastry for single-crust pie (9 inches)**
- 3 **tablespoons butter**
- 4 **cups thinly sliced zucchini (about 3 medium)**
- 1 **large onion, thinly sliced**
- 2 **large eggs**
- 2 **teaspoons dried parsley flakes**
- ½ **teaspoon each salt and garlic powder**
- ½ **teaspoon each dried basil and oregano**
- ¼ **teaspoon pepper**
- 2 **cups (8 ounces) part-skim shredded mozzarella cheese**
- 2 **teaspoons prepared mustard**

CHEESY ZUCCHINI QUICHE

1. Preheat the oven to 400°. Unroll the pastry sheet into a 9-in. pie plate; flute the edge. Refrigerate while preparing the filling.
2. In a large skillet, heat butter over medium heat. Add zucchini and onion; cook and stir until tender. Drain and cool slightly.
3. In a large bowl, whisk eggs and seasonings until blended. Stir in the mozzarella cheese and zucchini mixture. Spread mustard over pastry shell; add filling.
4. Bake quiche on a lower oven rack 35-40 minutes or until a knife inserted near center comes out clean and crust is golden brown. Cover edge loosely with foil during the last 15 minutes if needed to prevent overbrowning. Let stand 10 minutes before cutting.
PASTRY FOR SINGLE-CRUST PIE (9 INCHES) *Combine 1¼ cups of all-purpose flour and ¼ teaspoon salt; cut in ½ cup cold butter until crumbly.*

Gradually add 3-5 tablespoons ice water, tossing with a fork until dough holds together when pressed. Wrap in plastic wrap and refrigerate 1 hour.
FREEZE OPTION *Cover and freeze unbaked quiche. To use, thaw quiche in the refrigerator. Preheat oven to 400°. Bake quiche as directed, increasing time to 50-55 minutes.*
PER SERVING *1 slice equals 272 cal., 19 g fat (10 g sat. fat), 91 mg chol., 428 mg sodium, 17 g carb., 1 g fiber, 9 g pro.*

TOP TIP

To pick the freshest zucchini, look for a firm heavy squash that has a moist stem end and a shiny skin. Store zucchini in a plastic bag in the refrigerator crisper for four to five days. Do not wash until ready to use.

Spinach Hash Brown Frittata

PREP: 25 MIN. • **BAKE:** 35 MIN. + STANDING
MAKES: 8 SERVINGS

- 1 **large onion, finely chopped**
- 1 **tablespoon olive oil**
- 2 **garlic cloves, minced**
- 1 **package (10 ounces) frozen chopped spinach, thawed and squeezed dry**
- ¼ **teaspoon salt**
- ¼ **teaspoon pepper**
- 2 **ounces pancetta or bacon strips, finely chopped**
- 3 **cups frozen shredded hash brown potatoes, thawed**
- 8 **large eggs, lightly beaten**
- 1 **cup 2% milk**
- 1 **cup (4 ounces) fontina cheese, divided**
- 1 **cup (4 ounces) shredded cheddar cheese, divided**
- ¼ **cup minced fresh parsley**
- 1 **tablespoon Worcestershire sauce**
- 1 **teaspoon ground mustard**
- ¼ **teaspoon ground nutmeg**

1. Preheat oven to 350°. In a large skillet, saute the onion in oil until tender. Add the garlic; cook 1 minute longer. Stir in spinach, salt and pepper. Remove from heat.
2. In another skillet, cook pancetta over medium heat until crisp. Remove pancetta to paper towels with a slotted spoon; drain.
3. In a greased 11x7-in. baking dish, layer hash browns, spinach mixture and pancetta. In a large bowl, whisk eggs, milk, ½ cup fontina cheese, ½ cup cheddar cheese, parsley, Worcestershire sauce, mustard and nutmeg; pour over top. Sprinkle with remaining cheeses.
4. Bake, uncovered, 35-40 minutes or until a knife inserted near center comes out clean. Let stand 10 minutes before cutting.
PER SERVING *1 piece equals 281 cal., 19 g fat (9 g sat. fat), 225 mg chol., 542 mg sodium, 11 g carb., 2 g fiber, 18 g pro.*

Down East Blueberry Buckle

This recipe won a contest at my daughter's college. They shipped us lobsters as our prize, but the real reward was seeing the smile on our daughter's face.

—DIANNE VAN DER VEEN PLYMOUTH, MA

PREP: 15 MIN. • **BAKE:** 30 MIN.
MAKES: 9 SERVINGS

- 2 **cups all-purpose flour**
- ¾ **cup sugar**
- 2½ **teaspoons baking powder**
- ¼ **teaspoon salt**
- 1 **large egg**
- ¾ **cup 2% milk**
- ¼ **cup butter, melted**
- 2 **cups fresh or frozen blueberries**

TOPPING
- ½ **cup sugar**
- ⅓ **cup all-purpose flour**
- ½ **teaspoon ground cinnamon**
- ¼ **cup butter, softened**

1. Preheat oven to 375°. In a large bowl, whisk the flour, sugar, baking powder and salt. In another bowl, whisk the egg, milk and melted butter until blended. Add to flour mixture; stir just until moistened. Fold in the blueberries. Transfer to a greased 9-in.-square baking pan.
2. For the topping, in a small bowl, mix the sugar, flour and cinnamon. Using a fork, stir in softened butter until crumbly. Sprinkle over batter.
3. Bake 30-35 minutes or until a toothpick inserted in the center comes out clean (do not overbake). Cool in the pan on a wire rack. Serve warm or at room temperature.
NOTE *If using frozen blueberries, use without thawing to avoid discoloring the batter.*
PER SERVING *1 piece equals 354 cal., 12 g fat (7 g sat. fat), 49 mg chol., 277 mg sodium, 59 g carb., 2 g fiber, 5 g pro.*

DOWN EAST BLUEBERRY BUCKLE

FRUIT-FILLED FRENCH TOAST WRAPS

Fruit-Filled French Toast Wraps

Tortillas take the place of the bread in this French toast recipe. For a pretty finish, dust the wraps with confectioners' sugar.
—**DAWN JARVIS** BRECKENRIDGE, MN

START TO FINISH: 25 MIN.
MAKES: 2 SERVINGS

- ¾ **cup (6 ounces) vanilla yogurt**
- ⅔ **cup sliced ripe banana**
- 1 **large egg**
- ¼ **cup 2% milk**
- 1 **teaspoon ground cinnamon**
- ½ **teaspoon ground nutmeg**
- 2 **whole wheat tortillas (8 inches)**
- 2 **teaspoons butter**
- ⅔ **cup sliced fresh strawberries**
- ⅔ **cup fresh blueberries**
- ¼ **cup granola**
  Confectioners' sugar

1. In a small bowl, combine yogurt and banana. In a shallow bowl, whisk egg, milk, cinnamon and nutmeg. Dip both sides of each tortilla in the egg mixture. In a skillet, heat the butter over medium-high heat. Add tortilla; cook 1-2 minutes on each side or until golden brown.

2. Spoon the yogurt mixture down the center of the tortillas; top with the strawberries, blueberries and granola. Roll up; dust with confectioners' sugar.
PER SERVING *1 wrap equals 441 cal., 14 g fat (5 g sat. fat), 84 mg chol., 287 mg sodium, 68 g carb., 8 g fiber, 14 g pro.*

Beef, Potato & Egg Bake

How do I keep my family going all morning? I start with ground beef and sneak in some spinach!
—**JENNIFER FISHER**
AUSTIN, TX

PREP: 25 MIN. • **BAKE:** 45 MIN.
MAKES: 12 SERVINGS

- 1 **pound lean ground beef (90% lean)**
- 2 **teaspoons onion powder**
- 1½ **teaspoons salt, divided**
- 1 **teaspoon garlic powder**
- ½ **teaspoon rubbed sage**
- ½ **teaspoon crushed red pepper flakes**
- 1 **package (10 ounces) frozen chopped spinach, thawed and squeezed dry**
- 4 **cups frozen shredded hash brown potatoes**
- 14 **large eggs**
- 1 **cup fat-free ricotta cheese**
- ⅓ **cup fat-free milk**
- ¾ **to 1 teaspoon pepper**
- ¾ **cup shredded Colby-Monterey Jack cheese**
- 1⅓ **cups grape tomatoes, halved**

1. Preheat oven to 350°. In a large skillet, cook beef with onion powder, ½ teaspoon salt, garlic powder, sage and pepper flakes over medium heat 6-8 minutes or until no longer pink, breaking up beef into crumbles; drain. Stir in spinach. Remove from heat.

2. Spread the potatoes in a greased 13x9-in. baking dish; top with beef mixture. In a large bowl, whisk the eggs, ricotta cheese, milk, pepper and remaining salt; pour over top. Sprinkle with cheese. Top with tomatoes.

3. Bake, uncovered, 45-50 minutes or until a knife inserted near the center comes out clean. Let stand 5-10 minutes before serving.
PER SERVING *1 piece equals 218 cal., 11 g fat (5 g sat. fat), 250 mg chol., 489 mg sodium, 9 g carb., 1 g fiber, 20 g pro.* **Diabetic Exchanges:** *3 lean meat, ½ starch.*

BEEF, POTATO & EGG BAKE

BANANAS FOSTER BAKED FRENCH TOAST

Bananas Foster Baked French Toast

Mmm—bananas Foster for breakfast! Enjoy all the flavor of that classic dessert.
—**L.G. NASSON** QUINCY, MA

PREP: 20 MIN. + CHILLING • **BAKE:** 35 MIN.
MAKES: 6 SERVINGS

- ½ cup butter, cubed
- ⅔ cup packed brown sugar
- ½ cup heavy whipping cream
- ½ teaspoon ground cinnamon
- ½ teaspoon ground allspice
- ¼ cup chopped pecans, optional
- 3 large bananas, sliced
- 12 slices egg bread or challah (about ¾ pound)
- 1½ cups 2% milk
- 3 large eggs
- 1 tablespoon sugar
- 1 teaspoon vanilla extract

1. Place butter in a microwave-safe bowl; microwave the butter, covered, 30-45 seconds or until melted. Stir in brown sugar, heavy whipping cream, cinnamon, allspice and, if desired, pecans. Add the sliced bananas; toss gently to coat.

2. Transfer to a greased 13x9-in. baking dish. Arrange the bread over the top, trimming to fit as necessary.

3. Place the remaining ingredients in a blender; process just until blended. Pour over bread. Refrigerate, covered, 8 hours or overnight.

4. Preheat the oven to 375°. Remove the French toast from the refrigerator while the oven heats. Bake, uncovered, 35-40 minutes or until a knife inserted near center comes out clean. Let stand 5-10 minutes. Invert to serve.

PER SERVING *1 piece (calculated without pecans) equals 658 cal., 31 g fat (17 g sat. fat), 218 mg chol., 584 mg sodium, 84 g carb., 4 g fiber, 14 g pro.*

FAST FIX

Apple-Pear Puff Pancake

When I serve my easy oven pancake to guests, they think it took hours to make.
—**CAROL WILLIAMS** ST. JOSEPH, MO

START TO FINISH: 30 MIN.
MAKES: 6 SERVINGS

- 3 tablespoons butter
- 4 large eggs
- 1 cup 2% milk
- 1 cup all-purpose flour
- 1 tablespoon sugar
- ⅛ teaspoon ground nutmeg

FRUIT TOPPING

- 3 tablespoons butter
- 3 medium apples, sliced
- 3 medium pears, sliced
- 3 tablespoons sugar
- Maple syrup, optional

1. Preheat oven to 425°. Place the butter in a 10-in. ovenproof skillet; heat in the oven 2-3 minutes or until butter is melted. Tilt the pan to coat evenly with butter.

2. Place the eggs, milk, flour, sugar and nutmeg in a blender; cover and process until smooth. Pour puff pancake batter into the hot skillet. Bake 17-20 minutes or until the pancake is puffed and browned.

3. Meanwhile, for the fruit topping, heat the butter in a large skillet over medium heat. Add the apples, pears and sugar; cook 12-15 minutes or until apples and pears are tender, stirring occasionally.

4. Remove puff pancake from oven; fill with the fruit mixture and serve immediately. If desired, serve with maple syrup.

PER SERVING *1 serving (calculated without syrup) equals 367 cal., 16 g fat (9 g sat. fat), 158 mg chol., 170 mg sodium, 50 g carb., 5 g fiber, 8 g pro.*

APPLE-PEAR PUFF PANCAKE

Ham & Cheese Strata with Sun-Dried Tomatoes

Want to break away from the same old breakfast casserole? Try a hearty strata loaded with ham, cheese and sun-dried tomatoes. It's a welcome change of pace and feeds a hungry crowd.

—**KIM DEANE** FENTON, MO

PREP: 30 MIN. + CHILLING • **BAKE:** 45 MIN.
MAKES: 12 SERVINGS

- 1 cup cubed fully cooked ham
- 1 cup sun-dried tomatoes (not packed in oil), chopped
- 1 tablespoon minced fresh parsley
- 1½ teaspoons minced chives
- 1 loaf sourdough bread (1 pound), crust removed and cut into 1-inch cubes
- 2 cups (8 ounces) shredded cheddar cheese
- 12 large eggs
- 1½ cups 2% milk
- ½ cup heavy whipping cream
- 1 teaspoon salt
- ¼ teaspoon coarsely ground pepper
- ⅛ teaspoon ground nutmeg
- ⅛ teaspoon cayenne pepper
- 1 tablespoon butter, melted

1. In a small bowl, mix the ham, sun-dried tomatoes, parsley and chives. In a greased 13x9-in. baking dish, layer half of each of the following: bread cubes, ham mixture and cheese. Repeat the layers.

2. In a large bowl, whisk eggs, milk, heavy whipping cream and seasonings; pour over the layers. Drizzle with the melted butter. Refrigerate, covered, overnight.

3. Preheat oven to 350°. Remove strata from refrigerator while oven heats. Bake, uncovered, 45-50 minutes or until a knife inserted near center comes out clean. (Cover loosely with foil if top browns too quickly.) Let stand 5-10 minutes before cutting.

PER SERVING *1 piece equals 336 cal., 17 g fat (9 g sat. fat), 256 mg chol., 895 mg sodium, 27 g carb., 1 g fiber, 19 g pro.*

Diner Corned Beef Hash

This was my attempt to duplicate a favorite dish from a northern Arizona restaurant. We enjoy the hash with eggs and toast.

—**DENISE CHELPKA** PHOENIX, AZ

PREP: 10 MIN. • **COOK:** 25 MIN.
MAKES: 4 SERVINGS

- 1¼ pounds potatoes (about 3 medium), cut into ½-inch cubes
- 3 tablespoons butter
- ¾ cup finely chopped celery
- ¾ pound cooked corned beef, cut into ½-inch cubes (about 2½ cups)
- 4 green onions, chopped
- ¼ teaspoon pepper
  Dash ground cloves
- 2 tablespoons minced fresh cilantro

1. Place potatoes in a saucepan; add water to cover. Bring to a boil. Reduce the heat; cook, uncovered, 6-8 minutes or just until tender. Drain.

2. In a large nonstick skillet, heat the butter over medium-high heat. Add celery; cook and stir 4-6 minutes or until crisp-tender. Add potatoes; cook 6-8 minutes or until lightly browned, turning occasionally. Stir in corned beef; cook 1-2 minutes or until heated through. Sprinkle with green onions, pepper and cloves; cook 1-2 minutes longer. Stir in cilantro.

PER SERVING *1 cup equals 407 cal., 25 g fat (11 g sat. fat), 106 mg chol., 1,059 mg sodium, 27 g carb., 4 g fiber, 19 g pro.*

DINER CORNED BEEF HASH

Fluffy Pumpkin Pancakes

My daughters adore these tender, fluffy pancakes topped with butter, maple syrup and whipped cream. We freeze extras and pop them into the toaster on busy days.
—**MINDY BAUKNECHT** TWO RIVERS, WI

PREP: 15 MIN. • **COOK:** 10 MIN./BATCH
MAKES: 4 PANCAKES

- ⅓ **cup all-purpose flour**
- ⅓ **cup whole wheat flour**
- 2 **tablespoons sugar**
- ½ **teaspoon baking powder**
- ½ **teaspoon baking soda**
- ¼ **teaspoon pumpkin pie spice**
- ⅛ **teaspoon ground cinnamon**
  Dash salt
- 1 **large egg**
- ½ **cup fat-free milk**
- ⅓ **cup vanilla yogurt**
- ⅓ **cup canned pumpkin**
- 1 **tablespoon canola oil**
- ⅛ **teaspoon vanilla extract**
  Maple syrup

1. In a bowl, whisk the first eight ingredients. In another bowl, whisk the egg, milk, yogurt, pumpkin, oil and vanilla until blended. Add to the dry ingredients; stir just until moistened.

2. Lightly coat a griddle with cooking spray; heat over medium heat. Pour batter by ½ cupfuls onto griddle. Cook until bubbles on top begin to pop and bottoms are golden brown. Turn; cook until the second side is golden brown. Serve with syrup.

PER SERVING *2 pancakes (calculated without syrup) equals 360 cal., 11 g fat (2 g sat. fat), 109 mg chol., 579 mg sodium, 55 g carb., 5 g fiber, 13 g pro.*

DID YOU KNOW?

Chorizo is a coarsely ground fresh or smoked pork sausage that has Mexican, Spanish and Portuguese origins. Traditionally flavored with paprika or chili powder, which gives it its reddish color, chorizo sausage is often used in egg dishes, soups, stews, casseroles and a variety of Mexican and Tex-Mex dishes.

CHORIZO TOMATO STRATA

Chorizo Tomato Strata
Olé! South-of-the-border chorizo sausage is guaranteed to spice up your morning.
—**DONNA COWLEY** DEKALB, IL

PREP: 25 MIN. • **BAKE:** 35 MIN. + STANDING
MAKES: 12 SERVINGS

- ½ **pound uncooked chorizo**
- 1 **cup (4 ounces) shredded Gruyere cheese, divided**
- ¼ **cup minced fresh cilantro**
- 1 **garlic clove, halved**
- 1 **loaf (½ pound) day-old French bread, cut into 1-inch slices**
- 2 **large tomatoes, sliced**
- 8 **large eggs**
- 2 **cups milk**
- ¾ **teaspoon salt**
- ¾ **teaspoon pepper**
- ½ **teaspoon onion powder**
- ¼ **teaspoon crushed red pepper flakes**

1. Crumble the chorizo into a small skillet; cook and stir over medium heat until fully cooked. Drain. Stir in ⅓ cup cheese and cilantro.

2. Preheat the oven to 350°. Rub the cut side of garlic clove over the bread slices; discard the garlic. Place bread slices in a greased 13x9-in. baking dish. Top with the tomatoes, meat mixture and remaining cheese.

3. In a large bowl, whisk the eggs, milk, salt, pepper, onion powder and pepper flakes. Pour over casserole.

4. Bake, uncovered, 35-45 minutes or until a knife inserted near center comes out clean (cover loosely with foil if the top browns too quickly). Let stand 10 minutes before cutting.

PER SERVING *1 piece equals 242 cal., 14 g fat (6 g sat. fat), 172 mg chol., 597 mg sodium, 14 g carb., 1 g fiber, 15 g pro.*

BEEFY HUEVOS RANCHEROS

(5) INGREDIENTS | FAST FIX

Campfire Cheese Hash Brown Packets

Eating breakfast around the campfire? A simple foil packet of O'Brien potatoes, bacon and shredded cheese makes a hearty hash. It's sure to get you energized for outdoor fun.

—**GINA NISTICO** MILWAUKEE, WI

START TO FINISH: 30 MIN.
MAKES: 4 SERVINGS

1 package (28 ounces) frozen O'Brien potatoes, thawed
1¼ cups (5 ounces) shredded cheddar cheese, divided
8 bacon strips, cooked and chopped
½ teaspoon salt
¼ teaspoon pepper
   Hard-cooked eggs and pico de gallo, optional

1. Prepare the campfire or grill for medium-high heat. Toss potatoes with ¾ cup cheese, bacon, salt and pepper.
2. Divide the mixture among four 18x12-in. pieces of heavy-duty nonstick foil, placing the food on the dull side of foil. Fold foil around potato mixture, sealing tightly.
3. Place the packets over campfire or grill; cook 6-9 minutes on each side or until the potatoes are tender. Open the packets carefully to allow steam to escape; sprinkle with the remaining cheese. If desired, serve with eggs and pico de gallo.
PER SERVING *1 serving equals 329 cal., 15 g fat (9 g sat. fat), 37 mg chol., 708 mg sodium, 31 g carb., 5 g fiber, 14 g pro.*

TOP TIP

When I'm going camping or on a picnic, I like to freeze water in gallon or half-gallon jugs and use those ice jugs instead of ice cubes to keep the food in my cooler chilled. The blocks of ice won't melt as fast as cubes, and when they do, the water will stay in the jugs—not get the food wet.
—**KIM K.** CINCINNATI, OH

Beefy Huevos Rancheros

We use the eggs from our chickens to fix this Tex-Mex dish. Guests like that they can pile on whatever toppings they wish, from sour cream and chopped green onions to guacamole and salsa.

—**SANDRA LEONARD** PECULIAR, MO

PREP: 15 MIN. • **COOK:** 20 MIN.
MAKES: 6 SERVINGS

1 pound lean ground beef (90% lean)
1 small onion, finely chopped
2 cans (14½ ounces each) diced tomatoes
1 cup frozen corn
1 can (4 ounces) chopped green chilies
½ teaspoon salt
6 large eggs
¼ teaspoon pepper
6 tablespoons shredded cheddar cheese
6 flour tortillas (8 inches), warmed

Optional toppings: reduced-fat sour cream, guacamole, salsa and chopped green onions

1. In a large skillet, cook the beef and onion over medium heat 6-8 minutes or until the beef is no longer pink and onion is tender, breaking up beef into crumbles; drain and return to pan.
2. Drain tomatoes, reserving ½ cup liquid. Stir tomatoes, reserved liquid, corn, chilies and salt into beef mixture; bring to a simmer. With the back of a spoon, make six wells in beef mixture; add an egg to each well. Sprinkle with pepper. Cook, covered, 5-7 minutes or until egg whites are completely set.
3. Sprinkle with cheese. Serve with tortillas and toppings as desired.
PER SERVING *1 serving (calculated without toppings) equals 434 cal., 17 g fat (6 g sat. fat), 241 mg chol., 879 mg sodium, 41 g carb., 5 g fiber, 29 g pro.*

DAD'S BLUEBERRY BUTTERMILK PANCAKES

Dad's Blueberry Buttermilk Pancakes

Every Saturday without exception, my dad pulls out the griddle and cooks stacks of blueberry pancakes for us. The cornmeal, buttermilk and oats give his cakes that little something extra we can't resist.

—**GABRIELLE SHORT** PLEASANT HILL, IA

PREP: 15 MIN. + STANDING
COOK: 10 MIN./BATCH
MAKES: 12 PANCAKES

- 1 cup all-purpose flour
- 3 tablespoons cornmeal
- 3 tablespoons quick-cooking oats
- 3 tablespoons sugar
- 1 teaspoon baking powder
- ½ teaspoon baking soda
- ½ teaspoon salt
  Dash ground nutmeg
- 1 large egg
- 1½ cups buttermilk
- 2 tablespoons canola oil
- 1 teaspoon vanilla extract
- 1 cup fresh or frozen blueberries

1. In a large bowl, whisk the first eight ingredients. In another bowl, whisk egg, buttermilk, oil and vanilla until blended. Add to flour mixture; stir just until moistened (batter will be lumpy). Let stand 15 minutes.

2. Lightly grease a griddle or large nonstick skillet; heat over medium heat. Stir the blueberries into batter. Pour batter by ¼ cupfuls onto griddle or skillet. Cook until the bubbles on top begin to pop and the bottoms are golden brown. Turn; cook until second side is brown.

PER SERVING *3 pancakes equals 332 cal., 10 g fat (2 g sat. fat), 50 mg chol., 746 mg sodium, 52 g carb., 2 g fiber, 9 g pro.*

Easy Cheesy Loaded Grits

PREP: 35 MIN. • **BAKE:** 50 MIN. + STANDING
MAKES: 8 SERVINGS

- 1 pound mild or spicy bulk pork sausage
- 1 small onion, chopped
- 4 cups water
- ½ teaspoon salt
- 1 cup quick-cooking grits
- 3 cans (4 ounces each) chopped green chilies
- 1½ cups (6 ounces) shredded sharp cheddar cheese, divided
- 1½ cups (6 ounces) shredded Monterey Jack cheese, divided
- 2 tablespoons butter
- ¼ teaspoon hot pepper sauce
- 2 large eggs, lightly beaten
- ¼ teaspoon paprika
  Chopped fresh cilantro

1. Preheat oven to 325°. In a large skillet, cook sausage and onion over medium heat 6-8 minutes or until the sausage is no longer pink, breaking up sausage into crumbles; drain.

2. In a large saucepan, bring water and salt to a boil. Slowly stir in grits. Reduce heat to medium-low; cook, covered, about 5 minutes or until thickened, stirring occasionally. Remove from heat.

3. Add chilies, ¾ cup cheddar cheese, ¾ cup Jack cheese, butter and pepper sauce; stir until cheese is melted. Stir in eggs, then sausage mixture.

4. Transfer to a greased 13x9-in. baking dish. Top with the remaining cheeses; sprinkle with paprika. Bake, uncovered, 50-60 minutes or until golden brown and set. Let stand 10 minutes before serving. Sprinkle with cilantro.

PER SERVING *1 cup equals 399 cal., 28 g fat (15 g sat. fat), 116 mg chol., 839 mg sodium, 19 g carb., 2 g fiber, 18 g pro.*

A similar recipe inspired me to create Easy Cheesy Loaded Grits. My family loves all the add-ins, from the cheddar and Monterey Jack to the sausage.

—**JOAN HALLFORD** NORTH RICHLAND HILLS, TX

EASY CHEESY LOADED GRITS

EAT SMART **(5) INGREDIENTS** **FAST FIX**

Open-Faced Egg Sandwiches

I eat eggs for breakfast every day and came up with a new way to enjoy them.

—**VALERIE BELLEY** ST. LOUIS, MO

START TO FINISH: 15 MIN.
MAKES: 2 SERVINGS

- 4 large egg whites
- 2 large eggs
- 2 tablespoons grated Parmesan cheese
- 2 teaspoons butter, softened
- 2 slices whole wheat bread, toasted
- ⅛ teaspoon dried rosemary, crushed
- ⅛ teaspoon pepper

1. Heat a small nonstick skillet coated with cooking spray over medium-high heat. Whisk the egg whites, eggs and Parmesan cheese; add to the skillet. Cook and stir until set.

2. Spread butter over toasts; top with egg mixture. Sprinkle with rosemary and pepper. Serve immediately.

PER SERVING *1 sandwich equals 231 cal., 11 g fat (5 g sat. fat), 226 mg chol., 416 mg sodium, 13 g carb., 2 g fiber, 19 g pro.* **Diabetic Exchanges:** *2 lean meat, 1 starch, 1 fat.*

Spiced Bacon Twists

Extend the cooking time for these sweet spiced strips if you like crispy bacon.

—**GLENDA EVANS WITTNER** JOPLIN, MO

PREP: 10 MIN. • **BAKE:** 25 MIN.
MAKES: 5 SERVINGS

- ¼ cup packed brown sugar
- 1½ teaspoons ground mustard
- ⅛ teaspoon ground cinnamon
- ⅛ teaspoon ground nutmeg
  Dash cayenne pepper
- 10 center-cut bacon strips

1. Preheat oven to 350°. Combine the first five ingredients; rub over bacon on both sides. Twist bacon; place on a rack in a 15x10x1-in. baking pan.

2. Bake 25-30 minutes or until firm; bake longer if desired.

PER SERVING *2 bacon twists equals 75 cal., 4 g fat (1 g sat. fat), 15 mg chol., 212 mg sodium, 6 g carb., trace fiber, 5 g pro.* **Diabetic Exchanges:** *1 high-fat meat, ½ starch.*

EAT SMART **FAST FIX**

Cranberry-Walnut Oatmeal

START TO FINISH: 15 MIN.
MAKES: 4 SERVINGS

- 3½ cups water
- ¼ teaspoon salt
- 2 cups quick-cooking oats
- 3 tablespoons sugar
- 1 teaspoon vanilla extract
- 2 teaspoons cinnamon-sugar
- ½ cup whole-berry cranberry sauce
- ¼ cup chopped walnuts, toasted

1. In a large saucepan, bring water and salt to a boil. Stir in oats. Cook 1 minute over medium heat, stirring occasionally.

2. Remove from heat; stir in sugar and vanilla. Top servings with cinnamon-sugar, cranberry sauce and walnuts.

NOTE *To toast nuts, bake in a shallow pan in a 350° oven for 5-10 minutes or cook in a skillet over low heat until lightly browned, stirring occasionally.*

PER SERVING *1 cup equals 293 cal., 8 g fat (1 g sat. fat), 0 chol., 156 mg sodium, 53 g carb., 5 g fiber, 7 g pro.*

Give your morning bowl of comfort food a nutty crunch and tangy berry flavor. Cranberry-Walnut Oatmeal is such a treat on a chilly fall or winter day.

—**TEENA PETRUS** JOHNSTOWN, PA

CRANBERRY-WALNUT OATMEAL

Creamy Pumpkin Bubble Ring

While watching TV years ago, I saw a recipe I adapted into my caramel-coated pumpkin bubble ring. I often make it as a hostess gift or bake sale contribution. My children help by rolling the dough and cream cheese into balls.

—ANGELA COFFMAN KANSAS CITY, MO

PREP: 1 HOUR + RISING
BAKE: 25 MIN. + COOLING
MAKES: 1 LOAF (18 SERVINGS)

- ½ cup sugar
- 3 teaspoons active dry yeast
- 1½ teaspoons ground cinnamon
- 1 teaspoon salt
- ¼ teaspoon ground nutmeg
- 2½ to 3 cups all-purpose flour
- 1 cup canned pumpkin
- ¼ cup 2% milk
- 1 large egg
- ½ cup packed brown sugar
- ¼ cup corn syrup
- ¼ cup butter, cubed
- 1 cup chopped pecans
- 1 package (8 ounces) cream cheese, cut into 18 pieces

1. In a large bowl, mix the sugar, yeast, cinnamon, salt, nutmeg and 1½ cups flour. In a small saucepan, heat the pumpkin and milk to 120°-130°. Add to dry ingredients; beat on medium speed 2 minutes. Add egg; beat on high 2 minutes. Stir in enough remaining flour to form a soft dough.

2. Turn the dough onto a floured surface; knead until smooth and elastic, about 6-8 minutes. Place in a greased bowl, turning once to grease the top. Cover with plastic wrap and let rise in a warm place until doubled, about 1 hour.

3. In a small saucepan, combine the brown sugar, corn syrup and butter; cook and stir over medium heat until the sugar is dissolved. Pour half of the mixture into a greased 10-in. fluted tube pan; sprinkle with ½ cup pecans.

4. Punch the down dough; divide and shape into 18 balls. Flatten and wrap each ball around a piece of cream cheese, pinching to seal. Place nine balls in the prepared pan; top with the remaining brown sugar mixture and pecans. Top with the remaining balls.

MINI CARAMEL ROLLS

Cover with a kitchen towel; let rise in a warm place until doubled, about 45 minutes. Preheat oven to 350°.

5. Bake, uncovered, 25-30 minutes or until lightly browned. Cool in the pan 10 minutes before inverting onto a serving plate. Serve warm.

PER SERVING *1 piece equals 245 cal., 12 g fat (5 g sat. fat), 33 mg chol., 198 mg sodium, 31 g carb., 2 g fiber, 4 g pro.*

Mini Caramel Rolls

Your family will come running when they smell these goodies baking. The caramel rolls come together quickly thanks to a tube of refrigerated crescents.

—KAYLA WIEGAND CONGERVILLE, IL

PREP: 20 MIN. • **BAKE:** 15 MIN.
MAKES: 12 SERVINGS

- ⅓ cup packed brown sugar
- ⅓ cup butter, cubed
- 2 tablespoons light corn syrup
- 1½ teaspoons 2% milk
- 1 tube (8 ounces) refrigerated crescent rolls
- 2 teaspoons sugar
- ½ teaspoon ground cinnamon

1. Preheat oven to 375°. In a small saucepan, combine the brown sugar, butter, corn syrup and milk; cook and stir over medium heat until blended. Pour into a greased 9-in. pie plate.

2. Separate crescent dough into four rectangles; gently press perforations to seal. In a small bowl, mix the sugar and cinnamon; sprinkle evenly over the rectangles. Roll up jelly-roll style, starting with a long side; pinch the seams to seal.

3. Cut each roll into nine slices; place in prepared dish, cut side down. Bake 15-18 minutes or until golden brown. Cool 1 minute before inverting onto a serving plate.

PER SERVING *3 rolls equals 155 cal., 9 g fat (4 g sat. fat), 13 mg chol., 189 mg sodium, 17 g carb., trace fiber, 1 g pro.*

CHOCOLATE-FRUIT CREPES

Chocolate-Fruit Crepes

With a fudgy drizzle, these delicate crepes are luscious enough to serve as a dessert.
—LAURA MCDOWELL LAKE VILLA, IL

PREP: 30 MIN. + CHILLING
COOK: 5 MIN./BATCH
MAKES: 10 SERVINGS

- 1½ cups buttermilk
- 3 large eggs
- 3 tablespoons butter, melted
- 1 cup all-purpose flour
- 2 tablespoons sugar
- 2 tablespoons baking cocoa

FILLING
- 1 can (21 ounces) cherry pie filling
- 1 can (8½ ounces) sliced peaches, drained and chopped
- ½ teaspoon ground cinnamon
- ⅛ teaspoon almond extract
- ⅓ cup hot fudge ice cream topping, warmed
  Whipped cream, optional

1. In a large bowl, combine the buttermilk, eggs and butter. Combine the flour, sugar and baking cocoa; add to buttermilk mixture and mix well. Cover and refrigerate for 1 hour.
2. Heat a lightly greased 8-in. nonstick skillet over medium heat; pour 2 tablespoons batter into the center of skillet. Lift and tilt the pan to coat the bottom evenly. Cook until the top appears dry; turn and cook 15-20 seconds longer. Remove to a

wire rack. Repeat with remaining batter, greasing skillet as needed. When cool, stack crepes with waxed paper or paper towels in between.
3. In a microwave-safe bowl, combine the pie filling, peaches and cinnamon. Microwave, uncovered, on high for 3-4 minutes or until heated through, stirring once. Stir in extract. Spoon 2 tablespoons filling down the center of each crepe. Fold the sides of crepe over filling. Drizzle with hot fudge ice cream topping; garnish with whipped cream if desired.

PER SERVING *2 fruit-filled crepes (calculated without whipped cream) equals 241 cal., 6 g fat (3 g sat. fat), 74 mg chol., 109 mg sodium, 41 g carb., 1 g fiber, 5 g pro.*

Can't-Eat-Just-One Cinnamon Rolls

My go-to rolls vanish quickly—especially when I drop off a pan for my brothers!
—REGINA FARMWALD
WEST FARMNGTON, OH

PREP: 1 HOUR + RISING • **BAKE:** 20 MIN.
MAKES: 2 DOZEN

- 1 package (¼ ounce) active dry yeast
- 1 tablespoon sugar
- ¼ cup warm water (110° to 115°)
- 1 cup 2% milk
- ⅓ cup instant vanilla pudding mix (half of a 3.4-ounce package)

- 1 large egg
- ¼ cup butter, melted
- 1 teaspoon salt
- 3 to 3½ cups all-purpose flour

FILLING
- ¾ cup sugar
- 1 tablespoon ground cinnamon
- ¼ cup butter, melted

FROSTING
- ½ cup butter, softened
- 2 teaspoons vanilla extract
- 1 teaspoon water
- 1½ to 1¾ cups confectioners' sugar

1. In a small bowl, dissolve the yeast and 1 tablespoon sugar in warm water. In a large bowl, beat milk and pudding mix on low speed 1 minute. Let stand 1 minute or until soft-set. Add the egg, butter, salt, yeast mixture and 2 cups flour; beat on medium until smooth. Stir in enough remaining flour to form a soft dough (dough will be sticky).
2. Turn dough onto a floured surface; knead until smooth and elastic, about 6-8 minutes. Place in a greased bowl, turning once to grease the top. Cover with plastic wrap and let rise in a warm place until doubled, about 1 hour.
3. For filling, in a small bowl, mix the sugar and cinnamon. Punch down the dough; divide in half. Turn one portion of dough onto a lightly floured surface; roll into an 18x10-in. rectangle. Brush with half of the melted butter to within ¼ in. of the edges; sprinkle with half of the sugar mixture. Roll up jelly-roll style, starting with a long side; pinch seam to seal. Cut into 12 slices. Repeat with the remaining dough and filling ingredients.
4. Place all of the slices in a greased 13x9-in. baking pan, cut side down. Cover with a kitchen towel; let rise in a warm place until almost doubled, about 45 minutes. Preheat oven to 350°.
5. Bake 20-25 minutes or until golden brown. Cool in pan on a wire rack.
6. For frosting, in a small bowl, beat butter until creamy. Beat in vanilla, water and enough confectioners' sugar to reach desired consistency. Spread over warm rolls. Serve warm.

PER SERVING *1 cinnamon roll equals 199 cal., 8 g fat (5 g sat. fat), 29 mg chol., 187 mg sodium, 29 g carb., 1 g fiber, 2 g pro.*

⑤ INGREDIENTS **FAST FIX**

Chocolate Cinnamon Toast

If you have just 10 minutes in the morning, you can treat yourself to this simple but scrumptious toast. Spread bittersweet chocolate onto a slice of cinnamon bread, then pile on a layer of fresh strawberries and bananas. It's that easy!

—**JEANNE AMBROSE** MILWAUKEE, WI

START TO FINISH: 10 MIN.
MAKES: 1 SERVING

- 1 slice cinnamon bread
- 1 teaspoon butter, softened
- 2 tablespoons 60% cacao bittersweet chocolate baking chips
  Sliced banana and strawberries, optional

1. Spread both sides of cinnamon bread with butter. In a small skillet, toast bread over medium-high heat 2-3 minutes on each side, topping with the bittersweet chocolate baking chips after turning.

2. Remove from the heat; spread the melted chocolate evenly over the toast. If desired, top with fruit.

PER SERVING *1 serving (calculated without fruit) equals 235 cal., 13 g fat (8 g sat. fat), 10 mg chol., 131 mg sodium, 29 g carb., 3 g fiber, 4 g pro.*

Overnight Pumpkin French Toast Casserole

Cooking that doesn't keep me tied to the kitchen—that's what I'm all about. I fix this dish the night before breakfast with guests.

—**PATRICIA HARMON** BADEN, PA

PREP: 20 MIN. + CHILLING • **BAKE:** 65 MIN.
MAKES: 12 SERVINGS

- 1 loaf (1 pound) cinnamon-raisin bread
- 1 package (8 ounces) reduced-fat cream cheese, cut into ¾-inch cubes
- 8 large eggs
- 1 can (12 ounces) evaporated milk
- 1 cup canned pumpkin
- ⅔ cup packed brown sugar
- ½ cup fat-free milk
- 2 teaspoons ground cinnamon
- ¼ teaspoon ground nutmeg
- ¼ teaspoon ground ginger
- ⅛ teaspoon ground cloves
- ½ teaspoon salt
- ½ cup chopped pecans

  Confectioners' sugar, optional
  Maple syrup, warmed, optional

1. Cut each slice of bread in quarters. Arrange half of the bread in a greased 13x9-in. baking dish; layer with cubed cream cheese and remaining bread, pressing down slightly.

2. In a large bowl, whisk the eggs, evaporated milk, pumpkin, brown sugar, fat-free milk, spices and salt. Pour over top. Refrigerate, covered, overnight.

3. Preheat oven to 350°. Remove the casserole from the refrigerator while oven heats. Bake, covered, 40 minutes. Uncover; sprinkle with pecans. Bake, uncovered, 25-30 minutes or until lightly browned and a knife inserted near the center comes out clean.

4. Let stand 5-10 minutes. If desired, dust with confectioners' sugar and serve with maple syrup.

PER SERVING *1 piece (calculated without confectioners' sugar or maple syrup) equals 302 cal., 13 g fat (6 g sat. fat), 147 mg chol., 342 mg sodium, 36 g carb., 4 g fiber, 13 g pro.*

OVERNIGHT PUMPKIN
FRENCH TOAST CASSEROLE

(5) INGREDIENTS FAST FIX

Apple Sausage Puffs

I keep my recipe for sausage puffs close at hand when entertaining. Everyone loves them, and I need only four ingredients.

—VERONICA JOHNSON JEFFERSON CITY, MO

START TO FINISH: 25 MIN.
MAKES: 2 DOZEN

- 1 **pound bulk pork sausage**
- 1 **medium apple, finely chopped**
- 3 **ounces cream cheese, softened**
- 3 **tubes (8 ounces each) refrigerated crescent rolls**

1. Preheat oven to 375°. In a large skillet, cook sausage and apple over medium heat until meat is no longer pink; drain. Stir in cream cheese.

2. Unroll one tube of crescent dough; separate into eight triangles. Place 1 tablespoon filling on the long side of each triangle. Roll up, starting with the long side; pinch seams to seal.

3. Place point side down 2 in. apart on a greased baking sheet. Repeat with remaining crescent dough and filling. Bake 10-12 minutes or until golden brown. Serve warm.

PER SERVING *1 sausage puff equals 165 cal., 11 g fat (4 g sat. fat), 11 mg chol., 311 mg sodium, 12 g carb., trace fiber, 4 g pro.*

ORANGE RICOTTA PANCAKES

APPLE SAUSAGE PUFFS

FAST FIX

Orange Ricotta Pancakes

These yummy pancakes are so moist and tender, you could eat them without syrup!

—BREHAN KOHL ANCHORAGE, AK

START TO FINISH: 30 MIN.
MAKES: 12 PANCAKES

- 1½ **cups all-purpose flour**
- 3 **tablespoons sugar**
- 1½ **teaspoons baking powder**
- ½ **teaspoon baking soda**
- ¼ **teaspoon salt**
- 1 **large egg**
- 1 **cup part-skim ricotta cheese**
- ¾ **cup 2% milk**
- ½ **teaspoon grated orange peel**
- ½ **cup orange juice**
- ¼ **cup butter, melted**
- ½ **teaspoon vanilla extract**
  Maple syrup and confectioners' sugar, optional

1. In a bowl, whisk the first five ingredients. In another bowl, whisk the egg, ricotta cheese, milk, orange peel, orange juice, melted butter and vanilla until blended. Add to the dry ingredients; stir just until moistened.

2. Lightly grease a griddle; heat over medium heat. Pour pancake batter by ¼ cupfuls onto griddle. Cook until bubbles on top begin to pop and the bottoms are golden brown. Turn; cook until the second side is golden brown. Serve pancakes with maple syrup and confectioners' sugar if desired.

PER SERVING *3 pancakes (calculated without maple syrup and confectioners' sugar) equals 449 cal., 19 g fat (11 g sat. fat), 106 mg chol., 654 mg sodium, 54 g carb., 1 g fiber, 15 g pro.*

As a busy cook, I'm a huge fan of dishes that are versatile. Makeover Hash Brown Casserole is just as good with scrambled eggs for breakfast as it is with a big, meaty roast for Sunday dinner.

—KELLY KIRBY VICTORIA, BC

Makeover Hash Brown Casserole

PREP: 15 MIN. • **BAKE:** 40 MIN.
MAKES: 12 SERVINGS

- 1 package (30 ounces) frozen shredded hash brown potatoes, thawed
- 1 can (10¾ ounces) reduced-fat reduced-sodium condensed cream of chicken soup, undiluted
- 1 cup (4 ounces) shredded reduced-fat sharp cheddar cheese
- ⅔ cup reduced-fat sour cream
- 1 small onion, chopped
- ½ teaspoon salt
- ½ teaspoon pepper
- ¼ cup crushed cornflakes
- 1 tablespoon butter, melted

1. Preheat oven to 350°. In a large bowl, mix the first seven ingredients. Transfer to a 13x9-in. or 3-qt. baking dish coated with cooking spray.
2. In a small bowl, toss the crushed cornflakes with the melted butter; sprinkle over top. Bake 40-45 minutes or until golden brown.
PER SERVING ¾ cup equals 136 cal., 5 g fat (3 g sat. fat), 15 mg chol., 292 mg sodium, 19 g carb., 1 g fiber, 5 g pro.
Diabetic Exchanges: 1 starch, 1 fat.

Ricotta-Raisin Coffee Cake

Sharing this beautiful coffee cake with overnight guests is a joy. If you don't have cardamom or don't care for it, substitute nutmeg, cinnamon or allspice.
—CAROL GAUS ELK GROVE VILLAGE, IL

PREP: 15 MIN. + RISING
BAKE: 20 MIN. + COOLING
MAKES: 12 SERVINGS

- 1 loaf (1 pound) frozen bread dough, thawed
- 1 cup part-skim ricotta cheese
- ¼ cup honey
- ¼ teaspoon ground cardamom
- ¼ teaspoon almond extract
- 1 cup golden raisins
- ¼ cup confectioners' sugar
- 2 to 3 teaspoons fat-free milk

1. On a lightly floured surface, roll dough into a 15x9-in. rectangle. In a small bowl, combine cheese, honey, cardamom and extract. Spread filling to within ½ in. of edges. Sprinkle with raisins. Roll up jelly-roll style, starting with a long side; pinch seam to seal. Pinch ends together to form a ring.
2. Place ring seam side down in a parchment paper-lined 9-in. round baking pan. Cover and let rise until doubled, about 30 minutes.
3. Preheat oven to 350°. With a sharp knife, make 12 shallow slashes in top of ring. Bake 20-25 minutes or until golden brown. Cool on a wire rack. In a small bowl, combine confectioners' sugar and milk; drizzle over cake.
PER SERVING *1 slice equals 203 cal., 3 g fat (1 g sat. fat), 6 mg chol., 240 mg sodium, 37 g carb., 2 g fiber, 7 g pro.*

RICOTTA-RAISIN COFFEE CAKE

SPINACH-MUSHROOM SCRAMBLED EGGS

Holiday Brunch Casserole

Here's a great make-ahead breakfast for holidays when you want to spend more time with family and less in the kitchen.

—**NELDA CRONBAUGH** BELLE PLAINE, IA

PREP: 20 MIN. + CHILLING
BAKE: 30 MIN. + STANDING
MAKES: 12 SERVINGS

- 4 cups frozen shredded hash brown potatoes, thawed
- 1 pound bulk pork sausage, cooked and drained
- ½ pound bacon strips, cooked and crumbled
- 1 medium green pepper, chopped
- 1 green onion, chopped
- 2 cups (8 ounces) shredded cheddar cheese, divided
- 4 large eggs
- 3 cups 2% milk
- 1 cup reduced-fat biscuit/baking mix
- ½ teaspoon salt

1. In a large bowl, combine the first five ingredients; stir in 1 cup shredded cheddar cheese. Transfer to a greased 13x9-in. baking dish.

2. In another bowl, whisk the eggs, milk, baking mix and salt until blended; pour over the top. Sprinkle with the remaining cheddar cheese. Refrigerate, covered, overnight.

3. Preheat the oven to 375°. Remove the casserole from the refrigerator while the oven heats. Bake, uncovered, 30-35 minutes or until a knife inserted near center comes out clean. Let stand 10 minutes before cutting.

PER SERVING *1 piece equals 366 cal., 25 g fat (11 g sat. fat), 131 mg chol., 971 mg sodium, 16 g carb., 1 g fiber, 19 g pro.*

EAT SMART **FAST FIX**
Spinach-Mushroom Scrambled Eggs

My husband and I really loved a mushroom egg dish we tried at a restaurant. I created a healthier version that keeps the cheese and veggie flavor we crave.

—**RACHELLE MCCALLA** WAYNE, NE

START TO FINISH: 15 MIN.
MAKES: 2 SERVINGS

- 2 large eggs
- 2 large egg whites
- ⅛ teaspoon salt
- ⅛ teaspoon pepper
- 1 teaspoon butter
- ½ cup thinly sliced fresh mushrooms
- ½ cup fresh baby spinach, chopped
- 2 tablespoons shredded provolone cheese

1. In a small bowl, whisk the eggs, egg whites, salt and pepper until blended. In a small nonstick skillet, heat the butter over medium-high heat. Add mushrooms; cook and stir 3-4 minutes or until tender. Add the spinach; cook and stir until wilted. Reduce the heat to medium.

2. Add egg mixture; cook and stir just until eggs are thickened and no liquid egg remains. Stir in cheese.

PER SERVING *1 serving equals 162 cal., 11 g fat (5 g sat. fat), 226 mg chol., 417 mg sodium, 2 g carb., trace fiber, 14 g pro.* **Diabetic Exchange:** *2 medium-fat meat.*

HOLIDAY BRUNCH CASSEROLE

Classic Fruit Kolaches

For Christmas, shape these using festive cookie cutters instead of a biscuit cutter.

—GLEN & SUE ELLEN BORKHOLDER

STURGIS, MI

PREP: 35 MIN. + RISING
BAKE: 15 MIN./BATCH
MAKES: 2½ DOZEN

- 6 to 7 cups all-purpose flour
- ¼ cup sugar
- 2 packages (¼ ounce each) active dry yeast
- 2 teaspoons salt
- 2 cups 2% milk
- ½ cup butter, cubed
- ½ cup water
- 6 large egg yolks
- ¼ cup butter, melted
- 1 can (12 ounces) raspberry and/or apricot cake and pastry filling

ICING

- 3 cups confectioners' sugar
- ¼ cup butter, softened
- 2 teaspoons vanilla extract
- ½ teaspoon salt
- 4 to 6 tablespoons 2% milk

1. In a large bowl, combine 3 cups flour, sugar, yeast and salt. In a large saucepan, heat the milk, cubed butter and water to 120°-130°. Add to the dry ingredients; beat just until moistened. Add the egg yolks; beat until smooth. Stir in enough remaining flour to form a soft dough (the dough will be sticky). Do not knead. Cover and let rise until doubled, about 45 minutes.

2. Turn dough onto a floured surface; roll to ½-in. thickness. Cut with a floured 2½-in. biscuit cutter. Place 2 in. apart on lightly greased baking sheets. Brush with melted butter. Cover and let rise in a warm place until doubled, about 30 minutes.

3. Preheat oven to 350°. Using the back of a spoon, make an indentation in center of each roll. Spoon a heaping teaspoonful of the raspberry and/or apricot filling into each indentation. Bake 15-20 minutes or until golden brown. Remove from pans to wire racks to cool.

4. Combine the confectioners' sugar, butter, vanilla, salt and enough milk to achieve the desired consistency. Drizzle over the rolls.

CHOCOLATE PECAN WAFFLES

NOTE *This recipe was tested with Solo brand cake and pastry filling. Look for it in the baking aisle.*
PER SERVING *1 kolache equals 245 cal., 8 g fat (4 g sat. fat), 58 mg chol., 259 mg sodium, 40 g carb., 1 g fiber, 4 g pro.*

FAST FIX

Chocolate Pecan Waffles

Crisp, chocolaty, made-from-scratch waffles will have everyone at your table drooling! The recipe calls for raspberries, but feel free to substitute strawberries or bananas—they're just as yummy.

—LUCILLE MEAD ILION, NY

START TO FINISH: 30 MIN.
MAKES: 16 WAFFLES

- 3 large eggs
- 1 cup sugar
- 1 cup whole milk
- ½ cup butter, melted
- ¼ teaspoon vanilla extract
- 2 ounces unsweetened chocolate, melted and cooled
- 1½ cups all-purpose flour
- 1 teaspoon baking powder
- ½ teaspoon salt
- ¼ teaspoon baking soda
- ¼ cup chopped pecans
  Whipped topping and fresh raspberries, optional

1. In a large bowl, beat eggs and sugar until foamy; beat in the milk, butter and vanilla. Stir in chocolate.

2. In another bowl, combine the flour, baking powder, salt and baking soda. Stir in the chocolate mixture just until moistened. Fold in pecans.

3. Bake in a preheated waffle iron according to manufacturer's directions until golden brown. Serve with whipped topping and raspberries if desired.

FREEZE OPTION *Cool on wire racks. Freeze between layers of waxed paper in a resealable plastic freezer bag. To use, reheat in a toaster on medium setting. Or, microwave each on high 30-60 seconds or until heated through.*

PER SERVING *2 waffles (calculated without topping and berries) equals 389 cal., 21 g fat (11 g sat. fat), 112 mg chol., 358 mg sodium, 47 g carb., 2 g fiber, 7 g pro.*

DIANE MYERS'
HONEY CINNAMON BARS
PAGE 159

Potluck Pleasers

Wondering what to bring? Choose any of the **crowd-favorite foods** in this chapter of delicious, **larger-yield recipes.** You'll return home with an **empty dish**—but wish you had leftovers!

JENNIFER BABCOCK'S POTLUCK MACARONI & CHEESE
PAGE 160

ROBIN SPIRES' BUFFALO CHICKEN DEVILED EGGS
PAGE 165

SHERRY PITZER'S TANGY BARBECUE WINGS
PAGE 166

FAST FIX

Pasta Salad in a Jar

I love this make-ahead salad. When I pack a single serving for my husband's lunch at work, I tie a plastic fork to the jar.

—**PAT NEIHEISEL** LEETONIA, OH

START TO FINISH: 30 MIN.
MAKES: 16 SERVINGS (1 CUP EACH)

- 8 ounces each uncooked bow tie, medium pasta shells and wagon wheel pasta
- 2 cups Greek vinaigrette
- 3 cups cherry tomatoes, halved
- 1 medium red onion, finely chopped
- 1 jar (12 ounces) marinated quartered artichoke hearts, drained and coarsely chopped
- 1 jar (12 ounces) roasted sweet red peppers, drained and chopped
- 1 cup chopped fresh basil
- 1 cup grated Parmesan cheese
- 1 package (3½ ounces) sliced pepperoni
- 1 can (2¼ ounces) sliced ripe olives, drained

1. Cook pasta according to package directions for al dente. Drain pasta; rinse with cold water and drain well. Transfer to a large bowl or jar.
2. Add the vinaigrette to pasta; toss to coat. Add vegetables, basil, cheese, pepperoni and olives; toss to combine. If desired, transfer to covered jars. Refrigerate until serving.
PER SERVING *1 cup equals 375 cal., 20 g fat (4 g sat. fat), 11 mg chol., 690 mg sodium, 37 g carb., 2 g fiber, 9 g pro.*

HAM-CHEDDAR CHEESE BALL

PASTA SALAD IN A JAR

Ham-Cheddar Cheese Ball

Having a football party? Shape your cheese ball into a pigskin! You're sure to score big points with the sports fans in your crowd. A few strips of sliced Swiss are perfect for forming the laces on top.

—**MICHELE MOORE** MOORESVILLE, IN

PREP: 15 MIN. + CHILLING
MAKES: 4 CUPS

- ½ pound thinly sliced deli ham
- ½ medium onion, cut into wedges
- 2 cups (8 ounces) finely shredded cheddar cheese
- 2 packages (8 ounces each) cream cheese, cubed
- 1 cup chopped pecans
- 1 slice Swiss cheese
  Assorted crackers

1. Place the ham and onion in a food processor; pulse until finely chopped. Add the cheddar cheese; pulse until blended. Add the cream cheese; process until smooth.
2. Shape mixture into a football; press pecans into mixture. Wrap in plastic wrap; refrigerate at least 1 hour.
3. Cut Swiss cheese into strips; arrange over top for laces. Serve with crackers.
PER SERVING *2 tablespoons (calculated without crackers) equals 108 cal., 10 g fat (4 g sat. fat), 26 mg chol., 162 mg sodium, 1 g carb., trace fiber, 4 g pro.*

TOP TIP

Cheese balls are easy to make, but shaping them can be messy. To keep your hands and countertop clean, spoon the cheese mixture onto a piece of plastic wrap. Working from the underside of the wrap, pat the cheese mixture into a ball or other shape.

Honey Cinnamon Bars

My Aunt Ellie gave us the recipe for these honey-sweetened, cinnamon-spiced bars spread with a vanilla glaze. Enjoy one with your afternoon cup of coffee or tea.

—**DIANE MYERS** STAR, ID

PREP: 25 MIN. • **BAKE:** 10 MIN. + COOLING
MAKES: 3 DOZEN

- 1 **cup sugar**
- ¾ **cup canola oil**
- ¼ **cup honey**
- 1 **large egg**
- 2 **cups all-purpose flour**
- 1 **teaspoon baking soda**
- 1 **teaspoon ground cinnamon**
- ¼ **teaspoon salt**
- 1 **cup chopped walnuts, toasted**

GLAZE
- 1 **cup confectioners' sugar**
- 2 **tablespoons mayonnaise**
- 1 **teaspoon vanilla extract**
- 1 **to 2 tablespoons water**
  Additional toasted chopped walnuts, optional

1. Preheat oven to 350°. In a large bowl, beat sugar, oil, honey and egg until well blended. In another bowl, whisk flour, baking soda, cinnamon and salt; gradually beat into sugar mixture. Stir in 1 cup walnuts.

2. Spread the batter into a greased 15x10x1-in. baking pan. Bake 10-12 minutes or until golden brown (the edges will puff up). Cool completely on a wire rack.

3. For glaze, in a small bowl, mix confectioners' sugar, mayonnaise, vanilla and enough water to reach desired consistency; spread over top. If desired, sprinkle with additional walnuts. Let stand until set. Cut into bars. Refrigerate leftovers.

NOTE *To toast nuts, bake in a shallow pan in a 350° oven for 5-10 minutes or cook in a skillet over low heat until lightly browned, stirring occasionally.*

PER SERVING *1 bar (calculated without additional walnuts) equals 138 cal., 8 g fat (1 g sat. fat), 5 mg chol., 58 mg sodium, 17 g carb., trace fiber, 1 g pro.*

Grilled Sausages with Summer Vegetables

After 30 years of camping, we've acquired quite a collection of grilled recipes. Our sausage with vegetables would be great for any outdoor event.

—**NANCY DAUGHERTY** CORTLAND, OH

PREP: 35 MIN. • **GRILL:** 25 MIN.
MAKES: 12 SERVINGS

- ¾ **cup peach preserves**
- ½ **cup reduced-sodium soy sauce**
- 3 **tablespoons minced fresh gingerroot**
- 3 **tablespoons water**
- 3 **garlic cloves, minced**
  Dash hot pepper sauce, optional
- 4 **medium sweet red peppers**
- 1 **medium eggplant**
- 3 **small zucchini**
- 2 **small yellow summer squash**
- 12 **hot Italian pork or turkey sausage links (4 ounces each)**

1. Place the first five ingredients in a blender; if desired, add pepper sauce. Cover and process until blended.

2. Cut the peppers lengthwise in half; remove seeds. Cut eggplant lengthwise into ½-in.-thick slices. Cut zucchini and yellow squash lengthwise into quarters. Place all vegetables in a large bowl; drizzle with ½ cup peach sauce and toss to coat.

3. Moisten a paper towel with cooking oil; using long-handled tongs, rub on the grill rack to coat lightly. Grill the vegetables, covered, over medium heat 8-10 minutes or until tender and lightly charred, turning once. Cool slightly. Reduce the grill temperature to medium-low heat.

4. Cut the vegetables into bite-size pieces. Toss with additional ¼ cup sauce; keep warm.

5. Grill the sausages, covered, over medium-low heat 15-20 minutes or until a thermometer reads 160° for pork sausages (165° for turkey sausages), turning occasionally. Remove the sausages from the grill; toss with the remaining sauce. Serve with vegetables.

PER SERVING *1 sausage with 1 cup vegetables equals 362 cal., 22 g fat (9 g sat. fat), 60 mg chol., 1,099 mg sodium, 24 g carb., 3 g fiber, 17 g pro.*

GRILLED SAUSAGES WITH SUMMER VEGETABLES

GINGER SALMON WITH CUCUMBER LIME SAUCE

With the number of ingredients called for in my Ginger Salmon with Cucumber Lime Sauce recipe, it may seem complex. It's actually very easy to prepare!
—**NOELLE MYERS** GRAND FORKS, ND

Ginger Salmon with Cucumber Lime Sauce

PREP: 30 MIN. • **GRILL:** 10 MIN.
MAKES: 10 SERVINGS (2 CUPS SAUCE)

- 1 tablespoon grated lime peel
- ¼ cup lime juice
- 2 tablespoons olive oil
- 2 tablespoons rice vinegar or white wine vinegar
- 4 teaspoons sugar
- ½ teaspoon salt
- ½ teaspoon ground coriander
- ½ teaspoon freshly ground pepper
- ⅓ cup chopped fresh cilantro
- 1 tablespoon finely chopped onion
- 2 teaspoons minced fresh gingerroot
- 2 garlic cloves, minced
- 2 large cucumbers, peeled, seeded and chopped

SALMON
- ⅓ cup minced fresh gingerroot
- 1 tablespoon lime juice
- 1 tablespoon olive oil
- ½ teaspoon salt
- ½ teaspoon freshly ground pepper
- 10 salmon fillets (6 ounces each)

1. Place the first 13 ingredients in a blender. Cover and process until pureed.
2. In a small bowl, mix ginger, lime juice, oil, salt and pepper. Rub over flesh side of salmon fillets.
3. Moisten a paper towel with cooking oil; using long-handled tongs, rub on grill rack to coat lightly. Place salmon on grill rack, skin side down. Grill, covered, over medium-high heat 10-12 minutes or until fish just begins to flake easily with a fork. Serve with sauce.
PER SERVING *1 salmon fillet with 3 tablespoons sauce equals 327 cal., 20 g fat (4 g sat. fat), 85 mg chol., 372 mg sodium, 7 g carb., 1 g fiber, 29 g pro. Diabetic Exchanges: 4 lean meat, 1½ fat, ½ starch.*

Potluck Macaroni & Cheese

For your next potluck, try this wonderfully creamy mac from the slow cooker.
—**JENNIFER BABCOCK** CHICOPEE, MA

PREP: 25 MIN. • **COOK:** 2 HOURS
MAKES: 16 SERVINGS (¾ CUP EACH)

- 3 cups uncooked elbow macaroni
- 1 package (16 ounces) process cheese (Velveeta), cubed
- 2 cups (8 ounces) shredded Mexican cheese blend
- 2 cups (8 ounces) shredded white cheddar cheese
- 1¾ cups whole milk
- 1 can (12 ounces) evaporated milk
- ¾ cup butter, melted
- 3 large eggs, lightly beaten

1. Cook the macaroni according to the package directions for al dente; drain. Transfer to a greased 5-qt. slow cooker. Stir in remaining ingredients.
2. Cook, covered, on low 2 to 2½ hours or until a thermometer reads at least 160°, stirring once.
PER SERVING *¾ cup equals 405 cal., 28 g fat (17 g sat. fat), 82 mg chol., 661 mg sodium, 22 g carb., 1 g fiber, 18 g pro.*

POTLUCK MACARONI & CHEESE

Rustic Cranberry Tarts

At gatherings with family and friends, I'm always proud to serve this pair of simply elegant tarts. With a bubbly red filling and golden baked crust, they're absolutely beautiful. Best of all, the combination of sweet-tart fruit and rich, buttery pastry is scrumptious.

—**HOLLY BAUER** WEST BEND, WI

PREP: 15 MIN. • **BAKE:** 20 MIN./BATCH
MAKES: 2 TARTS (6 SERVINGS EACH)

- 1 cup orange marmalade
- ¼ cup sugar
- ¼ cup all-purpose flour
- 4 cups fresh or frozen cranberries, thawed
- 1 package (14.1 ounces) refrigerated pie pastry
- 1 large egg white, lightly beaten
- 1 tablespoon coarse sugar

1. Preheat the oven to 425°. In a large bowl, mix marmalade, sugar and flour; stir in cranberries.

2. Unroll one pastry sheet onto a parchment paper-lined baking sheet. Spoon half of the cranberry mixture over the pastry to within 2 in. of edge. Fold pastry edge over filling, pleating as you go and leaving a 5-in. opening in the center. Brush the folded pastry with egg white; sprinkle with half of the coarse sugar.

3. Bake 18-22 minutes or until crust is golden and filling is bubbly. Repeat with remaining ingredients. Transfer tarts to wire racks to cool.

PER SERVING *1 piece equals 260 cal., 9 g fat (4 g sat. fat), 6 mg chol., 144 mg sodium, 45 g carb., 2 g fiber, 2 g pro.*

Big John's Chili-Rubbed Ribs

When we think of summer grilling, it's ribs all the way! Here's a crowd favorite.

—**GINGER SULLIVAN** CUTLER BAY, FL

PREP: 20 MIN. + CHILLING
GRILL: 1½ HOURS
MAKES: 10 SERVINGS

- 3 tablespoons packed brown sugar
- 2 tablespoons paprika
- 2 tablespoons chili powder
- 3 teaspoons ground cumin
- 2 teaspoons garlic powder
- 1 teaspoon salt
- 6 pounds pork baby back ribs

GLAZE
- 1 cup reduced-sodium soy sauce
- 1 cup packed brown sugar
- ⅔ cup ketchup
- ⅓ cup lemon juice
- 1½ teaspoons minced fresh gingerroot

1. Mix the first six ingredients; rub over the ribs. Refrigerate, covered, 30 minutes.

2. Wrap the rib racks in large pieces of heavy-duty foil; seal tightly. Grill, covered, over indirect medium heat 1 to 1½ hours or until tender.

3. In a large saucepan, combine the glaze ingredients; cook, uncovered, over medium heat 6-8 minutes or until heated through and sugar is dissolved, stirring occasionally.

4. Carefully remove the ribs from foil. Place ribs over direct heat; brush with some of the glaze. Grill, covered, over medium heat 25-30 minutes or until browned, turning and brushing ribs occasionally with remaining glaze.

PER SERVING *1 serving equals 486 cal., 26 g fat (9 g sat. fat), 98 mg chol., 1,543 mg sodium, 34 g carb., 1 g fiber, 29 g pro.*

BIG JOHN'S CHILI-RUBBED RIBS

Sausage Bread Sandwiches

PREP: 30 MIN. • **BAKE:** 20 MIN.
MAKES: 4 SANDWICH LOAVES
(3 PIECES EACH)

- 1 **package (16 ounces) hot roll mix**
- 2 **pounds reduced-fat bulk pork sausage**
- 2 **tablespoons dried parsley flakes**
- 2 **teaspoons garlic powder**
- 1 **teaspoon onion powder**
- ½ **teaspoon dried oregano**
- 2 **cups (8 ounces) shredded part-skim mozzarella cheese**
- ½ **cup grated Parmesan cheese**
- 1 **large egg**
- 1 **tablespoon water**

1. Preheat oven to 350°. Prepare roll dough according to package directions.
2. Meanwhile, in a large skillet, cook the pork sausage over medium heat 8-10 minutes or until no longer pink, breaking meat into crumbles; drain. Stir in parsley flakes, garlic powder, onion powder and oregano.
3. Divide dough into four portions. On a lightly floured surface, roll each into a 14x8-in. rectangle. Top each with 1¼ cups sausage mixture to within 1 inch of the edges; sprinkle with ½ cup mozzarella cheese and 2 tablespoons Parmesan cheese. Roll up jelly-roll style, starting with a long side; pinch seams and ends to seal.
4. Transfer to greased baking sheets, seam side down. In a small bowl, whisk the egg with the water; brush over the loaves. Bake 20-25 minutes or until golden brown and heated through. Cool 5 minutes before slicing.

PER SERVING *1 piece equals 432 cal., 25 g fat (10 g sat. fat), 103 mg chol., 926 mg sodium, 27 g carb., 1 g fiber, 24 g pro.*

When I have time, I make Sausage Bread Sandwiches and keep them in the freezer. Then I pull them out for tailgating when we go to Kansas State football games.
—**DONNA ROBERTS** MANHATTAN, KS

SAUSAGE BREAD SANDWICHES

SWEET & SALTY PARTY MIX

SLOW COOKER

Sweet & Salty Party Mix

My husband doesn't care for traditional party mixes because he thinks they're either too salty or too sweet. He says this slow-cooked one is just right.
—**JACKIE BURNS** KETTLE FALLS, WA

PREP: 20 MIN. • **COOK:** 1 HOUR
MAKES: 16 SERVINGS (¾ CUP EACH)

- 3 **cups each Corn Chex, Rice Chex and Wheat Chex**
- 3 **cups miniature pretzels**
- 1 **cup dried cranberries**
- 1 **cup sliced almonds**
- ½ **cup butter, cubed**
- 1 **cup packed brown sugar**
- ¼ **cup corn syrup**
- ¼ **teaspoon baking soda**

1. Place cereal, pretzels, cranberries and almonds in a greased 6-qt. slow cooker; toss to combine. In a small saucepan, melt butter over medium heat; stir in the brown sugar and corn syrup. Bring to a boil; cook and stir 5 minutes. Remove from the heat; stir in baking soda. Drizzle over the cereal mixture and toss to coat.
2. Cook, covered, on low 1 hour, stirring halfway. Spread onto waxed paper; cool completely. Store in airtight containers.

PER SERVING *¾ cup equals 288 cal., 9 g fat (4 g sat. fat), 15 mg chol., 363 mg sodium, 51 g carb., 3 g fiber, 4 g pro.*

Cioppino-Mixed Green Salad

Living in California, called the "salad bowl" of the United States, inspires me to cook with nutritious veggies. Friends often request my cioppino dish for get-togethers.

—**CLEO GONSKE** REDDING, CA

PREP: 20 MIN. + MARINATING
MAKES: 10 SERVINGS

- 1 **cup Italian salad dressing**
- 1 **tablespoon minced fresh basil or 1 teaspoon dried basil**
- ¼ **cup dry white wine, optional**
- ¾ **pound peeled and deveined cooked shrimp (31-40 per pound)**
- 2 **cups lump crabmeat (about 10 ounces), drained**
- 16 **cups torn mixed salad greens**
- 2 **large tomatoes, seeded and coarsely chopped**
- 2 **jars (7½ ounces each) marinated quartered artichoke hearts, drained**
- 1 **large red onion, thinly sliced and separated into rings**
- 1 **can (6 ounces) pitted ripe olives, drained and quartered**
- 6 **hard-cooked large eggs, quartered lengthwise**
  Minced fresh parsley and lemon wedges, optional

1. In a bowl, mix dressing, basil and, if desired, wine. Add shrimp and crab; toss gently to combine. Refrigerate, covered, 2 hours.

2. Place the greens in a serving dish; top with tomatoes, artichoke hearts, onion, olives and eggs. Refrigerate, covered, 1 hour or until cold.

3. To serve, add the seafood mixture (with marinade) to salad; toss gently to combine. If desired, sprinkle with parsley and serve with lemon wedges.

PER SERVING *2 cups equals 285 cal., 17 g fat (3 g sat. fat), 190 mg chol., 888 mg sodium, 13 g carb., 3 g fiber, 18 g pro.*

SANDY'S CHOCOLATE CAKE

Sandy's Chocolate Cake

I wanted to enter the Greatest Cocoa Cake Contest in my home state, and I chose this as my submission. It received the top prize! Standing tall with three layers, the rich and velvety dessert is guaranteed to impress no matter where you serve it.

—**SANDY JOHNSON** TIOGA, PA

PREP: 30 MIN. • **BAKE:** 30 MIN. + COOLING
MAKES: 16 SERVINGS

- 1 **cup butter, softened**
- 3 **cups packed brown sugar**
- 4 **large eggs**
- 2 **teaspoons vanilla extract**
- 2⅔ **cups all-purpose flour**
- ¾ **cup baking cocoa**
- 3 **teaspoons baking soda**
- ½ **teaspoon salt**
- 1⅓ **cups sour cream**
- 1⅓ **cups boiling water**

FROSTING
- ½ **cup butter, cubed**
- 3 **ounces unsweetened chocolate, chopped**
- 3 **ounces semisweet chocolate, chopped**
- 5 **cups confectioners' sugar**
- 1 **cup (8 ounces) sour cream**
- 2 **teaspoons vanilla extract**

1. Preheat oven to 350°. Grease and flour three 9-in. round baking pans.

2. In a large bowl, cream the butter and brown sugar until light and fluffy. Add eggs, one at a time, beating well after each addition. Beat in the vanilla. In another bowl, whisk flour, cocoa, baking soda and salt; add to creamed mixture alternately with sour cream, beating well after each addition. Stir in the boiling water until blended.

3. Transfer to the prepared pans. Bake 30-35 minutes or until a toothpick inserted in center comes out clean. Cool in pans 10 minutes before removing to wire racks to cool completely.

4. For the frosting, in a metal bowl over simmering water, melt butter and chopped chocolates; stir until smooth. Cool slightly.

5. In a large bowl, combine the confectioners' sugar, sour cream and vanilla. Add chocolate mixture; beat until smooth. Spread frosting between layers and over top and sides of cake. Refrigerate leftovers.

PER SERVING *1 slice equals 685 cal., 29 g fat (18 g sat. fat), 115 mg chol., 505 mg sodium, 102 g carb., 3 g fiber, 7 g pro.*

JALAPENO POPPER & SAUSAGE DIP

SLOW COOKER

Jalapeno Popper & Sausage Dip

My workplace had an appetizer contest, and my jalapeno cheese dip won. Every time I take it somewhere, people empty the slow cooker.

—BEV SLABIK DILWORTH, MN

PREP: 15 MIN. • **COOK:** 3 HOURS
MAKES: 24 SERVINGS (¼ CUP EACH)

- 1 pound bulk spicy pork sausage
- 2 packages (8 ounces each) cream cheese, cubed
- 4 cups shredded Parmesan cheese (about 12 ounces)
- 1 cup (8 ounces) sour cream
- 1 can (4 ounces) chopped green chilies
- 1 can (4 ounces) diced jalapeno peppers
  Assorted fresh vegetables

1. In a large skillet, cook sausage over medium heat 6-8 minutes or until no longer pink, breaking into crumbles. Using a slotted spoon, transfer sausage to a 3-qt. slow cooker.

2. Stir in the cream cheese, Parmesan cheese, sour cream, green chilies and peppers. Cook, covered, on low 3 to 3½ hours or until heated through.

3. Stir dip before serving. Serve with vegetables.

PER SERVING ¼ cup (calculated without vegetables) equals 180 cal., 15 g fat (8 g sat. fat), 44 mg chol., 399 mg sodium, 2 g carb., trace fiber, 8 g pro.

SLOW COOKER

Cheesy Meatballs

Can meatballs be lucky? The guys in my family think so! They always request these when it's game time for our favorite team.

—JILL HILL DIXON, IL

PREP: 1 HOUR • **COOK:** 4 HOURS
MAKES: ABOUT 9 DOZEN

- 1 large egg
- ½ cup 2% milk
- 2 tablespoons dried minced onion
- 4 tablespoons chili powder, divided
- 1 teaspoon salt
- 1 teaspoon pepper
- 1½ cups crushed Ritz crackers (about 1 sleeve)
- 2 pounds ground beef
- 1 pound bulk pork sausage
- 2 cups shredded process cheese (Velveeta)
- 1 can (26 ounces) condensed tomato soup, undiluted
- 2½ cups water
- 1 cup packed brown sugar

1. Preheat oven to 400°. In a large bowl, whisk egg, milk, minced onion, 2 tablespoons chili powder, salt and pepper; stir in crushed crackers. Add beef, sausage and cheese; mix lightly but thoroughly.

2. Shape the mixture into 1-in. balls. Place the meatballs on greased racks in 15x10x1-in. baking pans. Bake 15-18 minutes or until browned.

3. Meanwhile, in a 5- or 6-qt. slow cooker, combine soup, water, brown sugar and remaining chili powder. Gently stir in the meatballs. Cook, covered, on low 4-5 hours or until meatballs are cooked through.

PER SERVING 1 meatball equals 51 cal., 3 g fat (1 g sat. fat), 11 mg chol., 104 mg sodium, 4 g carb., trace fiber, 2 g pro.

CHEESY MEATBALLS

Apple Caramel Cheesecake Bars

Here's a caramel apple, cheesecake and streusel-topped apple pie all rolled into one irresistible bar. It's hard not to sneak a few before I go to the potluck!

—**KATHERINE WHITE** CLEMMONS, NC

PREP: 30 MIN. • **BAKE:** 25 MIN. + CHILLING
MAKES: 3 DOZEN

- 2 **cups all-purpose flour**
- ½ **cup packed brown sugar**
- ¾ **cup cold butter, cubed**
- 2 **packages (8 ounces each) cream cheese, softened**
- ½ **cup plus 2 tablespoons sugar, divided**
- 1 **teaspoon vanilla extract**
- 2 **large eggs, lightly beaten**
- 3 **medium tart apples, peeled and finely chopped**
- ½ **teaspoon ground cinnamon**
- ¼ **teaspoon ground nutmeg**

STREUSEL
- ¾ **cup all-purpose flour**
- ¾ **cup packed brown sugar**
- ½ **cup quick-cooking oats**
- ⅓ **cup cold butter, cubed**
- ⅓ **cup hot caramel ice cream topping**

1. Preheat oven to 350°. In a small bowl, combine flour and brown sugar; cut in the butter until crumbly. Press into a well-greased 13x9-in. baking pan. Bake 15-18 minutes or until lightly browned.

2. Meanwhile, in a large bowl, beat cream cheese, ½ cup sugar and vanilla until smooth. Add the eggs; beat on low speed just until combined. Spread over the crust.

3. In a small bowl, toss apples with cinnamon, nutmeg and remaining sugar; spoon over the cream cheese layer. In another bowl, mix the flour, brown sugar and oats; cut in the butter until crumbly. Sprinkle streusel over the apple layer.

4. Bake 25-30 minutes or until the filling is set. Drizzle with the caramel ice cream topping; cool in the pan on a wire rack 1 hour. Refrigerate at least 2 hours. Cut into bars.

PER SERVING *1 bar equals 191 cal., 10 g fat (6 g sat. fat), 40 mg chol., 94 mg sodium, 23 g carb., 1 g fiber, 3 g pro.*

BUFFALO CHICKEN DEVILED EGGS

Buffalo Chicken Deviled Eggs

To treat my daughter Sara, who loves spicy buffalo chicken and deviled eggs, I created these. I think preparing and chilling them a day ahead makes the flavor even better.

—**ROBIN SPIRES** TAMPA, FL

PREP: 25 MIN. + CHILLING
MAKES: 2 DOZEN

- 12 **hard-cooked large eggs**
- ½ **cup crumbled blue cheese, divided**
- 2 **celery ribs, finely chopped**
- ½ **cup mayonnaise**
- ¼ **cup finely chopped cooked chicken breast**
- 3 **tablespoons minced fresh parsley**
- 1 **tablespoon Buffalo wing sauce or 1 teaspoon hot pepper sauce**
- ⅛ **teaspoon pepper**
   Additional Buffalo wing or hot pepper sauce

1. Cut eggs lengthwise in half. Remove yolks, reserving whites. In a bowl, mash yolks and ¼ cup cheese. Stir in celery, mayonnaise, chicken, parsley, wing sauce and pepper.

2. Spoon into egg whites. Refrigerate, covered, at least 1 hour before serving. To serve, sprinkle tops with remaining cheese and, if desired, drizzle with additional wing sauce.

PER SERVING *1 stuffed egg half equals 85 cal., 7 g fat (2 g sat. fat), 98 mg chol., 111 mg sodium, 1 g carb., trace fiber, 4 g pro.*

TOP TIP

When making deviled eggs to take to a potluck, I cut them the short way instead of the long way. After washing foam egg cartons thoroughly, I line them with mini muffin liners, then set my deviled egg halves inside so they sit snugly for traveling. At the potluck, I simply cut off the top of the carton and people help themselves.

—**JEAN STREHLOW** WEST ALLIS, WI

Big on Barbecue

Grab the napkins! Your potluck get-together or party will be a **hands-down winner** with these saucy slow-cooked and grilled specialties.

TANGY BARBECUE WINGS

SLOW COOKER
Slow Cooker BBQ Ham Sandwiches

My friends and family rave about these hot ham sandwiches and often ask me to make them for gatherings.

—DANA KNOX BUTLER, PA

PREP: 20 MIN. • **COOK:** 2 HOURS • **MAKES:** 16 SERVINGS

- 3 cups ketchup
- ¾ cup chopped onion
- ¾ cup chopped green pepper
- ¾ cup packed brown sugar
- ½ cup lemon juice
- ⅓ cup Worcestershire sauce
- 1 tablespoon prepared mustard
- 1¼ teaspoons ground allspice
- 1½ teaspoons liquid smoke, optional
- 3 pounds thinly sliced deli ham
- 16 kaiser or ciabatta rolls, split

1. In a large saucepan, combine the first eight ingredients; if desired, stir in liquid smoke. Bring to a boil. Reduce heat; simmer, uncovered, 5 minutes, stirring occasionally.
2. Place the ham in a 5- or 6-qt. slow cooker. Add the sauce; stir gently to combine. Cook, covered, on low 2-3 hours or until heated through. Serve on rolls.
PER SERVING *1 sandwich equals 348 cal., 4 g fat (trace sat. fat), 38 mg chol., 1,744 mg sodium, 57 g carb., 2 g fiber, 21 g pro.*

SLOW COOKER BBQ HAM SANDWICHES

SLOW COOKER
Tangy Barbecue Wings

When I brought a batch of my slow-simmered wings to share at work, they vanished before I could get a bite.

—SHERRY PITZER TROY, MO

PREP: 1 HOUR • **COOK:** 3 HOURS • **MAKES:** ABOUT 2 DOZEN WINGS

- 5 pounds chicken wings
- 2½ cups ketchup
- ⅔ cup white vinegar
- ⅔ cup honey
- ½ cup molasses
- 2 to 3 tablespoons hot pepper sauce
- 1 teaspoon salt
- 1 teaspoon Worcestershire sauce
- ½ teaspoon onion powder
- ½ teaspoon chili powder
- ½ to 1 teaspoon liquid smoke, optional

1. Preheat oven to 375°. Using a sharp knife, cut through the two wing joints; discard wing tips. Arrange remaining wing pieces in two greased 15x10x1-in. baking pans. Bake 30 minutes; drain. Turn wings; bake 20-25 minutes longer or until juices run clear.
2. Meanwhile, in a large saucepan, combine the remaining ingredients; bring to a boil. Reduce heat; simmer, uncovered, 30 minutes, stirring occasionally.
3. Drain wings. Place one-third of the chicken in a 5-qt. slow cooker; top with one-third of the sauce. Repeat layers twice. Cook, covered, on low 3-4 hours. Stir before serving.
NOTE *Uncooked chicken wing sections (wingettes) may be substituted for whole chicken wings.*
PER SERVING *1 wing (2 sections) equals 178 cal., 7 g fat (2 g sat. fat), 30 mg chol., 458 mg sodium, 19 g carb., trace fiber, 10 g pro.*

Barbecue Brats & Peppers

PREP: 15 MIN. • **COOK:** 6 HOURS • **MAKES:** 10 SERVINGS

- 2 bottles (12 ounces each) beer or nonalcoholic beer
- 1 bottle (18 ounces) barbecue sauce
- ½ cup ketchup
- 1 large sweet onion, halved and sliced
- 1 large sweet yellow pepper, cut into strips
- 1 large sweet orange pepper, cut into strips
- 1 jalapeno pepper, thinly sliced
- 1 serrano pepper, thinly sliced
- 10 uncooked bratwurst links
- 10 brat or hot dog buns, split

1. Place the first eight ingredients in a 5-qt. slow cooker; stir to combine. In a large skillet, brown bratwurst on all sides over medium-high heat; transfer to slow cooker.
2. Cook, covered, on low 6-8 hours or until sausages are cooked through and vegetables are tender. Serve bratwurst and pepper mixture on buns.
PER SERVING *1 serving equals 614 cal., 30 g fat (10 g sat. fat), 63 mg chol., 1,789 mg sodium, 66 g carb., 2 g fiber, 21 g pro.*

This is bratwurst country! Barbecue Brats & Peppers are a nice change of pace from the usual recipes.
—**MARIA ZRUCKY** KRONENWETTER, WI

BARBECUE BRATS & PEPPERS

LIP-SMACKIN' BBQ CHICKEN

Lip-Smackin' BBQ Chicken

Here's the first main dish I ever created. My children always tell their friends who come over for dinner that my grilled chicken is lip-smackin' good. That's high praise!
—**SUE THOMAS** MOORE, SC

PREP: 1¼ HOURS • **GRILL:** 25 MIN. • **MAKES:** 12 SERVINGS

- 2 cups ketchup
- 1 cup cider vinegar
- 1 cup water
- ¼ cup packed brown sugar
- ¼ cup reduced-sodium soy sauce
- ¼ cup molasses
- ¼ cup honey
- 2 tablespoons prepared mustard
- 3 teaspoons ground cumin
- ¼ teaspoon salt
- ¼ teaspoon pepper
- 6 pounds assorted bone-in chicken pieces

1. In a large saucepan, combine first 11 ingredients; bring to a boil. Reduce the heat; simmer, uncovered, 1 to 1½ hours or until thickened, stirring occasionally. Remove half of the sauce; reserve for brushing chicken. Keep remaining sauce warm for serving.
2. Grill chicken, covered, over medium heat 25-35 minutes or until juices run clear, turning occasionally and brushing with reserved sauce during the last 10 minutes. Serve with remaining sauce.
PER SERVING *1 serving equals 402 cal., 17 g fat (5 g sat. fat), 104 mg chol., 871 mg sodium, 27 g carb., trace fiber, 34 g pro.*

FIRE BEEF

Fire Beef

I first made this peppery beef using a recipe from my boss, who lived in Korea in the 1950s.

—LINDA MCCANE
CHESAPEAKE, VA

PREP: 20 MIN. + MARINATING
GRILL: 10 MIN. • **MAKES:** 10 SERVINGS

- 3 **pounds beef ribeye steaks**
- 3 **tablespoons sugar**
- ⅓ **cup reduced-sodium soy sauce**
- ¼ **cup canola oil**
- 3 **tablespoons toasted sesame seeds, crushed**
- 2 **garlic cloves, minced**
- 1½ **teaspoons hot pepper sauce**
- ¼ **teaspoon crushed red pepper flakes**
  Thinly sliced green onions, optional

1. Freeze ribeye steaks until firm, about 30 minutes. Cut the steaks crosswise into ¼-inch slices. Sprinkle with sugar; place in a large resealable plastic bag. Add the soy sauce, oil, sesame seeds, garlic, hot pepper sauce and red pepper flakes; seal the bag and turn to coat. Refrigerate 4 hours or overnight.

2. Thread sliced beef onto 10 metal or soaked wooden skewers; discard any remaining marinade. Grill the beef, covered, over medium heat 4-5 minutes on each side or until beef reaches desired doneness. If desired, sprinkle with green onions.

PER SERVING *1 skewer equals 363 cal., 27 g fat (9 g sat. fat), 80 mg chol., 317 mg sodium, 4 g carb., trace fiber, 25 g pro.*

Spiced Pumpkin Tiramisu

For a holiday version of classic Italian tiramisu, I mixed in pumpkin and spices. My brother and parents loved it. A new Christmas tradition was born!

—HEATHER CLARY DOWNINGTOWN, PA

PREP: 30 MIN. + CHILLING • **COOK:** 5 MIN.
MAKES: 12 SERVINGS

- 1 **cup water**
- 1 **cup brewed coffee**
- ⅔ **cup sugar**
- ⅔ **cup hazelnut liqueur**

PUMPKIN MIXTURE
- 2 **cartons (8 ounces each) mascarpone cheese**
- ¾ **cup canned pumpkin**
- 5 **tablespoons sugar, divided**
- 1½ **teaspoons ground cinnamon**
- ½ **teaspoon ground nutmeg**
- ¼ **teaspoon ground ginger**
- ¼ **teaspoon ground allspice**
- 1¼ **cups heavy whipping cream**

ASSEMBLY
- 54 **crisp ladyfinger cookies (about 16 ounces)**
- 1 **tablespoon sugar**
- ½ **teaspoon ground cinnamon**

1. In a small saucepan, combine the water, coffee, sugar and liqueur; cook and stir over medium-low heat until sugar is dissolved, about 3 minutes. Transfer to a shallow bowl; cool completely.

2. In a large bowl, mix mascarpone cheese, pumpkin, 3 tablespoons sugar and spices just until blended. In a small bowl, beat heavy cream until it begins to thicken. Add the remaining sugar; beat until soft peaks form. Fold into mascarpone mixture.

3. Quickly dip 18 ladyfingers into the coffee mixture, allowing the excess to drip off. Arrange in a single layer in a 13x9-in. dish. Spread with 1⅔ cups cheese mixture. Repeat layers twice.

4. Mix sugar and cinnamon; sprinkle over top. Refrigerate, covered, at least 8 hours or overnight.

NOTE *This recipe was prepared with Alessi brand ladyfinger cookies.*

PER SERVING *1 piece equals 491 cal., 28 g fat (15 g sat. fat), 121 mg chol., 88 mg sodium, 52 g carb., 1 g fiber, 7 g pro.*

FROZEN GRASSHOPPER TORTE

Frozen Grasshopper Torte

This cool chocolate-mint dessert was a hit when I served it at a ladies' meeting at our church. Feel free to use chopped candy canes instead of Oreos on top.

—**ELMA PENNER** OAK BLUFF, MB

PREP: 25 MIN. + FREEZING
MAKES: 12 SERVINGS

- 4 cups crushed Oreo cookies (about 40 cookies)
- ¼ cup butter, melted
- 1 pint (2 cups) vanilla ice cream, softened if necessary
- 2 cups heavy whipping cream
- 1 jar (7 ounces) marshmallow creme
- ¼ cup 2% milk
- ¼ to ½ teaspoon peppermint extract
- 3 drops green food coloring, optional

1. In a large bowl, combine crushed cookies and melted butter; toss until coated. Reserve ¼ cup mixture for the topping. Press the remaining mixture onto bottom of a 9-in. springform pan or 13x9-in. dish. Freeze 10 minutes. Spread ice cream over crust. Freeze, covered, until firm.

2. In a bowl, beat the cream until soft peaks form. In a large bowl, mix the marshmallow creme, milk, extract and, if desired, food coloring until blended. Fold in whipped cream.

3. Spread over the ice cream. Sprinkle with reserved cookie mixture. Freeze, covered, until firm.

PER SERVING *1 piece equals 385 cal., 24 g fat (12 g sat. fat), 56 mg chol., 256 mg sodium, 41 g carb., 2 g fiber, 3 g pro.*

---

(5) INGREDIENTS

Saltine Cracker Candy with Toasted Pecans

PREP: 15 MIN. • **BAKE:** 10 MIN. + CHILLING
MAKES: ABOUT 2 POUNDS

- 35 saltines
- 1 cup butter, cubed
- 1 cup packed brown sugar
- 2 cups (12 ounces) semisweet chocolate chips
- 1 cup chopped pecans, toasted

1. Preheat oven to 350°. Line a 15x10x1-in. baking pan with foil; grease the foil. Arrange the saltines in a single layer on foil.

2. In a large heavy saucepan, melt the butter over medium heat. Stir in the brown sugar. Bring to a boil; cook and stir 3-4 minutes or until the sugar is dissolved. Spread evenly over crackers.

3. Bake 8-10 minutes or until bubbly. Immediately sprinkle with semisweet chocolate chips. Allow the chocolate chips to soften for a few minutes, then spread over the top. Sprinkle with the pecans. Cool slightly.

4. Refrigerate, uncovered, 1 hour or until set. Break into pieces. Store in an airtight container.

NOTE *To toast nuts, bake in a shallow pan in a 350° oven for 5-10 minutes or cook in a skillet over low heat until lightly browned, stirring occasionally.*

PER SERVING *1 ounce equals 164 cal., 12 g fat (6 g sat. fat), 15 mg chol., 95 mg sodium, 16 g carb., 1 g fiber, 1 g pro.*

My kids and grandkids adore Saltine Cracker Candy with Toasted Pecans. And when the neighbor children find out I have some, they rush over, too!
—**LORRAINE CALAND** SHUNIAH, ON

SALTINE CRACKER CANDY WITH TOASTED PECANS

FELICIA SAATHOFF'S
FRESH HERB-BRINED
TURKEY *PAGE 187*

Holiday & Seasonal Celebrations

From Easter brunch to Christmas cookies and Halloween treats, all the **festive foods** you want for special occasions are right here. So go ahead—gather loved ones and **start celebrating!**

JACQUELYN BENSON'S MUSHROOM & SMOKED SALMON TARTS *PAGE 175*

CLARA COULSON MINNEY'S FRANKENSTEIN BOO-RITOS *PAGE 180*

SUE GRONHOLZ'S JOLLY GINGER REINDEER COOKIES *PAGE 199*

Springtime Brunch

On Easter Sunday, Mother's Day or any other spring occasion, this **sunny brunch menu** is a **wonderful way** to celebrate with loved ones.

Rhubread

We moved into a house with a yard full of rhubarb. To make the most of our new crop, we used the stalks to bake yummy loaves of bread spiced with cinnamon and dotted with pecans.

—**ERIKA ELLIOTT** PANOLA, IL

PREP: 15 MIN. • **BAKE:** 50 MIN. + COOLING
MAKES: 2 LOAVES (12 SLICES EACH)

- 3 **cups coarsely chopped fresh rhubarb (about 12 ounces)**
- 2 **tablespoons plus 1¾ cups sugar, divided**
- 1 **cup canola oil**
- 2 **large eggs**
- 1 **tablespoon vanilla extract**
- 3 **cups all-purpose flour**
- 1 **teaspoon salt**
- 1 **teaspoon baking soda**
- 1 **teaspoon ground cinnamon**
- ¼ **teaspoon baking powder**
- ½ **cup chopped pecans, optional**

1. Preheat the oven to 350°. Grease and flour two 8x4-in. loaf pans.
2. Toss the rhubarb with 2 tablespoons sugar; let stand while preparing batter.
3. In a large bowl, beat the oil, eggs, vanilla and remaining sugar until well blended. In another bowl, whisk next five ingredients; gradually beat into the oil mixture (batter will be thick). Stir in rhubarb mixture and, if desired, pecans.
4. Transfer to prepared pans. Bake 50-60 minutes or until a toothpick inserted in center comes out clean. Cool in pans 10 minutes before removing to a wire rack to cool.
PER SERVING *1 slice (calculated without pecans) equals 211 cal., 10 g fat (1 g sat. fat), 16 mg chol., 162 mg sodium, 29 g carb., 1 g fiber, 2 g pro.*

TOP TIP

Look for stalks of rhubarb that are firm and crisp. Tightly wrap unwashed stalks in a plastic bag and store them in the refrigerator for up to one week. Before using, wash stalks and remove any leaves, which are toxic. Thick stalks may be peeled with a vegetable peeler to remove fibrous strings.

TANGY POPPY SEED FRUIT SALAD

EAT SMART **FAST FIX**

Tangy Poppy Seed Fruit Salad

When you want to dress up your morning fruit, toss it with a tangy dressing of poppy seeds, honey and lime.

—**CARRIE HOWELL** LEHI, UT

START TO FINISH: 20 MIN. • **MAKES:** 10 SERVINGS

- 1 **can (20 ounces) unsweetened pineapple chunks, drained**
- 1 **pound fresh strawberries, quartered**
- 2 **cups fresh blueberries**
- 2 **cups fresh raspberries**
- 2 **medium navel oranges, peeled and sectioned**
- 2 **medium kiwifruit, peeled, halved and sliced**

DRESSING

- 2 **to 4 tablespoons honey**
- ½ **teaspoon grated lime peel**
- 2 **tablespoons lime juice**
- 2 **teaspoons poppy seeds**

Place all fruit in a large bowl. In a small bowl, whisk dressing ingredients. Drizzle over fruit; toss gently to combine.
PER SERVING *⅔ cup equals 117 cal., 1 g fat (trace sat. fat), 0 chol., 3 mg sodium, 29 g carb., 5 g fiber, 2 g pro.* **Diabetic Exchange:** *2 fruit.*

Cheesecake with Berry Sauce

This creamy cheesecake is a family tradition—I've even shipped it to my daughter as a special treat. Each piece gets a burst of flavor from the simple raspberry sauce.

—JEANETTE VOLKER WALTON, NE

PREP: 1 HOUR • **BAKE:** 50 MIN. + CHILLING • **MAKES:** 16 SERVINGS

- 1¾ cups graham cracker crumbs
- ¼ cup sugar
- ⅓ cup butter, melted

FILLING

- 5 packages (8 ounces each) cream cheese, softened
- 1 cup sugar
- 1 cup (8 ounces) sour cream
- ½ cup heavy whipping cream
- 2 teaspoons vanilla extract
- 7 large eggs, lightly beaten

TOPPINGS

- 1 package (12 ounces) frozen raspberries or blueberries, thawed
- ½ cup sugar
- 2 cups heavy whipping cream
- ½ cup confectioners' sugar
- 1 teaspoon vanilla extract

1. Preheat oven to 350°. Place a greased 10-in. springform pan on a double thickness of heavy-duty foil (about 18 in. square). Wrap foil securely around outside of pan. Place on a baking sheet.

2. In a small bowl, mix cracker crumbs and sugar; stir in butter. Press onto bottom and 1 in. up sides of prepared pan. Place on a baking sheet. Bake 8 minutes. Cool on a wire rack.

3. In a large bowl, beat cream cheese and sugar until smooth. Beat in sour cream, cream and vanilla. Add eggs; beat on low speed just until blended. Pour into crust. Place springform pan in a larger baking pan; add 1 in. of hot water to larger pan.

4. Bake 50-60 minutes or until the center is just set and the top appears dull. Remove springform pan from water bath. Cool the cheesecake on a wire rack for 10 minutes. Loosen sides from pan with a knife; remove foil. Cool 1 hour longer. Refrigerate overnight, covering when completely cooled.

5. For toppings, place berries and sugar in a food processor; process until blended. In a small bowl, beat the cream until it begins to thicken. Add confectioners' sugar and vanilla; beat until soft peaks form.

6. Remove the rim from springform pan. Serve cheesecake with sauce and whipped cream.

PER SERVING *1 slice equals 423 cal., 28 g fat (17 g sat. fat), 180 mg chol., 186 mg sodium, 37 g carb., 1 g fiber, 6 g pro.*

CHEESECAKE WITH BERRY SAUCE

Whole Wheat Waffles with Chicken & Spinach Sauce

While on a business trip years ago, I got the idea to combine waffles, chicken and a creamy spinach sauce.

—VICKI MELIES ELKHORN, NE

PREP: 25 MIN. • **BAKE:** 5 MIN./BATCH
MAKES: 12 SERVINGS

- 1 can (10¾ ounces) condensed cream of chicken soup, undiluted
- 1 package (10 ounces) frozen chopped spinach, thawed and squeezed dry
- ½ to ¾ cup 2% milk
- 1½ cups shredded cooked chicken

WAFFLES

- 3 cups white whole wheat flour
- 3 tablespoons sugar
- 4 teaspoons baking powder
- 1 teaspoon salt
- 2 large eggs
- 3 cups 2% milk
- ½ cup butter, melted
- 1 cup (4 ounces) shredded Swiss cheese

1. In a small saucepan, combine soup, spinach, ½ cup milk and chicken; cook over medium heat 5-7 minutes or until heated through, stirring occasionally. If desired, stir in additional milk for a thinner consistency. Remove from heat; cover to keep warm.

2. For the waffles, in a large bowl, whisk flour, sugar, baking powder and salt. In another bowl, whisk the eggs, milk and melted butter until blended. Add to the dry ingredients; stir just until moistened.

3. Bake in a preheated waffle iron according to manufacturer's directions until golden brown. Cut each waffle in half. Serve with the sauce; sprinkle with Swiss cheese.

PER SERVING *½ waffle and 3 tablespoons sauce equals 335 cal., 15 g fat (8 g sat. fat), 52 mg chol., 647 mg sodium, 34 g carb., 5 g fiber, 15 g pro.*

BRUNCH HASH & EGG BAKE

When I had a family of eight to cook for, Brunch Hash & Egg Bake was a lifesaver. Sometimes we sprinkle on Parmesan or cheddar cheese instead of the feta.
—LILY JULOW LAWRENCEVILLE, GA

Brunch Hash & Egg Bake

PREP: 45 MIN. • **BAKE:** 15 MIN.
MAKES: 8 SERVINGS

- 2 pounds Yukon Gold potatoes, peeled and cut into ¾-inch pieces
- 1 pound bulk Italian sausage
- 1 large onion, finely chopped
- ¼ cup olive oil
- ¼ teaspoon salt
- ¼ teaspoon pepper
- 8 large eggs
- 1 cup (4 ounces) crumbled feta cheese
- 3 tablespoons minced fresh parsley

1. Preheat the oven to 375°. Place the potatoes in a large saucepan; add water to cover. Bring to a boil. Reduce heat; cook, uncovered, 5-7 minutes or until almost tender. Drain.

2. Meanwhile, in a 12-in. ovenproof skillet, cook the Italian sausage and onion over medium heat 8-10 minutes or until the sausage is no longer pink, breaking up the sausage into crumbles. Remove sausage with a slotted spoon. Discard the drippings, wiping the skillet clean.

3. In the same skillet, heat oil over medium-high heat. Add the drained potatoes; sprinkle with the salt and pepper. Cook 10-15 minutes or until golden brown, turning the potatoes occasionally. Stir in sausage mixture. Remove from heat.

4. With the back of a spoon, make eight wells in the potato mixture. Break one egg into each well. Sprinkle with feta cheese.

5. Bake 12-15 minutes or until the egg whites are set and the yolks begin to thicken but are not hard. Sprinkle with minced parsley.

PER SERVING *1 serving equals 460 cal., 29 g fat (10 g sat. fat), 234 mg chol., 761 mg sodium, 29 g carb., 3 g fiber, 21 g pro.*

Apricot Lemonade Iced Tea

Every special occasion deserves a special beverage. This tea has a refreshing blend of lemonade, apricot nectar and mint.

—KAY CHON SHERWOOD, AR

PREP: 10 MIN. • **COOK:** 5 MIN. + COOLING
MAKES: 12 SERVINGS

- 4 cups water
- 7 individual tea bags
- 1 cup sugar
- 1 can (12 ounces) frozen lemonade concentrate, partially thawed
- 1 cup chilled apricot nectar
- 4 cups cold water
  Ice cubes
  Mint sprigs

1. In a saucepan, bring 4 cups water to a boil; remove from heat. Add tea bags; steep, covered, 5 minutes.
2. Discard tea bags. Stir in the sugar until dissolved; cool slightly. Transfer to a pitcher; cool completely.
3. Add the lemonade concentrate and chilled apricot nectar to the tea; stir in the cold water. Serve over ice with mint sprigs.
PER SERVING *¾ cup equals 148 cal., trace fat (trace sat. fat), 0 chol., 3 mg sodium, 38 g carb., trace fiber, trace pro.*

Mushroom & Smoked Salmon Tarts

We needed to clear out the refrigerator before moving into our new house, so we made a savory tart of smoked salmon and mushrooms. It was so good, it became a staple.

—JACQUELYN BENSON SOUTH BERWICK, ME

PREP: 30 MIN. + CHILLING • **BAKE:** 25 MIN.
MAKES: 2 TARTS (6 SERVINGS EACH)

- 1 package (14.1 ounces) refrigerated pie pastry
- 1 tablespoon olive oil
- 1 medium red onion, thinly sliced
- 1 tablespoon butter
- 4 cups sliced fresh mushrooms (about 10 ounces)
- ⅔ cup smoked salmon or lox
- ⅓ cup crumbled feta cheese
- 8 large eggs, divided use
- 4 teaspoons drained capers, divided
- ½ teaspoon salt, divided
- ½ teaspoon pepper, divided
- 2 teaspoons snipped fresh dill, optional, divided

1. Unroll the pastry sheets into two 9-in. fluted tart pans with removable bottoms; trim the edge. Refrigerate 30 minutes. Preheat oven to 400°.
2. Line unpricked pastry with a double thickness of foil. Fill with pie weights, dried beans or uncooked rice. Bake on a lower oven rack 10-15 minutes or until the edges are golden brown. Remove the foil and weights; bake 2-4 minutes longer or until bottom is golden brown. Cool on a wire rack. Reduce oven setting to 375°.
3. In a large skillet, heat the oil over medium-high heat. Add the onion; cook and stir 5-7 minutes or until tender and lightly browned. Remove from pan. Add butter and mushrooms; cook and stir 6-8 minutes or until mushrooms are tender. Cool slightly.
4. Place tart pans on separate baking sheets. Divide onion and mushrooms between crusts; top with the salmon and cheese. In a bowl, whisk 4 eggs, 2 teaspoons capers and ¼ teaspoon each salt and pepper; if desired, stir in 1 teaspoon dill. Pour over one of tarts. Repeat with remaining ingredients.
5. Bake 15-20 minutes or until a knife inserted near center comes out clean. Let stand 5 minutes before cutting.
NOTE *Tarts may also be prepared in two 9-in. springform pans or pie plates; bake as directed.*
PER SERVING *1 piece equals 239 cal., 15 g fat (6 g sat. fat), 136 mg chol., 382 mg sodium, 18 g carb., 1 g fiber, 8 g pro.*

MUSHROOM & SMOKED SALMON TARTS

Fourth of July Treats

Start the fireworks early by serving these summery desserts. From watermelon sorbet to strawberry bars, they'll make **eyes light up.**

Cape Cod Blueberry Pie

Here in the Northeast, people have been baking this pie since the 18th century. I prepare mine like the settlers did—with little wild berries and a topping of cream.

—NANCY O'CONNELL BIDDEFORD, ME

PREP: 45 MIN. + CHILLING • **COOK:** 10 MIN. + CHILLING
MAKES: 8 SERVINGS

> Pastry for single-crust pie (9 inches)
> 3 tablespoons all-purpose flour
> ¼ teaspoon salt
> 1 cup water, divided
> ¾ cup sugar
> 6 cups fresh blueberries, divided
> ½ teaspoon white vinegar
> Sweetened whipped cream or vanilla ice cream, optional

1. On a lightly floured surface, roll the pastry dough to a ⅛-in.-thick circle; transfer to a 9-in. pie plate. Trim pastry to ½ in. beyond rim of plate; flute edge. Refrigerate 30 minutes. Preheat oven to 425°.

2. Line the pastry with a double thickness of foil. Fill with pie weights, dried beans or uncooked rice. Bake on a lower oven rack 20-25 minutes or until the edges are golden brown. Remove the foil and weights; bake 3-6 minutes longer or until bottom is golden brown. Cool completely on a wire rack.

3. In a small bowl, mix the flour, salt and ⅓ cup water until blended. In a large saucepan, combine sugar, 1 cup blueberries and remaining water; bring to a boil. Stir in the flour mixture. Return to a boil, stirring constantly; cook and stir 4-6 minutes or until thickened. Stir in the vinegar and remaining blueberries; pour into crust. Refrigerate 4 hours or until filling is set. If desired, serve with whipped cream.

PASTRY FOR SINGLE-CRUST PIE (9 INCHES) *Combine 1¼ cups all-purpose flour and ¼ teaspoon salt; cut in ½ cup cold butter until crumbly. Gradually add 3-5 tablespoons ice water, tossing with a fork until dough holds together when pressed. Wrap in plastic wrap and refrigerate 1 hour.*

NOTE *Let pie weights cool before storing. Beans and rice may be reused for pie weights, but not for cooking.*

PER SERVING *1 piece (calculated without whipped cream) equals 307 cal., 12 g fat (7 g sat. fat), 30 mg chol., 230 mg sodium, 49 g carb., 3 g fiber, 3 g pro.*

RED, WHITE AND BLUE FROZEN LEMONADE

⑤ INGREDIENTS **FAST FIX**

Red, White and Blue Frozen Lemonade

With a base of blueberries and a garnish of maraschino cherries, frozen lemonade is perfect for the Fourth of July. It's as festive as it is refreshing on a hot summer afternoon.

—SHAWN CARLETON SAN DIEGO, CA

START TO FINISH: 10 MIN. • **MAKES:** 4 SERVINGS

> 1 cup lemon juice
> 1 cup sugar
> 4 cups ice cubes
> 1 cup fresh or frozen blueberries
> Maraschino cherries

Place the lemon juice, sugar and ice in a blender; cover and process until slushy. Divide the blueberries among four chilled glasses; muddle slightly. Add the frozen lemonade; top with maraschino cherries.

PER SERVING *¾ cup (calculated without cherries) equals 229 cal., trace fat (trace sat. fat), 0 chol., 1 mg sodium, 60 g carb., 1 g fiber, trace pro.*

Rhubarb-Berry Upside-Down Cake

I had extra rhubarb and wanted to use it for something different. A little experimenting resulted in my upside-down cake.

—JUNE PAUL PORTAGE, WI

PREP: 30 MIN. • **BAKE:** 35 MIN. + COOLING • **MAKES:** 8 SERVINGS

- 2 tablespoons butter
- 1¾ cups chopped fresh rhubarb
- ½ cup fresh blueberries
- 2 tablespoons dried cranberries
- 2 tablespoons brown sugar

CAKE

- 6 tablespoons butter, softened
- 1 cup sugar
- 1 tablespoon brown sugar
- 2 large eggs
- 1 tablespoon seedless strawberry jam
- 1 teaspoon vanilla extract
- 1¼ cups all-purpose flour
- 1½ teaspoons baking powder
- ½ teaspoon salt
- ½ cup 2% milk
- ¼ cup orange juice

1. Preheat oven to 350°. Place butter in an 11x7-in. baking dish. Place in oven 5-6 minutes or until butter is melted; carefully swirl to coat evenly.

2. Place rhubarb and berries in a bowl; sprinkle with sugar and toss to combine. Transfer to baking dish.

3. In a large bowl, beat the butter and sugars until blended. Add the eggs, one at a time, beating well after each addition. Beat in jam and vanilla. In a small bowl, whisk flour, baking powder and salt. Add to creamed mixture alternately with the milk and orange juice, beating well after each addition. Pour over fruit, spreading evenly.

4. Bake 35-45 minutes or until the top is golden brown and a toothpick inserted in the cake portion comes out clean. Cool 10 minutes.

5. Loosen edges of cake from pan with a knife; invert onto a serving plate. Serve warm or at room temperature.

PER SERVING *1 serving equals 344 cal., 13 g fat (8 g sat. fat), 78 mg chol., 343 mg sodium, 53 g carb., 1 g fiber, 5 g pro.*

Cornmeal Towers with Strawberries & Cream

My children love to help build these pancake towers. The kids measure, mix, whisk and layer the stacks. It's a family tradition!

—JOSIE SHAPIRO SAN FRANCISCO, CA

PREP: 40 MIN. • **COOK:** 5 MIN./BATCH • **MAKES:** 12 SERVINGS

- 3 egg whites
- 1 cup heavy whipping cream
- 1 cup cornmeal
- 1 cup all-purpose flour
- 1½ teaspoons baking powder
- ½ teaspoon ground cardamom
- ¼ teaspoon salt
- 1¼ cups 2% milk
- 1 cup whole-milk ricotta cheese
- ¼ cup orange juice
- 2 tablespoons honey
- 1 teaspoon almond extract
- 1 to 2 tablespoons butter
- 1 pound fresh strawberries, sliced
- 2 tablespoons sugar

1. Place the egg whites in a small bowl; let stand at room temperature 30 minutes. Meanwhile, in a small bowl, beat heavy whipping cream until soft peaks form; refrigerate, covered, until serving.

2. In a large bowl, whisk cornmeal, flour, baking powder, cardamom and salt. In another bowl, mix the milk, ricotta cheese, orange juice, honey and extract until blended. Add to cornmeal mixture; stir just until moistened. With clean beaters, beat the egg whites on high speed until stiff but not dry; fold into batter.

3. Heat a griddle or large nonstick skillet over medium heat; grease with butter. Filling a ¼-cup measure halfway with batter, pour batter onto griddle or skillet. Cook until edges begin to dry and bottoms are golden brown. Turn; cook until second side is golden brown. Cool pancakes slightly.

4. In a bowl, toss the strawberries with the sugar. For each serving, stack three pancakes, layering each pancake with strawberries and whipped cream.

PER SERVING *3 pancakes with 3 tablespoons each berries and whipped cream equals 245 cal., 11 g fat (7 g sat. fat), 40 mg chol., 167 mg sodium, 30 g carb., 2 g fiber, 7 g pro.*

CORNMEAL TOWERS WITH STRAWBERRIES & CREAM

STRAWBERRY-LIME BARS

Strawberry-Lime Bars

Sweet-tart fruit, salty pretzels and cream cheese make a scrumptious combination.
—**ALEXANDRA BARNETT** FOREST, VA

PREP: 25 MIN. + CHILLING
BAKE: 10 MIN. + COOLING
MAKES: 2 DOZEN

- 2 **cups finely crushed pretzels (about 6 ounces)**
- ¾ **cup sugar, divided**
- ¾ **cup butter, melted**
- 2 **cups boiling water**
- 1 **package (6 ounces) strawberry gelatin**
- 1 **pound fresh strawberries, chopped**
- 2 **packages (8 ounces each) cream cheese, softened**
- 1 **tablespoon grated lime peel**
- ¼ **cup lime juice**
- 1 **teaspoon vanilla extract**

1. Preheat oven to 350°. Place the crushed pretzels and ¼ cup sugar in a small bowl; stir in melted butter. Spread into an ungreased 15x10x1-in. baking pan. Bake 9-11 minutes or until golden brown. Cool completely.
2. Meanwhile, in a bowl, add boiling water to the gelatin; stir 2 minutes to completely dissolve. Gently stir in the strawberries. Cool slightly. Refrigerate 30 minutes.

3. In a large bowl, beat the cream cheese, lime peel, lime juice, vanilla and remaining sugar until blended. Stir in cooled pretzel mixture. Spread into an ungreased 13x9-in. baking pan. Top with berry mixture. Refrigerate, covered, 2 hours or until firm.
PER SERVING *1 bar equals 201 cal., 13 g fat (7 g sat. fat), 36 mg chol., 240 mg sodium, 21 g carb., 1 g fiber, 3 g pro.*

Coconut Cheesecake & Rhubarb Compote

When it comes to ways of using up excess rhubarb, this might be the ultimate!
—**WENDY RUSCH** TREGO, WI

PREP: 55 MIN.
BAKE: 1 HOUR 20 MIN. + CHILLING
MAKES: 16 SERVINGS (3½ CUPS COMPOTE)

- 14 **whole graham crackers**
- 1 **cup flaked coconut, toasted**
- ¼ **cup sugar**
- ⅓ **cup butter, melted**

CHEESECAKE
- 5 **packages (8 ounces each) cream cheese, softened**
- 1¼ **cups sugar**
- 1¼ **cups sour cream**
- 1 **tablespoon vanilla extract**
- 1 **tablespoon lemon or lime juice**
- 5 **large eggs, lightly beaten**
- 1 **cup flaked coconut**

COMPOTE
- 6 **cups chopped fresh rhubarb (about 1½ pounds)**
- 1 **cup sugar**
- ½ **cup orange juice or water**
  Additional toasted flaked coconut, optional

1. Preheat the oven to 325°. Place a greased 9-in. (3-in.-deep) springform pan on a double thickness of heavy-duty foil (about 18 in. square). Wrap the foil securely around the pan.
2. Break crackers into quarters; place in a food processor. Add coconut and sugar; pulse until fine crumbs form. While pulsing, add melted butter just until blended. Press onto bottom and 1½ in. up sides of prepared pan.
3. For the cheesecake, in a large bowl, beat the cream cheese and sugar until smooth. Beat in sour cream, vanilla and lemon juice. Add the eggs; beat on low speed just until blended. Fold in the coconut. Pour into crust. Place springform pan in a larger baking pan; add 1 in. of hot water to larger pan.
4. Bake 80-90 minutes or until center is just set and top appears dull. Remove springform pan from water bath. Cool cheesecake on a wire rack 10 minutes. Loosen sides from pan with a knife; remove foil. Cool 1 hour longer.
5. In a large saucepan, combine the rhubarb, sugar and orange juice; bring to a boil. Reduce the heat; simmer, uncovered, 7-9 minutes or until thickened. Cool slightly; transfer to a covered container. Refrigerate the cheesecake and rhubarb compote overnight, covering cheesecake when completely cooled.
6. Remove rim from springform pan. If desired, press additional coconut onto sides of cheesecake. Serve with compote, warmed if desired.
NOTE *To toast coconut, bake in a shallow pan in a 350° oven for 5-10 minutes or cook in a skillet over low heat until golden brown, stirring occasionally.*
PER SERVING *1 slice of cheesecake with 3 tablespoons compote (calculated without optional coconut) equals 589 cal., 38 g fat (23 g sat. fat), 159 mg chol., 434 mg sodium, 55 g carb., 2 g fiber, 8 g pro.*

Blueberry Zucchini Squares

On a box of muffin mix, I saw a lemony bar recipe that called for apples. I duplicated that idea from scratch using shredded zucchini and blueberries instead.

—SHELLY BEVINGTON HERMISTON, OR

PREP: 30 MIN. • **BAKE:** 30 MIN. + COOLING
MAKES: 2 DOZEN

- 2 cups shredded zucchini
- ½ cup buttermilk
- 1 tablespoon grated lemon peel
- 3 tablespoons lemon juice
- 1 cup butter, softened
- 2½ cups sugar
- 2 large eggs
- 3¾ cups plus 2 tablespoons all-purpose flour, divided
- 1 teaspoon baking soda
- ½ teaspoon salt
- 2 cups fresh or frozen blueberries

GLAZE

- 2 cups confectioners' sugar
- ¼ cup buttermilk
- 1 tablespoon grated lemon peel
- 2 teaspoons lemon juice
- ⅛ teaspoon salt

1. Preheat oven to 350°. Grease a 15x10x1-in. baking pan.
2. In a small bowl, combine zucchini, buttermilk, lemon peel and lemon juice; toss to combine. In a large bowl, cream butter and sugar until light and fluffy. Beat in the eggs, one at a time. In another bowl, whisk 3¼ cups flour, baking soda and salt; gradually add to creamed mixture alternately with zucchini mixture, mixing well after each addition. Toss blueberries with remaining flour; fold into batter.
3. Transfer batter to prepared pan, spreading evenly. Bake 30-35 minutes or until bars are light golden brown and a toothpick inserted in the center comes out clean. Cool completely in the pan on a wire rack.
4. In a small bowl, mix the glaze ingredients until smooth; spread over the top. Let stand until set.
NOTE *If using frozen blueberries, use without thawing to avoid discoloring the batter.*
PER SERVING *1 piece equals 270 cal., 8 g fat (5 g sat. fat), 36 mg chol., 197 mg sodium, 47 g carb., 1 g fiber, 3 g pro.*

EAT SMART ⑤ INGREDIENTS
Watermelon Chocolate Chip Sorbet

Summer and watermelon go hand in hand. This pretty sorbet is good even without the miniature chocolate chips, but they're fun to include because they look like the dark seeds inside a pink melon.

—RACHEL LEWIS DANVILLE, VA

PREP: 15 MIN. + CHILLING
PROCESS: 30 MIN. + FREEZING
MAKES: 1 QT.

- 1 cup sugar
- ½ cup water
- 3 cups chopped seedless watermelon
- 1 cup orange juice
- 2 tablespoons lime juice
- ½ cup miniature semisweet chocolate chips, optional

1. In a small saucepan, bring sugar and water to a boil. Reduce the heat; simmer, uncovered, 5 minutes, stirring occasionally to dissolve the sugar. Cool slightly.
2. Place melon in a food processor; process until pureed. Add citrus juices and cooled syrup; process until blended. Transfer to a large bowl; refrigerate, covered, 3 hours or until cold.
3. Pour into the cylinder of an ice cream freezer. Freeze according to manufacturer's directions; if desired, add chocolate chips during the last 10 minutes of processing. Transfer sorbet to freezer containers, allowing headspace for expansion. Freeze 2-4 hours or until firm.
PER SERVING *½ cup equals 131 cal., trace fat (trace sat. fat), 0 chol., 4 mg sodium, 33 g carb., trace fiber, trace pro.*

WATERMELON CHOCOLATE CHIP SORBET

Happy Halloween

The **thrills and chills** of October call for food that's just as fun. Here, you'll **scare up goodies** galore for a spooky menu or treat tray.

FRANKENSTEIN BOO-RITOS

---

⑤ INGREDIENTS **FAST FIX**

Sweet 'n' Spicy Munch

Everyone loves the sweet and salty blend in this simple snack mix, which requires just spiced gumdrops, candy corn and peanuts. Pack plastic bags of this colorful finger food inside bright paper cones or muffin cups for a take-home favor.

—SHANA REILEY THERESA, NY

START TO FINISH: 5 MIN. • **MAKES:** 2 QUARTS

- 1 **pound spiced gumdrops**
- 1 **pound candy corn**
- 1 **can (16 ounces) salted peanuts**

In a large bowl, combine the gumdrops, candy corn and peanuts. Store in an airtight container.
PER SERVING *1/2 cup equals 380 cal., 14 g fat (2 g sat. fat), 0 chol., 140 mg sodium, 60 g carb., 3 g fiber, 7 g pro.*

SWEET 'N' SPICY MUNCH

FAST FIX

Frankenstein Boo-ritos

Youngsters will get a charge out of these silly monster burritos. Even better, the mild-tasting filling will please the pickiest eaters. You may want to serve these year-round!

—CLARA COULSON MINNEY WASHINGTON COURT HOUSE, OH

START TO FINISH: 25 MIN. • **MAKES:** 8 SERVINGS

- 1 **envelope (5.6 ounces) Spanish rice and pasta mix**
- 2 **cups cubed cooked chicken**
- 1 **can (15¼ ounces) whole kernel corn, drained**
- 1 **can (14½ ounces) diced tomatoes, drained**
- 8 **spinach tortillas (10 inches)**
  Toppings: sour cream, blue corn tortilla chips, cubed and shredded cheese, ripe olives and sweet red pepper

1. In a large saucepan, prepare the rice mix according to the package directions. Stir in the chicken, corn and tomatoes; heat through.
2. Spoon about ⅔ cup rice mixture across center of each tortilla. Fold bottom and sides of tortilla over filling and roll up. Using toppings, create a face on each burrito.
PER SERVING *1 burrito (calculated without toppings) equals 396 cal., 8 g fat (2 g sat. fat), 31 mg chol., 1,118 mg sodium, 60 g carb., 4 g fiber, 19 g pro.*

Bubblin' Swamp Juice

Here's a thick, creamy beverage that reminds kids of mini marshmallow-topped hot cocoa—only it's Halloween green! If you like, add a few drops of peppermint extract to the mixture for a hint of mint. You can also garnish each mug with gummy insects for the ultimate in creepy appeal.
—*TASTE OF HOME* TEST KITCHEN

START TO FINISH: 10 MIN. • **MAKES:** 4 SERVINGS

- 4 cups whole milk
- 1 cup vanilla or white chips
- 12 drops green food coloring
- 8 drops yellow food coloring
- ¼ cup miniature marshmallows
- 4 centipede gummies

In a large saucepan, heat the milk and vanilla chips over medium heat. Whisk until the vanilla chips are melted and the mixture is blended (do not boil). Remove from the heat; stir in food coloring. Garnish with miniature marshmallows and candy.

PER SERVING *1 cup equals 417 cal., 22 g fat (13 g sat. fat), 33 mg chol., 149 mg sodium, 47 g carb., trace fiber, 10 g pro.*

HALLOWEEN ICE CREAM TREATS

BUBBLIN' SWAMP JUICE

⑤INGREDIENTS FAST FIX ▶
Halloween Ice Cream Treats

These chocolate-covered scoops on gingersnap cookies are easy to create, and children think they're super-cool. Vanilla ice cream is always a good choice, but feel free to try other flavors such as pumpkin. Don't forget the festive sprinkles!
—*TASTE OF HOME* TEST KITCHEN

START TO FINISH: 15 MIN. • **MAKES:** 4 SERVINGS

- 4 gingersnap cookies
- 4 scoops vanilla ice cream (about ¼ cup)
- 1 cup (6 ounces) semisweet chocolate chips
- 1 teaspoon shortening
  Orange and purple Halloween sprinkles

1. Place gingersnap cookies in a single layer on a waxed paper-lined baking sheet; top each with a scoop of vanilla ice cream. Freeze until firm.
2. In a small microwave-safe bowl, melt the chocolate and shortening; stir until smooth.
3. Remove one dessert at a time from the freezer. Dip in the melted chocolate; top with sprinkles. Freeze until serving. Repeat with remaining desserts.
PER SERVING *1 serving equals 342 cal., 20 g fat (11 g sat. fat), 22 mg chol., 79 mg sodium, 44 g carb., 3 g fiber, 4 g pro.*

CARAMEL NUT CAKE POPS

Caramel Nut Cake Pops

Chocolate cake, dulce de leche and nuts add up to one irresistible little bite.
—*TASTE OF HOME* TEST KITCHEN

PREP: 1½ HOURS + CHILLING
MAKES: 4 DOZEN

- 1 package chocolate cake mix (regular size)
- ¾ cup dulce de leche
- 48 lollipop sticks
- 2½ pounds milk chocolate candy coating, coarsely chopped
  Chopped cashews

1. Prepare and bake the cake mix according to the package directions, using a greased 13x9-in. baking pan. Cool completely on a wire rack.
2. Crumble the cake into a large bowl. Add dulce de leche and mix well. Shape into 1-in. balls. Place on baking sheets; insert sticks. Freeze for at least 2 hours or refrigerate for at least 3 hours or until cake balls are firm.
3. In a microwave, melt coating. Dip each ball in coating; allow excess to drip off. Coat with nuts. Insert pops into a foam block to stand. Let stand until set.
NOTE *This recipe was tested with Nestle La Lechera dulce de leche; look for it in the international foods section. If using Eagle Brand dulce de leche (caramel flavored sauce), thicken according to the package directions before using.*
PER SERVING *1 cake pop (calculated without cashews) equals 210 cal., 11 g fat (7 g sat. fat), 13 mg chol., 104 mg sodium, 28 g carb., 1 g fiber, 2 g pro.*

FAST FIX ▸
Spiderweb Dip with Bat Tortilla Chips

We host a yearly Halloween bash, and everyone looks forward to the spidery taco dip with bat-shaped dippers.
—**SONIA CANDLER** EDMONTON, AB

START TO FINISH: 30 MIN.
MAKES: ABOUT 1½ CUPS DIP AND ABOUT 7 DOZEN CHIPS

- 20 chipotle chili and pepper tortillas or flour tortillas (8 inches)
  Cooking spray
- ¾ teaspoon garlic salt
- ¾ teaspoon ground coriander
- ¾ teaspoon paprika
- ⅜ teaspoon pepper

DIP

- 1 package (8 ounces) cream cheese, softened
- ¾ cup salsa
- ½ cup prepared guacamole
- 1 to 2 tablespoons sour cream

1. Cut tortillas into bat shapes with a 3¾-in. cookie cutter. Place tortillas on baking sheets coated with cooking spray. Spritz tortillas with cooking spray. Combine garlic salt, coriander, paprika and pepper; sprinkle over tortillas. Bake at 350° for 5-8 minutes or until edges just begin to brown.
2. In a small bowl, combine softened cream cheese and salsa. Spread into a 9-in. pie plate. Carefully spread guacamole to within 1 in. of edges.
3. Place the sour cream in a small resealable plastic bag; cut a small hole in a corner of bag. Pipe thin concentric circles an inch apart over guacamole. Beginning with center circle, gently pull a knife through the circles toward outer edge. Wipe knife clean. Repeat to complete web. Serve with bat chips.
PER SERVING *2 tablespoons dip and 7 chips equals 338 cal., 14 g fat (5 g sat. fat), 22 mg chol., 704 mg sodium, 44 g carb., 1 g fiber, 9 g pro.*

SPIDERWEB DIP WITH BAT TORTILLA CHIPS

BEWITCHED CHILI

Pumpkin Mousse Dip

My daughter's Girl Scout leader shared her recipe for a fluffy pumpkin mousse served with sliced pears and gingersnaps.
—**MARY SLATER** BELPRE, OH

START TO FINISH: 10 MIN.
MAKES: 16 SERVINGS

- 1 **cup canned pumpkin**
- ½ **cup confectioners' sugar**
- 1 **package (3 ounces) cream cheese, softened**
- ½ **teaspoon ground cinnamon**
- 1 **carton (8 ounces) frozen whipped topping, thawed**
  Gingersnap cookies and/or pear slices

In a large bowl, beat the pumpkin, sugar, cream cheese and cinnamon until smooth. Fold in the whipped topping. Refrigerate until serving. Serve with cookies and pear slices.
PER SERVING *¼ cup (calculated without cookies and pears) equals 78 cal., 4 g fat (4 g sat. fat), 6 mg chol., 16 mg sodium, 8 g carb., 1 g fiber, 1 g pro.*

TOP TIP

Pumpkin Mousse Dip (above) would be delicious with other dippers as well. For example, try vanilla wafers, plain or flavored graham crackers, shortbread cookies or sliced apples.

PUMPKIN MOUSSE DIP

Bewitched Chili

One pot and 30 minutes—yes, please! Children love this chunky sausage chili, and busy moms do, too. Arrange chips on top for an instant witch's hat.
—**JANICE WESTMORELAND**
BROOKSVILLE, FL

START TO FINISH: 30 MIN.
MAKES: 12 SERVINGS (3 QT.)

- 1 **pound bulk pork sausage**
- 1 **large onion, chopped**
- 2 **cans (16 ounces each) chili beans, undrained**
- 1 **can (28 ounces) crushed tomatoes**
- 3 **cups water**
- 1 **can (4 ounces) chopped green chilies**
- 1 **envelope chili seasoning mix**
- 2 **tablespoons sugar**
- 12 **round blue tortilla chips, halved**
- 12 **triangular blue tortilla chips**

1. In a Dutch oven, cook sausage and onion over medium heat 5-7 minutes or until the sausage is no longer pink, breaking up sausage into crumbles; drain. Add the beans, tomatoes, water, chilies, chili seasoning mix and sugar; bring to a boil. Reduce heat; simmer, covered, 20 minutes to allow flavors to blend, stirring frequently.
2. Top each serving with two halved round tortilla chips and one triangular tortilla chip inserted vertically into the chili between the round halves to resemble a witch's hat.
FREEZE OPTION *Freeze cooled chili in freezer containers. To use, partially thaw in the refrigerator overnight. Heat through in a saucepan, stirring occasionally and adding a little water if necessary.*
PER SERVING *1 cup equals 230 cal., 10 g fat (3 g sat. fat), 14 mg chol., 744 mg sodium, 31 g carb., 6 g fiber, 9 g pro.*

Turkey Day Feast

Thanksgiving is all about family and great food. Look right here for a **mouthwatering bird** and everything you could want on the side.

CALIFORNIA CITRUS & AVOCADO SALAD

California Citrus & Avocado Salad reminds me of my childhood in the Sunshine State.
—**CATHERINE CASSIDY** MILWAUKEE, WI

FAST FIX
Apple Cider Smash

A smash is a fruity chilled cocktail— so refreshing. It's a great way to use the apples and cider you bought at the orchard.
—**MOFFAT FRAZIER** NEW YORK, NY

START TO FINISH: 20 MIN. • **MAKES:** 16 SERVINGS

- 2 **cups finely chopped Gala or other red apples (about 2 small)**
- 2 **cups finely chopped Granny Smith apples (about 2 small)**
- 2½ **cups bourbon**
- ⅔ **cup apple brandy**
- 4 **teaspoons lemon juice**
  Ice cubes
- 5⅓ **cups chilled sparkling apple cider**

1. In a bowl, toss the apples to combine. In a small pitcher, mix bourbon, brandy and lemon juice.
2. To serve, fill each of 16 rocks glasses halfway with ice. To each, add ¼ cup apple mixture and 3 tablespoons bourbon mixture; top each with ⅓ cup cider.
PER SERVING ¾ cup equals 152 cal., trace fat (trace sat. fat), 0 chol., 3 mg sodium, 13 g carb., 1 g fiber, trace pro.

APPLE CIDER SMASH

EAT SMART **FAST FIX**
California Citrus & Avocado Salad

START TO FINISH: 25 MIN. • **MAKES:** 12 SERVINGS

- 10 **cups torn Bibb or Boston lettuce**
- 1½ **cups orange sections (about 2 medium oranges)**
- 1 **cup ruby red grapefruit sections (about 1 medium grapefruit)**
- 2 **medium ripe avocados, peeled and cubed**
- 3 **tablespoons ruby red grapefruit juice**
- 3 **tablespoons extra virgin olive oil**
- 2 **teaspoons honey**
- ½ **teaspoon salt**
- ¾ **cup crumbled queso fresco or feta cheese**
- ¼ **cup pistachios, chopped**

Place lettuce, oranges, grapefruit and avocados in a large bowl. In a small bowl, whisk grapefruit juice, oil, honey and salt until blended. Drizzle over salad and toss gently to coat. Sprinkle with cheese and pistachios. Serve immediately.
PER SERVING 1 cup equals 132 cal., 9 g fat (2 g sat. fat), 5 mg chol., 134 mg sodium, 10 g carb., 3 g fiber, 4 g pro.
Diabetic Exchanges: 2 fat, 1 vegetable.

Mashed Potatoes with Cheddar

Who doesn't love fluffy homemade mashed potatoes? I think they're even better when I mix in sharp cheddar. For an extra-creamy texture, my mother would add heavy whipping cream in place of the half-and-half.

—DARLENE BRENDEN SALEM, OR

PREP: 15 MIN. • **COOK:** 30 MIN. • **MAKES:** 8 SERVINGS

- 3 pounds potatoes, peeled and cubed (about 6 cups)
- 1 to 1¼ cups half-and-half cream
- 3 tablespoons butter
- 1 teaspoon salt
- 3 cups (12 ounces) shredded extra-sharp cheddar cheese

1. Place the potatoes in a 6-qt. stockpot; add water to cover. Bring to a boil. Reduce heat; cook, uncovered, 15-20 minutes or until tender. Meanwhile, in a small saucepan, heat the half-and-half cream, butter and salt until butter is melted, stirring occasionally.
2. Drain potatoes; return to pot. Mash potatoes, gradually adding cream mixture. Stir in cheese.
PER SERVING ¾ cup equals 348 cal., 21 g fat (14 g sat. fat), 71 mg chol., 614 mg sodium, 25 g carb., 2 g fiber, 14 g pro.

MASHED POTATOES WITH CHEDDAR

BACON & FONTINA
STUFFED MUSHROOMS

Bacon & Fontina Stuffed Mushrooms

These are also known as my "piled-high cheesy stuffed mushrooms." They're an instant hit no matter where I serve them. I like the fact that I need only six ingredients to create the yummy filling, and then just a drizzle of oil.

—TAMMY REX NEW TRIPOLI, PA

PREP: 30 MIN. • **BAKE:** 10 MIN. **MAKES:** 2 DOZEN

- 4 ounces cream cheese, softened
- 1 cup (4 ounces) shredded fontina cheese
- 8 bacon strips, cooked and crumbled
- 4 green onions, chopped
- ¼ cup chopped oil-packed sun-dried tomatoes
- 3 tablespoons minced fresh parsley
- 24 large fresh mushrooms (about 1¼ pounds), stems removed
- 1 tablespoon olive oil

1. Preheat oven to 425°. In a small bowl, mix the first six ingredients until blended. Arrange the mushroom caps in a greased 15x10x1-in. baking pan, stem side up. Spoon about 1 tablespoon filling into each.
2. Drizzle the tops with oil. Bake, uncovered, 9-11 minutes or until golden brown and mushrooms are tender.
PER SERVING 1 stuffed mushroom equals 60 cal., 5 g fat (2 g sat. fat), 13 mg chol., 105 mg sodium, 2 g carb., trace fiber, 3 g pro.

CARROT CAKE WITH PECAN FROSTING

My husband constantly requests Carrot Cake with Pecan Frosting. I think he may be its biggest fan! Feel free to leave out the nuts—it's yummy with or without them.
—**ADRIAN BADON** DENHAM SPRINGS, LA

PER SERVING *1 slice equals 557 cal., 27 g fat (10 g sat. fat), 72 mg chol., 358 mg sodium, 74 g carb., 2 g fiber, 6 g pro.*

FAST FIX
Giblet Turkey Gravy

Made-from-scratch turkey gravy with giblets is a holiday tradition in our house. This recipe features a little minced fresh sage and a splash of white wine.
—**JEFF LOCKE** ARMA, KS

START TO FINISH: 25 MIN.
MAKES: 16 SERVINGS

- ¼ **cup cornstarch**
- 4 **cups chicken stock, divided**
- 1 **tablespoon butter**
- 1 **tablespoon olive oil**
  Giblets from 1 turkey, finely chopped
- ½ **cup dry white wine or additional chicken stock**
- 2 **tablespoons minced fresh sage or 2 teaspoons dried sage leaves**
- ¼ **teaspoon salt**
- ¼ **teaspoon pepper**

1. In a small bowl, mix the cornstarch and ½ cup chicken stock until smooth. In a large saucepan, heat the butter and oil over medium-high heat. Add the giblets; cook and stir 5-8 minutes or until browned.
2. Add the wine and sage to the pan; cook 3-5 minutes, stirring to loosen browned bits from the pan. Add the remaining stock; bring to a boil. Stir in cornstarch mixture; return to a boil. Reduce heat; simmer 3-5 minutes or until thickened to desired consistency, stirring occasionally. Stir in the salt and pepper.
PER SERVING *¼ cup equals 50 cal., 2 g fat (1 g sat. fat), 49 mg chol., 191 mg sodium, 2 g carb., trace fiber, 4 g pro.*

TOP TIP

When I need shredded carrots in a hurry for a cake or other recipe, I simply put baby carrots in my food processor. In just minutes, the carrots are ready to use.
—**MILDRED B.** BOULDER, CO

Carrot Cake with Pecan Frosting

PREP: 35 MIN. • **BAKE:** 40 MIN. + COOLING
MAKES: 16 SERVINGS

- 1 **cup shortening**
- 2 **cups sugar**
- 4 **large eggs**
- 1 **can (8 ounces) unsweetened crushed pineapple, undrained**
- 2½ **cups all-purpose flour**
- 2 **teaspoons ground cinnamon**
- 1 **teaspoon baking powder**
- 1 **teaspoon baking soda**
- ¾ **teaspoon salt**
- 3 **cups shredded carrots (about 6 medium carrots)**

FROSTING
- 1 **package (8 ounces) reduced-fat cream cheese**
- ½ **cup butter, softened**
- 1 **teaspoon vanilla extract**
- 3¾ **cups confectioners' sugar**
- 1 **cup chopped pecans**

1. Preheat oven to 325°. Line bottoms of two greased 9-in. round baking pans with parchment paper; grease paper.
2. In a large bowl, cream shortening and sugar until fluffy. Add the eggs, one at a time, beating well after each addition. Beat in crushed pineapple. In another bowl, whisk the flour, cinnamon, baking powder, baking soda and salt; gradually add to the creamed mixture. Stir in carrots.
3. Transfer the batter to prepared pans. Bake 40-45 minutes or until a toothpick inserted in center comes out clean. Cool in pans 10 minutes before removing to wire racks; remove paper. Cool completely.
4. In a large bowl, beat the cream cheese, butter and vanilla until blended. Gradually beat in confectioners' sugar until smooth. Stir in pecans.
5. Spread frosting between layers and over top and sides of cake. Refrigerate until serving.

Fresh Herb-Brined Turkey

Brining is all about producing a tender, juicy bird by adding moisture. Our brine blends parsley, rosemary and thyme.

—**FELICIA SAATHOFF** VASHON, WA

PREP: 40 MIN. + BRINING
BAKE: 2½ HOURS + STANDING
MAKES: 16 SERVINGS

- 4 quarts water
- 2 cups sugar
- 1½ cups salt
- 10 fresh parsley sprigs
- 10 fresh thyme sprigs
- 5 fresh rosemary sprigs
- 7 bay leaves
- 4 teaspoons crushed red pepper flakes
- 4 teaspoons whole peppercorns
- 4½ quarts cold water
- 2 turkey-size oven roasting bags
- 1 turkey (14 to 16 pounds)

TURKEY
- 2 tablespoons olive oil
- ½ teaspoon pepper
- ½ teaspoon salt, optional

1. In a large stockpot, combine the first nine ingredients; bring to a boil. Cook and stir until the sugar and salt are dissolved. Remove from the heat. Add cold water to cool the brine to room temperature.

2. Place one oven roasting bag inside the other. Place the turkey inside both bags; pour in cooled brine. Seal bags, pressing out as much air as possible; turn to coat turkey. Place in a shallow roasting pan. Refrigerate 18-24 hours, turning occasionally.

3. Preheat oven to 350°. Remove the turkey from brine; rinse and pat dry. Discard the brine. Place turkey on a rack in a shallow roasting pan, breast side up. Tuck the wings under turkey; tie drumsticks together. Rub oil over outside of turkey; sprinkle with pepper and, if desired, salt.

4. Roast, uncovered, 2½-3 hours or until a thermometer inserted in thickest part of thigh reads 170°-175°. (Cover loosely with foil if the turkey browns too quickly.)

5. Remove the turkey from the oven; tent with foil. Let stand 20 minutes before carving.

NOTE *If using a prebasted turkey, omit ½ teaspoon salt sprinkled on outside of turkey.*
PER SERVING *9 ounces cooked turkey with skin equals 480 cal., 23 g fat (7 g sat. fat), 215 mg chol., 258 mg sodium, trace carb., trace fiber, 63 g pro.*

Sausage & Corn Bread Dressing

For a hearty and satisfying side, try this version of corn bread dressing with Italian sausage and steak sauce.

—**MANDY NALL** MONTGOMERY, AL

PREP: 30 MIN. • **BAKE:** 40 MIN.
MAKES: 12 SERVINGS

- 1 package (19½ ounces) Italian turkey sausage links, casings removed
- 4 medium onions, chopped (about 3 cups)
- ½ cup chopped celery
- 6 cups cubed day-old white or French bread
- 6 cups coarsely crumbled corn bread
- 2 large eggs
- 2 tablespoons steak sauce
- 2 teaspoons onion salt
- 2 teaspoons poultry seasoning
- 2 teaspoons dried parsley flakes
- 1 teaspoon garlic powder
- 1 teaspoon baking powder
- 2½ to 3 cups reduced-sodium chicken broth

1. Preheat oven to 350°. In a 6-qt. stockpot, cook sausage over medium heat 6-8 minutes or until no longer pink, breaking into crumbles. Remove with a slotted spoon, reserving the drippings in pot.

2. Add the onions and celery to the drippings; cook and stir 6-8 minutes or until tender. Remove from the heat; stir in the sausage. Add cubed bread and corn bread; toss to combine.

3. In a small bowl, whisk eggs, steak sauce, seasonings and baking powder until blended; stir into bread mixture. Stir in enough chicken broth to reach desired moistness.

4. Transfer to a greased 13x9-in. or 3-qt. baking dish. Bake 40-50 minutes or until lightly browned.

PER SERVING *¾ cup equals 240 cal., 6 g fat (1 g sat. fat), 48 mg chol., 1,112 mg sodium, 35 g carb., 3 g fiber, 11 g pro.*

SAUSAGE & CORN BREAD DRESSING

NORTHWOODS WILD RICE SALAD

Northwoods Wild Rice Salad

Here's my Minnesota version of a vintage German slaw served at church suppers.

—JEANNE HOLT

MENDOTA HEIGHTS, MN

PREP: 20 MIN. + CHILLING
COOK: 40 MIN. + COOLING
MAKES: 8 SERVINGS

⅔ cup uncooked wild rice

2 cans (14 ounces each) sauerkraut, rinsed and well drained

1 medium apple, peeled and chopped

¾ cup chopped celery

¾ cup shredded carrot (about 1 large carrot)

½ cup finely chopped red onion

DRESSING

½ cup sugar

⅓ cup cider vinegar

3 tablespoons canola oil

¼ teaspoon salt

¼ teaspoon pepper

3 tablespoons minced fresh parsley

1 tablespoon minced fresh tarragon or 1 teaspoon dried tarragon

¾ cup chopped walnuts, toasted

1. Cook wild rice according to package directions. Cool completely.

2. In a large bowl, combine sauerkraut, apple, celery, carrot, red onion and cooled wild rice. In a small bowl, whisk the first five dressing ingredients until the sugar is dissolved; stir in parsley and tarragon. Add to the sauerkraut mixture; toss to combine.

3. Refrigerate salad, covered, at least 4 hours to allow the flavors to blend. Stir in walnuts just before serving.

NOTE *To toast nuts, bake in a shallow pan in a 350° oven for 5-10 minutes or cook in a skillet over low heat until lightly browned, stirring occasionally.*

PER SERVING *¾ cup equals 290 cal., 17 g fat (1 g sat. fat), 0 chol., 747 mg sodium, 33 g carb., 5 g fiber, 5 g pro.*

Scalloped Sweet Corn Casserole

PREP: 25 MIN. • **BAKE:** 50 MIN.
MAKES: 8 SERVINGS

- 4 teaspoons cornstarch
- ⅔ cup water
- ¼ cup butter, cubed
- 3 cups fresh or frozen corn
- 1 can (5 ounces) evaporated milk
- ¾ teaspoon plus 1½ teaspoons sugar, divided
- ½ teaspoon plus ¾ teaspoon salt, divided
- 3 large eggs
- ¾ cup 2% milk
- ¼ teaspoon pepper
- 3 cups cubed bread
- 1 small onion, chopped
- 1 cup Rice Krispies, slightly crushed
- 3 tablespoons butter, melted

1. Preheat oven to 350°. In a small bowl, mix cornstarch and water until smooth. In a large saucepan, heat butter over medium heat. Stir in corn, evaporated milk, ¾ teaspoon sugar and ½ teaspoon salt; bring just to a boil. Stir in cornstarch mixture; return to a boil, stirring constantly. Cook and stir 1-2 minutes or until thickened; cool slightly.

2. In a large bowl, whisk eggs, milk, pepper and the remaining sugar and salt until blended. Stir in bread, onion and corn mixture. Transfer to a greased 8-in.-square or 1½-qt. baking dish.

3. Bake, uncovered, for 40 minutes. In a small bowl, toss Rice Krispies with melted butter; sprinkle over casserole. Bake 10-15 minutes longer or until golden brown.

FREEZE OPTION *Cool unbaked casserole, reserving Rice Krispies topping for baking; cover and freeze. To use, partially thaw in refrigerator overnight. Remove from refrigerator 30 minutes before baking. Preheat the oven to 350°. Bake casserole as directed, increasing time as necessary to heat through and for a thermometer inserted in center to read 165°.*

PER SERVING *⅔ cup equals 258 cal., 15 g fat (8 g sat. fat), 104 mg chol., 604 mg sodium, 26 g carb., 2 g fiber, 8 g pro.*

EAT SMART

Butternut Squash with Maple Syrup

Loaded with flavor, this roasted butternut squash is wonderful hot or cold.

—**MARIE WILLETTE** BELLOWS FALLS, VT

PREP: 25 MIN. • **BAKE:** 35 MIN.
MAKES: 10 SERVINGS

- 1 medium butternut squash, peeled and cut into 1-inch cubes (about 12 cups)
- 4 tablespoons olive oil, divided
- ¾ teaspoon salt
- ¼ teaspoon pepper
- 2 tablespoons minced fresh gingerroot
- 3 garlic cloves, minced
- ¼ teaspoon crushed red pepper flakes, optional
- 2 medium leeks (white portion only) or ½ large sweet onion, finely chopped
- ⅓ cup maple syrup
- 1 cup roasted sweet red peppers, coarsely chopped

1. Preheat oven to 425°. In a large bowl, toss squash with 2 tablespoons oil, salt and pepper; divide between two ungreased 15x10x1-in. baking pans. Roast 35-45 minutes or until tender, stirring occasionally and switching position of pans halfway.

2. In a skillet, heat remaining oil over medium heat. Add ginger, garlic and, if desired, red pepper flakes; cook and stir 1 minute. Add leeks; cook and stir 3-4 minutes longer or until tender. Stir in maple syrup; bring to a boil. Reduce heat; simmer, uncovered, 2-3 minutes or until syrup is slightly reduced.

3. Place the squash in a large bowl. Add the red peppers and leek mixture; toss to combine.

PER SERVING *¾ cup equals 178 cal., 6 g fat (1 g sat. fat), 0 chol., 279 mg sodium, 32 g carb., 7 g fiber, 2 g pro.* **Diabetic Exchanges:** *2 starch, 1 fat.*

BUTTERNUT SQUASH WITH MAPLE SYRUP

Christmas Dinner

It comes just **once each year**—the moment loved ones first lay eyes on your yuletide feast. Make it a moment **they'll never forget!**

CITRUS-MOLASSES GLAZED HAM

Overnight Layered Lettuce Salad

Here's a favorite from a church cookbook I've had for 40 years. I think the bacon is the key—it adds savory flavor and crunch.
—**MARY BREHM** CAPE CORAL, FL

PREP: 20 MIN. + CHILLING • **MAKES:** 16 SERVINGS

- 1 **medium head iceberg lettuce, torn**
- 1 **medium green pepper, chopped**
- 1 **small sweet red pepper, chopped**
- 1 **medium onion, sliced and separated into rings**
- 2 **cups frozen peas (about 10 ounces)**
- 1 **cup mayonnaise**
- 2 **tablespoons sugar**
- 1 **cup (4 ounces) shredded cheddar cheese**
- 12 **bacon strips, cooked and crumbled**
- ¾ **cup dried cranberries**

1. In a 4-qt. or 13x9-in. glass dish, layer the first five ingredients. In a small bowl, mix the mayonnaise and sugar; spoon over salad, spreading to cover.
2. Sprinkle the top with cheese, bacon and cranberries. Refrigerate, covered, overnight.
PER SERVING *1 cup equals 206 cal., 16 g fat (4 g sat. fat), 19 mg chol., 250 mg sodium, 11 g carb., 2 g fiber, 5 g pro.*

OVERNIGHT LAYERED LETTUCE SALAD

Citrus-Molasses Glazed Ham

We're always searching for new ways to enjoy our state's famous citrus crop, which is plentiful during the holiday season. Orange and grapefruit juices make a delectable glaze for ham.
—**CHARLENE CHAMBERS** ORMOND BEACH, FL

PREP: 15 MIN. • **BAKE:** 2 HOURS • **MAKES:** 12 SERVINGS

- 1 **fully cooked bone-in ham (7 to 9 pounds)**
- **GLAZE**
- ½ **cup grapefruit juice**
- ½ **cup orange juice**
- ¼ **cup molasses**
- 3 **tablespoons honey**
- 1 **tablespoon packed brown sugar**
- 1 **tablespoon Dijon mustard**
- 3 **teaspoons coarsely ground pepper**

1. Preheat oven to 325°. Place ham on a rack in a shallow roasting pan. Using a sharp knife, score the surface of ham with ¼-in.-deep cuts in a diamond pattern. Cover and bake 1¾-2¼ hours or until a thermometer reads 130°.
2. Meanwhile, in a large saucepan, combine the grapefruit juice and orange juice. Bring to a boil; cook 6-8 minutes or until the liquid is reduced by half. Stir in the remaining ingredients; return to a boil. Reduce the heat; simmer, uncovered, 12-15 minutes or until thickened.
3. Remove the ham from the oven. Brush with ⅓ cup glaze. Bake the ham, uncovered, 15-20 minutes longer or until a thermometer reads 140°, basting occasionally with the remaining glaze.
PER SERVING *5 ounces cooked ham equals 272 cal., 7 g fat (2 g sat. fat), 116 mg chol., 1,424 mg sodium, 14 g carb., trace fiber, 39 g pro.*

Holiday White Fruitcake

Years ago, when I attended Koloa Missionary Church in Hawaii, a friend shared her wonderful white fruitcake recipe with me. Now every year at Christmastime, I bake at least 60 loaves!

—**EILEEN SOKOLOWSKI** CHANDLER, AZ

PREP: 20 MIN. • **BAKE:** 50 MIN. + COOLING
MAKES: 4 LOAVES (16 SLICES EACH)

- 1 package (8 ounces) chopped mixed candied fruit
- 1¼ cups golden raisins
- 1 cup chopped walnuts, toasted
- 3 cups all-purpose flour, divided
- 2 cups butter, softened
- 2 cups sugar
- 6 large eggs

1. Preheat oven to 275°. Line the bottoms of four greased 9x5-in. loaf pans with parchment paper; grease the paper.
2. In a small bowl, toss the mixed candied fruit, golden raisins and toasted walnuts with ½ cup flour. In a large bowl, cream the butter and sugar until light and fluffy. Add eggs, one at a time, beating well after each addition. Gradually beat in the remaining flour. Fold in the candied fruit mixture.
3. Transfer to prepared pans. Bake 50-60 minutes or until a toothpick inserted in center comes out clean. Cool in pans 10 minutes before removing to wire racks to cool.
NOTE *To toast nuts, bake in a shallow pan in a 350° oven for 5-10 minutes or cook in a skillet over low heat until lightly browned, stirring occasionally.*
PER SERVING *1 slice equals 133 cal., 7 g fat (4 g sat. fat), 33 mg chol., 61 mg sodium, 16 g carb., 1 g fiber, 2 g pro.*

HOLIDAY WHITE FRUITCAKE

PEANUT BUTTER CHOCOLATE FUDGE

Peanut Butter Chocolate Fudge

When making fudge, I get the whole family involved. My daughter watches the clock, my husband stirs and my son is a taste tester!

—JENNIFER GILBERT BRIGHTON, MI

PREP: 20 MIN. • **COOK:** 20 MIN. + CHILLING
MAKES: 4 POUNDS (117 PIECES)

2 teaspoons butter

CHOCOLATE LAYER

2 cups sugar
1 can (5 ounces) evaporated milk (⅔ cup)
5 tablespoons butter, cubed
½ teaspoon salt
1 jar (7 ounces) marshmallow creme
½ teaspoon vanilla extract
2 cups (12 ounces) semisweet chocolate chips

PEANUT BUTTER LAYER

2 cups sugar
1 can (5 ounces) evaporated milk (⅔ cup)
5 tablespoons butter, cubed
½ teaspoon salt
1 jar (7 ounces) marshmallow creme
½ cup creamy peanut butter
1 teaspoon vanilla extract
Coarsely chopped chocolate-covered or salted peanuts, optional

1. Line a 13x9-in. pan with foil; grease foil with 2 teaspoons butter.
2. For chocolate layer, in a large heavy saucepan, combine sugar, evaporated milk, cubed butter and salt. Bring to a rapid boil over medium heat, stirring constantly; cook and stir until a candy thermometer reads 234° (soft-ball stage), about 4 minutes. Remove from heat; stir in marshmallow creme and vanilla until blended. Stir in chocolate chips until melted. Immediately spread into prepared pan.
3. For peanut butter layer, in another large heavy saucepan, combine the sugar, evaporated milk, cubed butter and salt. Bring to a rapid boil over medium heat, stirring constantly; cook and stir until a candy thermometer reads 234° (soft-ball stage), about 4 minutes. Remove from the heat; stir in marshmallow creme, peanut butter and vanilla until blended. Immediately spread over chocolate layer. If desired, sprinkle with coarsely chopped nuts. Refrigerate for 3 hours or until firm, covering when cooled.
4. Using the foil, lift the fudge out of pan. Remove the foil; cut fudge into 1-in. squares. Store between layers of waxed paper in an airtight container.
PER SERVING 1 piece (calculated without peanuts) equals 71 cal., 3 g fat (1 g sat. fat), 4 mg chol., 40 mg sodium, 12 g carb., trace fiber, 1 g pro.

Icebox Potato Rolls

The dough for these melt-in-your-mouth rolls can be made days ahead. I love that!
—BARB LINNERUD BOILING SPRINGS, SC

PREP: 1 HOUR + RISING • **BAKE:** 15 MIN.
MAKES: ABOUT 2½ DOZEN

1¼ pounds potatoes, peeled and cubed (about 3½ cups)
¾ cup sugar
2 teaspoons salt
1 package (¼ ounce) active dry yeast
5½ to 6 cups bread flour
1 cup 2% milk
½ cup water
½ cup shortening
3 large eggs
⅓ cup butter, melted

1. Place potatoes in a saucepan; add water to cover. Bring to a boil. Reduce heat; cook, uncovered, 10-15 minutes or until tender. Drain; return to pan. Mash potatoes (you should have about 2 cups). Cool slightly.
2. In a large bowl, mix sugar, salt, yeast and 2 cups flour. In a small saucepan, heat the milk, water and shortening to 120°-130°. Add to dry ingredients; beat on medium speed 2 minutes. Add eggs and potatoes; beat on high 2 minutes. Stir in enough remaining flour to form a soft dough (dough will be very sticky).
3. Do not knead. Place the dough in a large greased bowl. Cover with greased plastic wrap; refrigerate overnight.
4. Punch down the dough. Using a tablespoon dipped in melted butter, drop three spoonfuls of dough into a greased muffin cup. Repeat, redipping spoon in butter. Cover with greased plastic wrap; let rise in a warm place until almost doubled, about 45 minutes. Preheat oven to 375°.
5. Brush tops with remaining melted butter. Bake 12-15 minutes or until golden brown. Cool in pans 5 minutes. Remove to wire racks; serve warm.
NOTE *Dough can be made up to 3 days before baking. Prepare the dough as directed, refrigerating it for 1-3 days and punching it down every 24 hours. Shape and bake rolls as directed.*
PER SERVING 1 roll equals 181 cal., 6 g fat (2 g sat. fat), 25 mg chol., 187 mg sodium, 26 g carb., 1 g fiber, 4 g pro.

Featuring a filling that's tinted with with jam, Raspberry Red Bakewell Tart is ideal for Christmas. I first had this British dessert while in Dubai with the Navy.

—CRYSTAL SCHLUETER
NORTHGLENN, CO

Raspberry Red Bakewell Tart

PREP: 30 MIN. + FREEZING
BAKE: 30 MIN. + COOLING
MAKES: 12 SERVINGS

- 1 **sheet refrigerated pie pastry**
- 1 **egg white, lightly beaten**

FILLING
- ¼ **cup seedless raspberry jam**
- ⅔ **cup butter, softened**
- ¾ **cup sugar**
- 3 **large eggs**
- 1 **large egg yolk**
- 1 **tablespoon baking cocoa**
- 2 **teaspoons red paste food coloring**
- 1 **cup ground almonds**

ICING
- 2½ **cups confectioners' sugar**
- 3 **tablespoons water**
- ¼ **teaspoon almond extract**

1. Preheat oven to 350°. Unroll pastry sheet into a 9-in. fluted tart pan with removable bottom; trim even with rim. Freeze 10 minutes.
2. Line unpricked pastry with a double thickness of foil. Fill with pie weights, dried beans or uncooked rice. Bake 12-15 minutes or until edges are golden brown.
3. Remove foil and weights; brush bottom of crust with egg white. Bake 6-8 minutes longer or until golden brown. Cool on a wire rack.
4. Spread jam over bottom of crust. In a bowl, cream butter and sugar until light and fluffy. Gradually beat in eggs, egg yolk, cocoa and food coloring. Fold in ground almonds. Spread over jam.
5. Bake 30-35 minutes or until filling is set. Cool completely on a wire rack.
6. In a small bowl, mix confectioners' sugar, water and extract until smooth; drizzle or pipe over tart. Refrigerate leftovers.
NOTE *Let the pie weights cool before storing. Beans and rice may be reused for pie weights, but not for cooking.*
PER SERVING *1 slice equals 404 cal., 20 g fat (9 g sat. fat), 92 mg chol., 181 mg sodium, 53 g carb., 1 g fiber, 5 g pro.*

Twice-Baked Cheddar Potato Casserole

With bacon, cheddar and sour cream, ordinary potatoes become extraordinary.
—**KYLE COX** SCOTTSDALE, AZ

PREP: 70 MIN. • **BAKE:** 15 MIN.
MAKES: 12 SERVINGS

- 8 **medium baking potatoes (about 8 ounces each)**
- ½ **cup butter, cubed**
- ⅔ **cup sour cream**
- ⅔ **cup 2% milk**
- 1 **teaspoon salt**
- ¾ **teaspoon pepper**
- 10 **bacon strips, cooked and crumbled, divided**
- 2 **cups (8 ounces) shredded cheddar cheese, divided**
- 4 **green onions, chopped, divided**

1. Preheat oven to 425°. Scrub the potatoes; pierce several times with a fork. Bake 45-60 minutes or until tender. Remove from oven; reduce oven setting to 350°.
2. When potatoes are cool enough to handle, cut each potato lengthwise in half. Scoop out the pulp; place in a large bowl. Discard shells. Mash pulp with butter; stir in sour cream, milk, salt and pepper.
3. Reserve ¼ cup crumbled bacon for topping. Gently fold the remaining bacon, 1 cup cheddar cheese and half of the onions into the potato mixture (do not overmix).
4. Transfer to a greased 11x7-in. baking dish. Top with the remaining cheese and onions; sprinkle with the reserved bacon. Bake 15-20 minutes or until heated through and cheese is melted.
PER SERVING *⅔ cup equals 301 cal., 19 g fat (11 g sat. fat), 57 mg chol., 517 mg sodium, 22 g carb., 2 g fiber, 10 g pro.*

TWICE-BAKED CHEDDAR POTATO CASSEROLE

Merry Cookies

Sweeten the season with Christmas goodies of all kinds, from **cute cutouts** to **chunky bars** your holiday guests will snatch up in a flash.

Snow-Capped Mocha Fudge Drops

Just about everyone is happy to see chocolate in one form or another on a dessert platter. Dipped in melted white candy coating for a snow-capped look, my drops are fudgy and have a touch of mocha flavor.

—PATRICIA HARMON BADEN, PA

PREP: 40 MIN. • **BAKE:** 10 MIN./BATCH + COOLING
MAKES: ABOUT 3½ DOZEN

- 1 cup (6 ounces) semisweet chocolate chips, divided
- ½ cup butter, cubed
- 1 tablespoon instant coffee granules or espresso powder
- ¾ cup sugar
- ¾ cup packed brown sugar
- 2 large eggs
- 2 teaspoons vanilla extract
- 2 cups all-purpose flour
- ¼ cup baking cocoa
- ½ teaspoon baking powder
- ¼ teaspoon salt
- ½ cup chopped pecans or walnuts
- 10 ounces white candy coating, melted
  White edible glitter and/or red and green colored sugar

1. Preheat oven to 350°. In a large microwave-safe bowl, microwave ½ cup chips and butter until butter is melted; stir until chocolate is melted. Stir in the coffee granules; cool slightly.
2. Whisk in sugars. Whisk in eggs, one at a time, and vanilla until blended. In small bowl, whisk the flour, cocoa, baking powder and salt; stir into chocolate mixture. Stir in pecans and remaining chips.
3. Drop dough by tablespoonfuls 1 in. apart onto ungreased baking sheets. Bake 8-10 minutes or until set. Cool on the pans 2 minutes. Remove to wire racks to cool completely.
4. Dip the tops of the cookies into the melted white candy coating; sprinkle with the glitter and/or colored sugar. Let stand until set.
NOTE *Edible glitter is available from Wilton Industries. Call 800-794-5866 or visit* wilton.com.
PER SERVING *1 cookie (calculated without edible glitter) equals 131 cal., 6 g fat (4 g sat. fat), 15 mg chol., 43 mg sodium, 19 g carb., 1 g fiber, 1 g pro.*

Triple Chocolate Candy Cane Cookies

Every year, I prepare these drizzled treats knowing they'll be among the first of my Christmas baked goods to disappear.
—PRISCILLA YEE CONCORD, CA

PREP: 40 MIN. • **BAKE:** 10 MIN./BATCH + COOLING
MAKES: ABOUT 3 DOZEN

- ¾ cup butter, softened
- 1 cup sugar
- 1 large egg
- 1¾ cups all-purpose flour
- ½ cup baking cocoa
- ¼ teaspoon salt
- ¼ teaspoon baking soda
- 3 ounces white baking chocolate, chopped
- 2 teaspoons canola oil, divided
- 3 ounces semisweet chocolate, chopped
- ¼ cup crushed candy canes (about 10 miniature)

1. Preheat oven to 350°. In a small bowl, cream butter and sugar until light and fluffy. Beat in the egg. In another bowl, whisk flour, cocoa, salt and baking soda; gradually beat into creamed mixture.
2. Shape the cookie dough into 1-in. balls; place 2 in. apart on ungreased baking sheets. Flatten to 2-in. rounds with the bottom of a glass. Bake 6-8 minutes or until set (do not overbake). Cool on pans 5 minutes. Remove to wire racks to cool completely.
3. In a microwave, melt white chocolate with 1 teaspoon oil; stir until smooth. Drizzle over the cookies. Repeat with the semisweet chocolate and remaining oil. Sprinkle tops with crushed candy canes; let stand until set.
PER SERVING *1 cookie equals 115 cal., 6 g fat (3 g sat. fat), 15 mg chol., 63 mg sodium, 15 g carb., 1 g fiber, 1 g pro.*

TRIPLE CHOCOLATE CANDY CANE COOKIES

NANNY'S FRUITCAKE COOKIES

Nanny's Fruitcake Cookies

My grandmother always made a holiday fruitcake. I turned her recipe into a cookie I nibble with a cup of tea.
—**AMANDA DIGGES** SOUTH WINDSOR, CT

PREP: 35 MIN. + CHILLING • **BAKE:** 15 MIN./BATCH
MAKES: ABOUT 4 DOZEN

1⅔ **cups chopped pecans or walnuts**
1⅓ **cups golden raisins**
 1 **cup pitted dried plums, chopped**
⅔ **cup dried apricots, finely chopped**
½ **cup dried cranberries**
¼ **cup Triple Sec**
 1 **cup butter, softened**
½ **cup sugar**
⅓ **cup packed light brown sugar**
½ **teaspoon ground nutmeg**
 1 **large egg**
2⅔ **cups all-purpose flour**

1. Place the first five ingredients in a large bowl. Drizzle with Triple Sec; toss to combine. Let stand, covered, overnight.
2. In a large bowl, cream butter, sugars and nutmeg until light and fluffy. Beat in the egg. Gradually beat in the flour. Stir in fruit mixture.
3. Divide the cookie dough in half; shape each portion into a 12x3x1-in. rectangular log. Wrap each in plastic wrap; refrigerate overnight or until firm.
4. Preheat the oven to 350°. Unwrap and cut the dough crosswise into ½-in. slices. Place 2 in. apart on ungreased baking sheets. Bake 13-16 minutes or until edges are light brown. Remove from pans to wire racks to cool.
PER SERVING *1 cookie equals 131 cal., 7 g fat (3 g sat. fat), 14 mg chol., 37 mg sodium, 17 g carb., 1 g fiber, 2 g pro.*

⑤ INGREDIENTS
Pecan Cutout Cookies

Pecans and a handful of kitchen staples—sugar, butter, flour and vanilla— are all you'll need to bake a batch of these cutouts.
—**LOUISE REISLER** BONDUEL, WI

PREP: 35 MIN. • **BAKE:** 10 MIN./BATCH + COOLING
MAKES: ABOUT 4 DOZEN

 2 **cups pecan halves (8 ounces)**
 1 **cup sugar, divided**
 2 **cups all-purpose flour**
 1 **cup cold butter, cubed**
VANILLA SUGAR
⅔ **cup sugar**
½ **teaspoon vanilla extract**

1. Preheat oven to 325°. Place the pecans and ½ cup sugar in a food processor; process until pecans are finely ground. Transfer to a large bowl.
2. Stir the flour and remaining sugar into pecan mixture; cut in butter until crumbly. Transfer the mixture to a clean work surface; knead gently to form a smooth dough, about 2 minutes. (Mixture will be very crumbly at first, but will come together and form a dough as it is kneaded.) Divide dough in half.
3. On a lightly floured surface, roll each portion of dough to ¼-in. thickness. Cut with a floured 3-in. cookie cutter. Place 1 in. apart on ungreased baking sheets.
4. Bake 10-12 minutes or until the edges begin to brown. Cool on the pans 5 minutes. Meanwhile, in a shallow bowl, mix vanilla sugar ingredients until blended.
5. Dip warm cookies in vanilla sugar to coat; cool completely on wire racks. Store in airtight containers.
PER SERVING *1 cookie equals 109 cal., 7 g fat (3 g sat. fat), 10 mg chol., 34 mg sodium, 12 g carb., 1 g fiber, 1 g pro.*

PECAN CUTOUT COOKIES

My family adores just about any dessert that has cream cheese. I think Cranberry Eggnog Cheesecake Bars are even better when left to chill in the fridge overnight.
—**CARMELL CHILDS** FERRON, UT

CRANBERRY EGGNOG CHEESECAKE BARS

Cranberry Eggnog Cheesecake Bars

PREP: 20 MIN. • **BAKE:** 50 MIN. + CHILLING
MAKES: 2 DOZEN

- 1 package spice cake mix (regular size)
- 2½ cups old-fashioned oats
- ¾ cup butter, melted
- 2 packages (8 ounces each) cream cheese, softened
- ½ cup sugar
- ⅛ teaspoon ground nutmeg
- ½ cup eggnog
- 2 tablespoons all-purpose flour
- 3 large eggs
- 1 can (14 ounces) whole-berry cranberry sauce
- 2 tablespoons cornstarch

1. Preheat the oven to 350°. Line a 13x9-in. baking pan with parchment paper, letting the ends extend up sides; grease paper. In a large bowl, combine cake mix and oats; stir in melted butter.

Reserve 1⅓ cups crumb mixture for the topping; press remaining mixture onto bottom of prepared pan.
2. In a large bowl, beat the cream cheese, sugar and nutmeg until smooth. Gradually beat in the eggnog and flour. Add eggs; beat on low speed just until blended. Pour over crust.
3. In a small bowl, mix the cranberry sauce and cornstarch until blended; spoon over cheesecake layer, spreading over the top. Sprinkle with reserved crumb mixture.
4. Bake 50-55 minutes or until edges are brown and center is almost set. Cool 1 hour on a wire rack.
5. Refrigerate at least 2 hours. Lifting with parchment paper, remove from the pan. Cut into bars.
NOTE *This recipe was tested with commercially prepared eggnog.*
PER SERVING *1 bar equals 282 cal., 15 g fat (8 g sat. fat), 62 mg chol., 254 mg sodium, 34 g carb., 1 g fiber, 4 g pro.*

Cranberry Swirl Biscotti

Crunchy glazed biscotti is ideal for dunking into a hot cup of coffee, cocoa or tea.
—**LISA KILCUP** GIG HARBOR, WA

PREP: 20 MIN. • **BAKE:** 40 MIN. + COOLING
MAKES: ABOUT 2½ DOZEN

- ⅔ cup dried cranberries
- ½ cup cherry preserves
- ½ teaspoon ground cinnamon
- ½ cup butter, softened
- ⅔ cup sugar
- 2 large eggs
- 1 teaspoon vanilla extract
- 2¼ cups all-purpose flour
- ¾ teaspoon baking powder
- ¼ teaspoon salt
GLAZE
- ¾ cup confectioners' sugar
- 1 tablespoon 2% milk
- 2 teaspoons butter, melted
- 1 teaspoon almond extract

1. Preheat oven to 325°. Place the dried cranberries, cherry preserves and cinnamon in a food processor; process until smooth.
2. In a large bowl, cream butter and sugar until light and fluffy. Beat in eggs and vanilla. In another bowl, whisk the flour, baking powder and salt; gradually beat into creamed mixture.
3. Divide the cookie dough in half. On a lightly floured surface, roll each half of dough into a 12x8-in. rectangle. Spread each with half of the cranberry mixture; roll up jelly-roll style, starting with a short side.
4. Place rolls 4 in. apart on a lightly greased baking sheet, seam side down. Bake 25-30 minutes or until lightly browned.
5. Carefully transfer rolls to a cutting board; cool 5 minutes. Using a serrated knife, cut crosswise into ½-in. slices. Place slices upright on lightly greased baking sheets.
6. Bake 15-20 minutes longer or until centers are firm and dry. Remove from pans to wire racks.
7. In a small bowl, mix the glaze ingredients. Drizzle glaze over warm cookies; cool completely. Store in an airtight container.
PER SERVING *1 cookie equals 120 cal., 4 g fat (2 g sat. fat), 23 mg chol., 58 mg sodium, 20 g carb., trace fiber, 1 g pro.*

Candy Cane Shortbread Bars

I created these goodies for my daughter, who's a big fan of mint. Crushed candy canes dress them up for the holiday.

—**SUSAN CIUFFREDA** HUNTERSVILLE, NC

PREP: 30 MIN. • **BAKE:** 20 MIN. + COOLING
MAKES: 2 DOZEN

- 1 cup butter, softened
- 1 cup packed brown sugar
- 1 large egg yolk
- 1½ teaspoons peppermint extract
- 2 cups all-purpose flour

BUTTERCREAM
- 2 cups confectioners' sugar
- ¼ cup butter, melted
- 2 tablespoons 2% milk
- ½ teaspoon peppermint extract
- 2 drops red food coloring, optional

TOPPING
- 9 ounces white baking chocolate, melted and cooled slightly
- ¾ cup crushed candy canes (about 10 regular)

1. Preheat the oven to 350°. Line a 13x9-in. baking pan with parchment paper, letting the ends extend up sides.
2. In a large bowl, cream the butter and brown sugar until light and fluffy. Beat in egg yolk and extract. Gradually beat in the flour. Press evenly into the prepared pan.
3. Bake 16-19 minutes or until edges are brown. Cool completely in the pan on a wire rack.
4. In a bowl, combine the buttercream ingredients; beat until smooth. Spread over the shortbread. Carefully spread white baking chocolate over the top. Sprinkle with crushed candy canes; let stand until set.
5. Lifting with the parchment paper, remove from pan. Cut into bars.
PER SERVING *1 bar equals 265 cal., 13 g fat (8 g sat. fat), 33 mg chol., 97 mg sodium, 37 g carb., trace fiber, 2 g pro.*

DID YOU KNOW?

Extracts are distilled essential oils from plant materials that are then dissolved in alcohol. Peppermint and vanilla are just two of many varieties.

Peppermint Brownie Cups

Brownie lovers—here are the Christmas cookies for you! They look fancy when you pipe the homemade frosting in the center and sprinkle on baking chips.

—**LINDA BIBBO** CHAGRIN FALLS, OH

PREP: 40 MIN.
BAKE: 15 MIN./BATCH + COOLING
MAKES: 4 DOZEN

- 1 cup butter, cubed
- 1 cup plus 3 tablespoons milk chocolate chips
- 3 ounces unsweetened chocolate, chopped
- 3 large eggs
- 1¼ cups sugar
- 1 tablespoon instant coffee granules
- 2 teaspoons vanilla extract
- ½ teaspoon peppermint extract
- ⅔ cup all-purpose flour
- 1½ teaspoons baking powder
- ½ teaspoon salt

FROSTING
- 1½ cups confectioners' sugar
- 1 cup butter, softened
- 1 teaspoon peppermint extract
- 1 jar (7 ounces) marshmallow creme
    Peppermint crunch baking chips

1. Preheat the oven to 350°. Line 48 mini-muffin cups with paper or foil liners.
2. In a metal bowl over simmering water, melt the butter, chocolate chips and unsweetened chocolate; stir until smooth. Cool slightly.
3. In a large bowl, beat the eggs, sugar and coffee granules until blended. Stir in the extracts and chocolate mixture. In another bowl, whisk flour, baking powder and salt; gradually add to the chocolate mixture, mixing well.
4. Fill prepared cups three-fourths full. Bake 12-14 minutes or until a toothpick inserted in center comes out clean (do not overbake). Cool in pans 5 minutes before removing to wire racks to cool completely.
5. For the frosting, in a small bowl, beat the confectioners' sugar, butter and peppermint extract until smooth. Fold in marshmallow creme. Pipe or spread frosting over brownie cups; sprinkle with peppermint baking chips.
PER SERVING *1 brownie cup (calculated without peppermint baking chips) equals 160 cal., 10 g fat (6 g sat. fat), 33 mg chol., 116 mg sodium, 17 g carb., trace fiber, 1 g pro.*

PEPPERMINT BROWNIE CUPS

RED VELVET PEPPERMINT THUMBPRINTS

Red Velvet Peppermint Thumbprints

If you like classic red velvet cake, you'll love these yummy drizzled thumbprints.
—**PRISCILLA YEE** CONCORD, CA

PREP: 30 MIN.
BAKE: 10 MIN./BATCH + COOLING
MAKES: ABOUT 4 DOZEN

- 1 **cup butter, softened**
- 1 **cup sugar**
- 1 **large egg**
- 4 **teaspoons red food coloring**
- 1 **teaspoon peppermint extract**
- 2½ **cups all-purpose flour**
- 3 **tablespoons baking cocoa**
- 1 **teaspoon baking powder**
- ¼ **teaspoon salt**
- 2 **cups white baking chips**
- 2 **teaspoons canola oil**
- ¼ **cup crushed peppermint candies**

1. Preheat the oven to 350°. In a large bowl, cream butter and sugar until light and fluffy. Beat in egg, food coloring and extract. In another bowl, whisk flour, cocoa, baking powder and salt; gradually beat into creamed mixture.
2. Shape into 1-in. balls. Place 1 in. apart on ungreased baking sheets. Press a deep indentation in center of each with the end of a wooden spoon handle.
3. Bake for 9-11 minutes or until set. Remove from the pans to wire racks to cool completely.
4. In a microwave, melt baking chips with oil; stir until smooth. Spoon a scant teaspoon filling into each cookie. Drizzle tops with remaining mixture. Sprinkle with candy. Let stand until set.
PER SERVING *1 cookie equals 118 cal., 7 g fat (4 g sat. fat), 16 mg chol., 63 mg sodium, 14 g carb., trace fiber, 1 g pro.*

Snow Angel Cookies

How divine! Adorable angels are sure to disappear in a hurry at Christmastime. Cinnamon, nutmeg and cloves give them spice. After piping the frosting, sprinkle on coarse sugar for a glistening finish.
—**CAROLYN MOSELEY** DAYTON, OH

PREP: 40 MIN. + CHILLING
BAKE: 15 MIN./BATCH + COOLING
MAKES: ABOUT 5 DOZEN

- 1 **cup butter, softened**
- 1 **cup sugar**
- 1½ **teaspoons vanilla extract**
- 2 **large eggs**
- 3½ **cups all-purpose flour**
- 1 **teaspoon ground cinnamon**
- ½ **teaspoon baking powder**
- ½ **teaspoon salt**
- ¼ **teaspoon ground nutmeg**
- ¼ **teaspoon ground cloves**

FROSTING
- 9 **cups confectioners' sugar**
- ¾ **cup shortening**
- ½ **cup lemon juice**
- 4 **to 6 tablespoons water**
  Coarse sugar, optional

1. In a large bowl, beat butter, sugar and vanilla until blended. Beat in eggs, one at a time. In another bowl, whisk flour, cinnamon, baking powder, salt, nutmeg and cloves; gradually beat into creamed mixture.
2. Divide dough in half. Shape each portion of dough into a disk; wrap in plastic wrap. Refrigerate 1 hour or until firm enough to roll.
3. Preheat oven to 350°. On a lightly floured surface, roll each portion of dough to ⅛-in. thickness. Cut with a floured 4-in. angel cookie cutter. Place 1 in. apart on ungreased baking sheets.
4. Bake 12-14 minutes or until edges begin to brown. Remove from pans to wire racks to cool completely.
5. For frosting, beat confectioners' sugar, shortening, juice and enough water to reach spreading consistency. Spread or pipe over cookies; sprinkle with coarse sugar if desired.
PER SERVING *1 cookie (calculated without coarse sugar) equals 162 cal., 6 g fat (3 g sat. fat), 14 mg chol., 53 mg sodium, 27 g carb., trace fiber, 1 g pro.*

SNOW ANGEL COOKIES

JOLLY GINGER
REINDEER COOKIES

I noticed that a gingerbread-man cookie cutter looks like Rudolph's head when turned upside down. Soon after, I had a team of Jolly Ginger Reindeer Cookies.
—SUE GRONHOLZ BEAVER DAM, WI

Jolly Ginger Reindeer Cookies

PREP: 50 MIN. + CHILLING
BAKE: 10 MIN./BATCH + COOLING
MAKES: ABOUT 4 DOZEN

- ½ cup butter, softened
- 1 cup packed brown sugar
- 1 large egg
- ¾ cup molasses
- 3½ cups all-purpose flour
- 2 teaspoons ground ginger
- 1 teaspoon baking powder
- 1 teaspoon baking soda
- 1 teaspoon ground cinnamon
- 1 teaspoon ground allspice

ROYAL ICING

- 2 cups confectioners' sugar
- 2 tablespoons plus 2 teaspoons water
- 4 teaspoons meringue powder
- ¼ teaspoon cream of tartar
- 1 to 2 tablespoons miniature semisweet chocolate chips
- 1 to 2 tablespoons Red Hots

1. In a large bowl, cream butter and brown sugar until light and fluffy. Beat in egg and molasses. In another bowl, whisk the flour, ginger, baking powder, baking soda, cinnamon and allspice; gradually beat into creamed mixture.

2. Divide dough in half. Shape each portion of dough into a disk; wrap in plastic wrap. Refrigerate 1 hour or until firm enough to roll.

3. Preheat oven to 350°. On a lightly floured surface, roll each portion of dough to ¼-in. thickness. Cut with a floured 3-in. gingerbread boy-shaped cookie cutter. Place 1 in. apart on greased baking sheets.

4. Bake 10-12 minutes or until set. Cool on the pans 1 minute. Remove to wire racks to cool completely.

5. For royal icing, in a bowl, combine confectioners' sugar, water, meringue powder and cream of tartar; beat on low speed just until blended. Beat on high 4-5 minutes or until stiff peaks form. Keep unused icing covered at all times with a damp cloth. If necessary, beat again on high speed to restore texture.

6. To decorate cookies, place the gingerbread boys on a work surface with heads toward you. Pipe antlers onto legs. With icing, attach miniature chocolate chips for eyes and Red Hots for noses. Let stand until set. Store in airtight containers.

PER SERVING *1 cookie equals 106 cal., 2 g fat (1 g sat. fat), 9 mg chol., 58 mg sodium, 21 g carb., trace fiber, 1 g pro.*

STEVE RIEMERSMA'S
SMOOTH CHOCOLATE PIE
PAGE 211

Family Best

These family cooks learned from the very best—**Mom and Dad.** In this chapter, you'll find classic dishes passed down from generation to generation, building **all-new memories** along the way.

ARGE SALVATORI'S DAD'S GREEK SALAD
PAGE 207

GLORIA MEZIKOFSKY'S SWEET POTATO & CARROT CASSEROLE *PAGE 205*

MELISSA BEYER'S GRANDMA'S SEAFOOD CHOWDER *PAGE 213*

Stir-Fry for Supper

Belly laughs and fun stories make **home cooking** even better. This reader reminisces about how her **adventurous mom** inspired dinner celebrations.

RECIPES & STORY BY **JOY ZACHARIA** | CLEARWATER, FL

At least once a month, my rowdy family gets together for dinner (and laughs) at one of our homes. The lively group includes my sisters, our families and memories of our beloved mom, Betty.

My mother passed down her love of all foods, from new-to-me fruits and vegetables to exotic international cuisine. Now, when experimenting in my own kitchen, I use that inspiration to make unexpected creations, which I pack with plenty of nutritious ingredients.

Like most siblings, my sisters and I delight in a little competition. So when it's my turn to cook, I strive for a wow-worthy meal that won't tie me to the kitchen all day. I have the latest gossip to catch up on, after all!

For one of our wintertime gatherings, I threw together a bright and spicy stir-fry, starring fresh spinach I'd picked up at the local farmers market. From the first taste, I was sure everybody would go crazy for it.

These dinners are super casual, and people just come as they are. The only goal is to have a simple celebration of eating great food with our favorite people: our big, beautiful, boisterous family.

⑤ INGREDIENTS

Jasmine Rice with Coconut & Cherries

PREP: 10 MIN. • **COOK:** 20 MIN. + STANDING • **MAKES:** 4 SERVINGS

- 2½ cups water
- 1 tablespoon olive oil
- ¾ teaspoon salt
- 1½ cups uncooked jasmine rice
- ⅓ cup dried cherries
- ¼ cup chopped salted peanuts
- 1 teaspoon grated orange peel
- ¼ cup flaked coconut, toasted

1. In a large saucepan, bring the water, oil and salt to a boil. Stir in the rice; return to a boil, stirring once. Reduce heat; simmer, covered, 15-17 minutes or until water is absorbed.

JASMINE RICE WITH COCONUT & CHERRIES

2. Stir in dried cherries, peanuts and orange peel; let stand, covered, 10 minutes. Sprinkle with coconut.

NOTE *To toast coconut, bake in a shallow pan in a 350° oven for 5-10 minutes or cook in a skillet over low heat until golden brown, stirring occasionally.*

PER SERVING *1 cup equals 411 cal., 10 g fat (3 g sat. fat), 0 chol., 498 mg sodium, 71 g carb., 3 g fiber, 7 g pro.*

SPICY BEEF & PEPPER STIR-FRY

Spicy Beef & Pepper Stir-Fry

PREP: 20 MIN. + STANDING • **COOK:** 10 MIN. • **MAKES:** 4 SERVINGS

- 1 **pound beef top sirloin steak, cut into thin strips**
- 1 **tablespoon minced fresh gingerroot**
- 3 **garlic cloves, minced, divided**
- ¼ **teaspoon pepper**
- ¾ **teaspoon salt, divided**
- 1 **cup light coconut milk**
- 2 **tablespoons sugar**
- 1 **tablespoon Sriracha Asian hot chili sauce**
- ½ **teaspoon grated lime peel**
- 2 **tablespoons lime juice**
- 2 **tablespoons canola oil, divided**
- 1 **large sweet red pepper, cut into thin strips**
- ½ **medium red onion, thinly sliced**
- 1 **jalapeno pepper, seeded and thinly sliced**
- 4 **cups fresh baby spinach**
- 2 **green onions, thinly sliced**
- 2 **tablespoons chopped fresh cilantro**

1. In a large bowl, toss the beef with ginger, 2 cloves garlic, pepper and ½ teaspoon salt; let stand 15 minutes. In a small bowl, whisk coconut milk, sugar, chili sauce, lime peel, lime juice and remaining salt until blended.

2. In a large skillet, heat 1 tablespoon oil over medium-high heat. Add beef; stir-fry 2-3 minutes or until no longer pink. Remove from pan.

3. Stir-fry red pepper, red onion, jalapeno and remaining garlic in remaining oil 2-3 minutes or just until vegetables are crisp-tender. Stir in coconut milk mixture; heat through. Add spinach and beef; cook until spinach is wilted and beef is heated through, stirring occasionally. Sprinkle with green onions and cilantro.

PER SERVING ¾ *cup equals 312 cal., 16 g fat (5 g sat. fat), 46 mg chol., 641 mg sodium, 15 g carb., 2 g fiber, 26 g pro.* **Diabetic Exchanges:** *3 lean meat, 2 fat, 1 vegetable, ½ starch.*

Dishes to Cherish

This **Massachusetts mom** welcomes you to her kitchen, where she whips up golden brown popovers and other scrumptious **Passover sides** that make her family proud.

RECIPES & STORY BY **GLORIA "GLO" MEZIKOFSKY** | WAKEFIELD, MA

CHAROSET

My fondest memories of my mother, Cecelia Liftman, are of the chats we had after school in our small second-floor apartment in Lynn, Massachusetts, where she cooked and baked with a match-lit gas stove.

Mom was a to-the-letter cook who never let me lift a finger. Even so, the many heart-to-heart talks we had influenced my life as an educator (I taught English, speech therapy and special education) and as a wife. And they influenced me as a mother and grandmother, too.

Mom made beautiful meals after spending most days in her family's grocery store. She learned to cook from my Russian grandmother, born in Kiev, whose mouthwatering homemade strudels flew off the grocery counter.

Before Passover, Mom changed all the dishes and cleared the house of every last bread crumb. We replaced the bread with unleavened matzo crackers, using them to scoop up a delicious mix of fruit and nuts called charoset.

After I got married, cooking became one of my favorite pastimes. And when I retired, I wrote a cookbook—*Dessert Gems*—and started a cooking show, *Glo's Kitchen*.

My dear mom passed away in 1985. She would be so surprised.

EAT SMART ⑤ **INGREDIENTS**
Charoset

PREP: 15 MIN. + CHILLING • **MAKES:** 6 SERVINGS

- 3 **medium Gala or Fuji apples, peeled and chopped**
- ½ **cup finely chopped walnuts, toasted**
- 2 **tablespoons sweet red wine or grape juice**
- 2 **tablespoons sugar**
- 1 **teaspoon ground cinnamon**
  Matzo crackers, optional

1. In a large bowl, toss the apples and walnuts with sweet red wine. Mix the sugar and cinnamon; sprinkle over the apple mixture and toss to combine.

2. Refrigerate, covered, 1 hour before serving. If desired, serve with matzo crackers.

NOTE *To toast nuts, bake in a shallow pan in a 350° oven for 5-10 minutes or cook in a skillet over low heat until lightly browned, stirring occasionally.*

PER SERVING *¾ cup (calculated without matzo crackers) equals 116 cal., 7 g fat (1 g sat. fat), 0 chol., trace sodium, 14 g carb., 2 g fiber, 2 g pro.* **Diabetic Exchanges:** *1 fat, ½ starch, ½ fruit.*

PASSOVER POPOVERS

SWEET POTATO & CARROT CASSEROLE

(5) INGREDIENTS
Passover Popovers

PREP: 25 MIN. • **BAKE:** 20 MIN. + STANDING • **MAKES:** 1 DOZEN

- 1 cup water
- ½ cup safflower oil
- ⅛ to ¼ teaspoon salt
- 1 cup matzo cake meal
- 7 large eggs

1. Preheat the oven to 450°. Generously grease 12 muffin cups. In a large saucepan, bring the water, safflower oil and salt to a rolling boil. Add the matzo cake meal all at once and beat until blended. Remove the mixture from the heat; let stand 5 minutes.

2. Transfer mixture to a blender. Add two eggs; process, covered, until blended. Continue adding eggs, one at a time, and process until incorporated. Process 2 minutes longer or until mixture is smooth.

3. Fill the prepared muffin cups three-fourths full. Bake 18-22 minutes or until puffed, very firm and golden brown. Turn off the oven (do not open oven door); leave popovers in oven 10 minutes. Immediately remove popovers from pan to a wire rack. Serve hot.

NOTE *This recipe was tested with Manischewitz cake meal. Look for it in the baking aisle or kosher foods section.*

PER SERVING *1 popover equals 174 cal., 12 g fat (2 g sat. fat), 109 mg chol., 66 mg sodium, 11 g carb., trace fiber, 5 g pro.*

Sweet Potato & Carrot Casserole

PREP: 55 MIN. • **BAKE:** 25 MIN. + STANDING • **MAKES:** 12 SERVINGS

- ½ cup golden raisins
- 3½ pounds medium sweet potatoes (about 6 potatoes)
- 4 large carrots, cut into 1½-inch pieces
- ¼ cup butter or nondairy margarine
- 1½ cups packed brown sugar
- ⅓ cup orange juice

1. Preheat oven to 375°. In a small bowl, cover raisins with hot water; let stand 30 minutes.

2. Place the sweet potatoes in a 6-qt. stockpot; add water to cover. Bring to a boil. Reduce the heat; cook, uncovered, 15-20 minutes or just until tender. Remove sweet potatoes and cool slightly. Add carrots to same pot of boiling water; cook, uncovered, 15-20 minutes or until tender; drain.

3. Peel sweet potatoes; cut crosswise into 1½-in.-thick slices. Arrange sweet potatoes and carrots in a greased 13x9-in. baking dish, cut sides down.

4. Drain the raisins. In a small saucepan, melt butter over medium heat; stir in raisins. Add brown sugar and orange juice, stirring to dissolve sugar. Pour over vegetables.

5. Bake, uncovered, 25-30 minutes or until heated through and the sauce is bubbly; if desired, baste occasionally with sauce. Let stand 10 minutes; toss before serving.

PER SERVING *¾ cup equals 307 cal., 4 g fat (2 g sat. fat), 10 mg chol., 69 mg sodium, 67 g carb., 5 g fiber, 3 g pro.*

Sizzlin' on the Grill

This East Coast clan is a meat-and-potatoes family. With **Dad at the grill** and friends gathered around, they throw a party of **mythic proportions.**

RECIPES & STORY BY **ARGE SALVATORI** | WALDWICK, NJ

I grew up in Queens, New York, with my younger brother, Dino; our Italian-American mom, Rosemarie; and our father, Thanasis, who came to this country from the Greek village of Orchomenos.

We tended to be very traditional—Mom prepared the meals, and the whole family gathered around the dinner table to eat together every night. But for parties and holidays, Dad was always the cook, and he always went big.

We'd welcome up to 60 guests to our celebrations, which often included a whole lamb, goat and pig all roasting on a spit. On top of that, we'd usually have six different salads, cheese and spinach pies, and classic Greek pastries and cookies from the bakery. These were quite the feasts!

My dad does it right. He seasons his dishes with lots of garlic, oregano, fresh black pepper, olive oil, red wine vinegar, and mild and sharp feta cheese, all imported from Greece.

A couple of years ago, I wanted to learn Dad's secrets and techniques, but he never uses a recipe. My solution was to start recording him cooking, step by step, on my cellphone.

Thanks to those videos, I've mastered the recipes I adore, and now my husband, Billy, loves them just as much as I do.

⑤ INGREDIENTS

Roasted Greek Potatoes with Feta Cheese

PREP: 15 MIN. • **BAKE:** 40 MIN. • **MAKES:** 8 SERVINGS

- ⅔ **cup water**
- ½ **cup olive oil**
- 3 **tablespoons lemon juice**
- 4 **garlic cloves, minced**
- 2 **teaspoons dried oregano**
- 1 **teaspoon salt**
- ½ **teaspoon pepper**
- 3 **pounds Yukon Gold potatoes (about 6 medium), each cut into eight wedges**
- ¾ **cup crumbled feta cheese**

ROASTED GREEK POTATOES WITH FETA CHEESE

1. Preheat oven to 450°. In a small bowl, whisk the first seven ingredients. Arrange potatoes evenly in a shallow roasting pan. Pour water mixture over top.

2. Roast 40-50 minutes or until potatoes are golden brown and tender. Sprinkle with cheese.

PER SERVING *¾ cup equals 308 cal., 15 g fat (3 g sat. fat), 6 mg chol., 405 mg sodium, 38 g carb., 3 g fiber, 5 g pro.*

GRILLED RIBEYES WITH
BROWNED GARLIC BUTTER

Dad's Greek Salad

START TO FINISH: 20 MIN. • **MAKES:** 8 SERVINGS

- 4 large tomatoes, seeded and coarsely chopped
- 2½ cups thinly sliced Persian cucumbers (about 6) or English cucumber
- 1 small red onion, halved and thinly sliced
- ¼ cup olive oil
- 3 tablespoons red wine vinegar
- ¼ teaspoon salt
- ⅛ teaspoon pepper
- ¼ teaspoon dried oregano, optional
- ¾ cup pitted Greek olives
- ¾ cup (3 ounces) crumbled feta cheese

Place the tomatoes, cucumbers and onion in a large bowl. In a small bowl, whisk the oil, red wine vinegar, salt, pepper and, if desired, oregano until blended. Drizzle over salad; toss to coat. Top with olives and cheese.

PER SERVING *¾ cup equals 148 cal., 12 g fat (2 g sat. fat), 6 mg chol., 389 mg sodium, 7 g carb., 2 g fiber, 3 g pro.* **Diabetic Exchanges:** *2 vegetable, 2 fat.*

DAD'S GREEK SALAD

(5) INGREDIENTS FAST FIX
Grilled Ribeyes with Browned Garlic Butter

START TO FINISH: 25 MIN. • **MAKES:** 8 SERVINGS

- 6 tablespoons unsalted butter, cubed
- 2 garlic cloves, minced
- 4 beef ribeye steaks (about 1 inch thick and 12 ounces each)
- 1½ teaspoons salt
- 1½ teaspoons pepper

1. In a small heavy saucepan, melt butter with garlic over medium heat. Heat 4-6 minutes or until butter is golden brown, stirring constantly. Remove from heat.

2. Season the steaks with salt and pepper. Grill, covered, over medium heat or broil 4 in. from heat 5-7 minutes on each side or until the meat reaches desired doneness (for medium-rare, a thermometer should read 145°; medium, 160°; well-done, 170°).

3. Gently warm garlic butter over low heat. Cut steaks into thick slices; serve with garlic butter.

PER SERVING *4 ounces cooked beef with 2 teaspoons garlic butter equals 449 cal., 36 g fat (16 g sat. fat), 123 mg chol., 521 mg sodium, 1 g carb., trace fiber, 30 g pro.*

Dumplings for Dinner

Pull out your biggest stockpot for Mom's cooking at its coziest. It's time for a delectably **creamy soup** and a perfectly **refreshing salad** on the side.

RECIPES & STORY BY **ERIKA MONROE-WILLIAMS** | SCOTTSDALE, AZ

PEAR & POMEGRANATE SALAD

When I was a child, I'd watch my mother cook for hours, waiting for the time I'd be old enough to tie on an apron of my own. Soon enough, I was learning to bake cookies and prepare Sunday brunch comfort food, like crepes and French toast, at her side.

When I began cooking by myself, I had some some pretty amazing kitchen disasters. You name it, I've burned it, undercooked it, spilled it or just plain ruined it. Luckily, these mistakes actually helped me make my recipes foolproof.

Now I know exactly what not to do at almost every turn in the kitchen, and I'm teaching those tricks to my own daughter, Madison. She's already such a good baker, making her grandma's apricot shortbread cookies without a hitch.

I often re-create my mom's recipes, too, including her chicken and dumplings. That dish harkens back to my childhood and nippy days when we devoured those cute little balls of dough swimming in a hot, rich broth.

After a few tweaks to the recipe, such as adding cream and white wine, I've come up with a dinner we all adore. When Mom eats it, she asks for my secrets to making the recipe even better.

The classic dishes that warm me up body and soul are my favorites. When the first bite whisks me back to childhood, I know the recipe is perfect, no matter how imperfectly it began.

Try bowls of chicken and dumplings with a great side—Pear & Pomegranate Salad. It's a fresh, cool complement to a hearty main dish.

FAST FIX
Pear & Pomegranate Salad

START TO FINISH: 25 MIN. • **MAKES:** 4 SERVINGS

- ¼ cup apple juice
- 2 tablespoons canola oil
- 1 tablespoon cider vinegar
- 1 tablespoon white balsamic vinegar or white wine vinegar
- ⅛ teaspoon onion powder
- ⅛ teaspoon coarsely ground pepper
  Dash salt
- 3 medium Bosc pears
- 1 head Boston or Bibb lettuce (about 6 ounces), torn
- 1 cup pomegranate seeds
- 1 cup coarsely chopped pecans, toasted
- ¾ cup crumbled Boursin garlic and fine herbs cheese (half of a 5.2-ounce package) or garlic and herb feta cheese

1. In a blender, combine the first seven ingredients. Cut one pear lengthwise in half; peel, core and coarsely chop one pear half. Add the chopped pear to blender; cover and process until blended. Cut remaining pears and pear half lengthwise into ¼-in. slices.

2. Arrange the lettuce on four plates. Top with the pears, pomegranate seeds and pecans; sprinkle with the cheese. Drizzle with the dressing; serve immediately.

NOTES *Boursin garlic and fine herbs cheese, sold in a 5.2-ounce package, has a firmer texture than the spreadable cheese product. To toast nuts, bake in a shallow pan in a 350° oven for 5-10 minutes or cook in a skillet over low heat until lightly browned, stirring occasionally.*

PER SERVING *1 serving equals 388 cal., 29 g fat (4 g sat. fat), 6 mg chol., 74 mg sodium, 34 g carb., 7 g fiber, 4 g pro.*

The Best Chicken & Dumplings

PREP: 25 MIN. • **COOK:** 1 HOUR 10 MIN.
MAKES: 8 SERVINGS (3 QUARTS)

- ¾ cup all-purpose flour, divided
- ½ teaspoon salt
- ½ teaspoon freshly ground pepper
- 1 broiler/fryer chicken (about 3 pounds), cut up
- 2 tablespoons canola oil
- 1 large onion, finely chopped
- 2 medium carrots, finely chopped
- 2 celery ribs, finely chopped
- 3 garlic cloves, minced
- 6 cups chicken stock
- ½ cup white wine or apple cider
- 2 teaspoons sugar
- 2 bay leaves
- 5 whole peppercorns

DUMPLINGS

- 1⅓ cups all-purpose flour
- 2 teaspoons baking powder
- ¾ teaspoon salt
- ⅔ cup 2% milk
- 1 tablespoon butter, melted

SOUP

- ½ cup heavy whipping cream
- 2 teaspoons minced fresh parsley
- 2 teaspoons minced fresh thyme
  Additional salt and pepper to taste

1. In a shallow bowl, mix ½ cup flour, salt and pepper. Add chicken, one piece at a time, and toss to coat; shake off excess. In a 6-qt. stockpot, heat oil over medium-high heat. Brown chicken in batches on all sides; remove from pan.

2. Add onion, carrots and celery to same pan; cook and stir 6-8 minutes or until onion is tender. Add the garlic; cook and stir 1 minute longer. Stir in ¼ cup flour until blended. Gradually add stock, stirring constantly. Stir in wine, sugar, bay leaves and peppercorns. Return chicken to pan; bring to a boil. Reduce heat; simmer, covered, 20-25 minutes or until chicken juices run clear.

3. Meanwhile, in a bowl, whisk flour, baking powder and salt. In another bowl, whisk milk and melted butter until blended. Add to flour mixture; stir just until moistened (do not overmix). Drop by rounded tablespoons onto a parchment paper-lined baking sheet; set aside.

4. Remove chicken from stockpot; cool slightly. Discard bay leaves and skim fat from soup. Remove skin and bones from chicken and discard. Using two forks, coarsely shred meat into 1- to 1½-in. pieces; return to soup. Cook, covered, on high until mixture reaches a simmer.

5. Drop the dumplings on top of simmering soup, a few at a time. Reduce heat to low; cook, covered, 15-18 minutes or until a toothpick inserted in center of dumplings comes out clean (do not lift cover while simmering). Gently stir in cream, parsley and thyme. Season with additional salt and pepper to taste.

PER SERVING *1½ cups equals 470 cal., 24 g fat (8 g sat. fat), 104 mg chol., 892 mg sodium, 29 g carb., 2 g fiber, 32 g pro.*

THE BEST CHICKEN & DUMPLINGS

The Gift of Pie

A **pie recipe** handed down through generations tastes so much like home. Here, **family bakers** tell all about the special pies—and the special people—they **give thanks** for.

CINNAMON-SUGAR APPLE PIE

The Pie Lady—that's how my Grandma Huegerich was known in her corner of rural Iowa. It was my mom who taught me to bake pie, though. As she explained to me time and again, "Grandma was never one to give out her recipes."

I can't say I blame Grandma. To share a pie is one thing, but to reveal a recipe is quite another. So I learned to bake my mother's apple pie, a true classic that included just apples, sugar, cinnamon, lemon and butter, tucked into a lard crust from a recipe Grandma had actually shared.

A few tweaks later, I found a guy who solemnly pronounced my version better than his nonna's. We married not long after!

I've held on to that recipe. These days, there's a teenage boy in our home—one who tends to whisper upon waking, "Apple pie?"

I catch myself regretting that he never had a chance to know my grandmother. But then I watch him eat a slice of pie and sigh exactly like her—and I realize he actually knows her quite well.

Here's my recipe for apple pie baked in a cast-iron skillet. You can also use a 9-inch deep-dish pie plate.

—RENEE SCHETTLER ROSSI NEW YORK, NY

Cinnamon-Sugar Apple Pie

PREP: 1 HOUR + CHILLING • **BAKE:** 65 MIN. + COOLING
MAKES: 10 SERVINGS

- 2½ **cups all-purpose flour**
- ½ **teaspoon salt**
- 1¼ **cups cold lard**
- 6 **to 8 tablespoons cold 2% milk**

FILLING
- 2½ **cups sugar**
- 1 **teaspoon ground cinnamon**
- ½ **teaspoon ground ginger**
- 9 **cups thinly sliced peeled tart apples (about 9 medium)**
- 1 **tablespoon bourbon, optional**
- 2 **tablespoons all-purpose flour**
- **Dash salt**
- 3 **tablespoons cold butter, cubed**

TOPPING
- 1 **tablespoon 2% milk**
- 2 **teaspoons coarse sugar**

1. In a large bowl, mix the flour and salt; cut in lard until crumbly. Gradually add the milk, tossing with a fork until dough holds together when pressed. Divide dough in half. Shape each into a disk; wrap in plastic wrap. Refrigerate 1 hour or overnight.

2. For filling, in a large bowl, mix the sugar, cinnamon and ginger. Add the apples; toss to coat. Cover; let stand 1 hour to allow the apples to release juices, stirring occasionally.

3. Drain the apples, reserving the syrup. Place syrup and, if desired, bourbon in a small saucepan; bring to a boil. Reduce heat; simmer, uncovered, 20-25 minutes or until the mixture thickens slightly and turns a medium amber color. Remove from heat; cool completely.

4. Preheat oven to 400°. Toss the drained apples with the flour and salt. On a lightly floured surface, roll one half of the pie pastry dough to a ⅛-in.-thick circle; transfer to a 10-in. cast-iron or other deep ovenproof skillet. Trim the pastry even with the rim. Add apple mixture. Pour cooled syrup over top; dot with butter.

5. Roll remaining dough to a ⅛-in.-thick circle. Place over filling. Trim, seal and flute edge. Cut slits in top. Brush milk over pastry; sprinkle with coarse sugar. Place on a foil-lined baking sheet. Bake 20 minutes.

6. Reduce oven setting to 350°. Bake 45-55 minutes longer or until the crust is golden brown and the filling is bubbly. Cool on a wire rack.

PER SERVING *1 piece equals 633 cal., 30 g fat (12 g sat. fat), 34 mg chol., 169 mg sodium, 90 g carb., 2 g fiber, 4 g pro.*

y birthday is in late November, so my mom often morphed our Thanksgiving pumpkin pie into my birthday "cake" and had all the family sing for me. This update on her recipe adds more of our favorite ingredient, ginger. I think the pie tastes best after it's nice and chilled. Birthday candles are optional!

—**EMILY TYRA** MILWAUKEE, WI

Gingery Pumpkin Pie

PREP: 30 MIN. + CHILLING • **BAKE:** 50 MIN.
MAKES: 8 SERVINGS (1½ CUPS WHIPPED CREAM)

1¼ cups all-purpose flour
1 tablespoon minced fresh gingerroot
¼ teaspoon ground allspice
¼ teaspoon salt
½ cup butter, cubed
3 to 5 tablespoons ice water

FILLING
2 large eggs
1 large egg yolk
1 can (15 ounces) solid-pack pumpkin
1¼ cups heavy whipping cream
⅔ cup packed brown sugar
1 teaspoon ground cinnamon
1 teaspoon minced fresh gingerroot
1 teaspoon molasses
¼ teaspoon ground ginger
¼ teaspoon ground allspice
⅛ teaspoon ground cardamom
⅛ teaspoon ground cloves

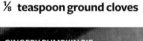
GINGERY PUMPKIN PIE

WHIPPED CREAM
¾ cup heavy whipping cream
1 tablespoon maple syrup
¼ teaspoon ground cinnamon

1. In a small bowl, mix the flour, ginger, allspice and salt; cut in the butter until crumbly. Gradually add the ice water, tossing with a fork until the dough holds together when pressed. Shape into a disk; wrap in plastic wrap. Refrigerate 1 hour or overnight.
2. Preheat oven to 375°. On a lightly floured surface, roll dough to a ⅛-in.-thick circle; transfer to a 9-in. pie plate. Trim the pastry to ½ in. beyond the rim of the plate; flute the edge. In a large bowl, whisk the filling ingredients until blended; pour into crust.
3. Bake on a lower oven rack 50-60 minutes or until a knife inserted near center comes out clean. Cool on a wire rack; serve or refrigerate within 2 hours.
4. For the whipped cream, in a small bowl, beat the heavy whipping cream until it begins to thicken. Add the maple syrup and cinnamon; beat until soft peaks form. Serve the whipped cream with pie.
PER SERVING *1 piece with 3 tablespoons whipped cream equals 504 cal., 36 g fat (22 g sat. fat), 182 mg chol., 226 mg sodium, 42 g carb., 2 g fiber, 6 g pro.*

prepared a pie with my mom—just the two of us—and our family devoured every slice. With rich chocolaty flavor in both the crust and filling, it's doubly decadent.

—**STEVE RIEMERSMA** ALLEGAN, MI

Smooth Chocolate Pie

PREP: 25 MIN. + FREEZING • **MAKES:** 8 SERVINGS

1½ cups finely crushed chocolate wafers (about 24 wafers)
⅓ cup butter, melted
3 ounces cream cheese, softened
2 tablespoons sugar
4 ounces German sweet chocolate, melted
⅓ cup 2% milk
1 carton (8 ounces) frozen whipped topping, thawed
   Additional melted German sweet chocolate, optional

1. In a small bowl, mix the chocolate wafer crumbs and melted butter. Press onto the bottom and up the sides of an ungreased 9-in. pie plate.
2. In a bowl, beat cream cheese and sugar until blended. Gradually beat in melted German sweet chocolate and milk. Refrigerate 10 minutes.
3. Fold the whipped topping into the chocolate mixture; spoon into the crust. Freeze 4 hours or until firm. If desired, drizzle with additional melted German sweet chocolate before serving.
PER SERVING *1 piece (calculated without chocolate drizzle) equals 383 cal., 24 g fat (15 g sat. fat), 33 mg chol., 293 mg sodium, 39 g carb., 2 g fiber, 4 g pro.*

Bring on the Biscuits

It's what this family of cooks waits for all year: **Christmas brunch** starring Grandma's special seafood chowder ladled over golden biscuits. There's **a lot to love** about a tradition like this.

RECIPES & STORY BY **MELISSA BEYER** | UTICA, NY

GRANDMA'S BISCUITS

In all my life, I've missed Christmas at my grandma's only once. After opening presents at my parents' house, we always head to the home my grandparents built in Utica, New York.

My mother is the youngest of seven siblings, and all seven, their spouses and kids cram into the small house to celebrate the day with an amazing brunch—eggs, sausage and Gram's rich, creamy chowder over biscuits.

Gram is a cancer survivor and more active than I am—she works out and drives a red convertible. She cooks almost every day of the year.

I guess you could say cooking and school are in my DNA. I teach family and consumer science, and my mom and grandpa both worked for our town's school district. Not too long ago, Gram retired after many years of cooking for the local middle school kids.

I can't say how long she's been stirring up pots of her Christmas chowder, but she has definitely perfected it! Grandpa discovered the recipe in a magazine and asked her to try it. Over the years, Gram has made it her own.

She prepares the recipe each year for Christmas morning—the only time I've ever had it. Gram triples the ingredients for our feast and lets it simmer in a huge slow cooker.

I have her recipe, which really is too good to reserve for one day of the year. But I can't bring myself to indulge on my own. To me, Christmas wouldn't be the same if I ate the chowder at any other time.

Homemade biscuits add a warm and comforting touch to any meal. Gram always bakes a batch of from-scratch biscuits to go with her seafood chowder. The tender, golden goodies absolutely melt in your mouth.

I've shared both of Gram's special Christmastime recipes here. I hope your family enjoys them as much as our family has!

⑤ INGREDIENTS **FAST FIX**

Grandma's Biscuits

START TO FINISH: 25 MIN. • **MAKES:** 10 BISCUITS

- 2 **cups all-purpose flour**
- 3 **teaspoons baking powder**
- 1 **teaspoon salt**
- ⅓ **cup shortening**
- ⅔ **cup 2% milk**
- 1 **large egg, lightly beaten**

1. Preheat oven to 450°. In a large bowl, whisk flour, baking powder and salt. Cut in shortening until mixture resembles coarse crumbs. Add milk; stir just until moistened.

2. Turn dough onto a lightly floured surface; knead gently 8-10 times. Pat dough into a 10x4-in. rectangle. Cut rectangle lengthwise in half; cut crosswise to make ten squares.

3. Place 1 in. apart on an ungreased baking sheet; brush the tops with egg. Bake 8-10 minutes or until golden brown. Serve warm.

PER SERVING *1 biscuit equals 165 cal., 7 g fat (2 g sat. fat), 20 mg chol., 371 mg sodium, 20 g carb., 1 g fiber, 4 g pro.*

Grandma's Seafood Chowder

PREP: 15 MIN. • **COOK:** 25 MIN. • **MAKES:** 10 SERVINGS (3¼ QUARTS)

- 3 tablespoons plus ¼ cup butter, divided
- 1 pound sliced fresh mushrooms
- ⅓ cup all-purpose flour
- 1 teaspoon salt
- ⅛ teaspoon pepper
- 4 cups half-and-half cream
- 1½ cups 2% milk
- 1 pound haddock fillets, skin removed, cut into 1-inch pieces
- 1 pound uncooked medium shrimp, peeled and deveined
- 2 cups frozen peas (about 10 ounces)
- ¾ cup shredded cheddar cheese
- 1 cup lump crabmeat (about 5 ounces), drained
- 1 jar (4 ounces) diced pimientos, drained
- 1 teaspoon paprika

1. In a 6-qt. stockpot, heat 3 tablespoons butter over medium-high heat. Add the mushrooms; cook and stir 8-10 minutes or until tender. Remove from the pot.

2. In same pot, heat remaining butter over medium heat. Stir in flour, salt and pepper until smooth; gradually whisk in cream and milk. Bring to a boil, stirring constantly; cook and stir 2-3 minutes or until thickened.

3. Stir in haddock, shrimp, peas and sauteed mushrooms; cook 5-7 minutes or until the fish just begins to flake easily with a fork and shrimp turn pink. Add the cheese, crab and pimientos; stir gently until the cheese is melted. Sprinkle servings with paprika.

PER SERVING *1¼ cups equals 390 cal., 23 g fat (14 g sat. fat), 176 mg chol., 596 mg sodium, 14 g carb., 2 g fiber, 28 g pro.*

GRANDMA'S SEAFOOD CHOWDER

RENA MCCALMENT'S SHORTCAKE WITH FRESH RHUBARB SAUCE *PAGE 217*

Field Editor Favorites

Taste of Home Field Editors have countless **rave-winning recipes** in their kitchen collections. Page through this chapter for some of the **most popular dishes** served up by these avid cooks.

**JANE WHITTAKER'S
SLOW COOKER SPAGHETTI &
MEATBALLS** *PAGE 219*

**LINDA SCHEND'S
CHOCOLATE CHIP RED VELVET
WHOOPIE PIES** *PAGE 221*

**ANN SHEEHY'S
PEA & PEPPER PASTA SALAD**
PAGE 224

Savory Pumpkin Quiche

This fall-flavored dish satisfies a seasonal craving I get for all things pumpkin. With bacon, vegetables and Parmesan cheese, the quiche is great any time of day. I like to vary the mushrooms, sometimes using baby portobello or cremini.

—**RACHEL GARCIA** COLORADO SPRINGS, CO

PREP: 15 MIN. • **BAKE:** 50 MIN. + STANDING
MAKES: 8 SERVINGS

- 3 **large eggs**
- 1 **can (15 ounces) solid-pack pumpkin**
- 1 **can (5 ounces) evaporated milk**
- ½ **pound bacon strips, cooked and crumbled**
- ½ **cup sliced mushrooms**
- ¼ **cup finely chopped onion**
- ¼ **cup finely chopped green pepper**
- ½ **cup grated Parmesan cheese**
- 1 **tablespoon all-purpose flour**
- 1 **frozen deep-dish pie shell**

1. Preheat oven to 375°. In a large bowl, whisk the eggs, pumpkin and evaporated milk until blended. Stir in the bacon, mushrooms, onion and pepper. Toss the Parmesan cheese with the flour; stir into egg mixture. Pour into pie shell.

2. Bake quiche on a lower oven rack 50-60 minutes or until a knife inserted near center comes out clean. Let stand 15 minutes before cutting.

PER SERVING *1 slice equals 231 cal., 13 g fat (5 g sat. fat), 96 mg chol., 417 mg sodium, 18 g carb., 2 g fiber, 11 g pro.*

⑤ INGREDIENTS FAST FIX ▶

Creamy Fudge Frosting

For every occasion that calls for a rich frosting, keep this fudgy favorite in mind. Just a handful of ordinary ingredients and 15 minutes are all it takes to prepare this luscious homemade topper.

—**LINDA SCHEND** KENOSHA, WI

START TO FINISH: 15 MIN.
MAKES: 1½ CUPS

- 4 **ounces unsweetened chocolate, chopped**
- ¼ **cup butter, cubed**
- 1 **can (5 ounces) evaporated milk**
- 1 **cup sugar**
- ¼ **teaspoon vanilla extract**

1. Melt the chocolate and butter in a metal bowl over barely simmering water. Stir until smooth.

2. Place evaporated milk, sugar and vanilla in a blender; cover and process 1 minute to dissolve sugar. Add warm chocolate mixture; cover and process just until mixture thickens to desired consistency, about 30 seconds. Store in refrigerator.

PER SERVING *1½ tablespoons equals 129 cal., 8 g fat (5 g sat. fat), 11 mg chol., 35 mg sodium, 17 g carb., 1 g fiber, 2 g pro.*

Sue's Chocolate Zucchini Cake

What makes eyes light up faster than a freshly baked chocolate cake? Here's one you'll want to keep in your recipe file.

—**SUE FALK** WARREN, MI

PREP: 20 MIN. • **BAKE:** 25 MIN. + COOLING
MAKES: 15 SERVINGS

- 2 **cups all-purpose flour**
- 2 **cups sugar**
- ½ **cup dark baking cocoa**
- 1½ **teaspoons ground cinnamon**
- 1 **teaspoon baking powder**
- 1 **teaspoon baking soda**
- 1 **teaspoon salt**
- 2 **large eggs**
- ¾ **reduced-fat plain yogurt**
- ¼ **cup canola oil**
- 2 **teaspoons vanilla extract**
- 2 **cups shredded zucchini**
  Confectioners' sugar, optional

1. Preheat the oven to 350°. Grease a 13x9-in. baking pan.

2. In a large bowl, whisk the first seven ingredients. In another bowl, whisk the eggs, plain yogurt, oil and vanilla until blended. Add to flour mixture; stir just until moistened. Stir in the shredded zucchini.

3. Transfer batter to prepared pan. Bake 25-30 minutes or until the top springs back when lightly touched.

4. Cool completely in the pan on a wire rack. If desired, dust with confectioners' sugar before serving.

PER SERVING *1 piece equals 227 cal., 5 g fat (1 g sat. fat), 25 mg chol., 287 mg sodium, 43 g carb., 1 g fiber, 4 g pro.*

CREAMY FUDGE FROSTING
SUE'S CHOCOLATE ZUCCHINI CAKE

In spring when she had a crop of ripe red stalks, my mother-in-law chopped them up for scrumptious Shortcake with Fresh Rhubarb Sauce. It was a wonderful treat after a long cold winter!

—RENA MCCALMENT HARPSVILLE, IN

Shortcake with Fresh Rhubarb Sauce

PREP: 30 MIN. • **BAKE:** 30 MIN.
MAKES: 9 SERVINGS (2¼ CUPS SAUCE)

- 1½ cups chopped fresh rhubarb
- ¼ cup shortening
- ¾ cup sugar
- 1 large egg
- 1¼ cups all-purpose flour
- ¾ teaspoon baking powder
- ¼ teaspoon salt
- ¼ teaspoon baking soda
- ¼ teaspoon ground cinnamon
- ½ cup 2% milk
- ¼ cup chopped walnuts or pecans

SAUCE
- ¾ to 1 cup sugar
- ½ cup water
- 4 cups cubed fresh rhubarb (1-inch)
  Dash ground cinnamon, optional

1. Preheat the oven to 350°. Grease an 8-in.-square baking pan. In a heatproof bowl, cover rhubarb with boiling water; let stand 5 minutes. Drain and pat dry.
2. Meanwhile, in a bowl, cream the shortening and sugar until blended. Beat in the egg. In another bowl, whisk the flour, baking powder, salt, baking soda and cinnamon; add to creamed mixture alternately with the milk, beating well after each addition.
3. Fold in the drained rhubarb and chopped walnuts. Transfer to the prepared pan; bake 30-35 minutes or until a toothpick inserted in the center comes out clean. Cool in the pan on a wire rack.
4. In a small saucepan, combine sugar and water; bring to a boil, stirring to dissolve the sugar. Stir in the rhubarb; return to a boil. Reduce heat; simmer, uncovered, 10-12 minutes or until the rhubarb is softened. If desired, stir in cinnamon. Serve over warm shortcake.

PER SERVING *1 piece with ¼ cup sauce equals 294 cal., 9 g fat (2 g sat. fat), 22 mg chol., 152 mg sodium, 51 g carb., 2 g fiber, 4 g pro.*

ZUCCHINI CHEDDAR SAUTE

FAST FIX

Zucchini Cheddar Saute

Tired of making bread with your zucchini? Try my sauteed side dish sprinkled with cheese.

—MARGARET DRYE
PLAINFIELD, NH

START TO FINISH: 25 MIN.
MAKES: 4 SERVINGS

- 3 tablespoons butter
- ¾ cup chopped onion
- 1½ teaspoons dried basil
- 4 cups coarsely shredded zucchini
- 1 large garlic clove, minced
- ¾ teaspoon salt
- ¼ teaspoon pepper
- 1 cup (4 ounces) shredded cheddar cheese
- 2 medium tomatoes, cut into ¾-inch pieces
- 3 tablespoons sliced ripe olives

1. In a large skillet, heat butter over medium heat. Add onion and basil; cook and stir 4-5 minutes or until onion is tender. Add the zucchini and garlic; cook and stir over medium-high heat 2-3 minutes or just until zucchini is tender. Stir in salt and pepper.
2. Top with cheese, tomatoes and ripe olives. Cook, covered, on low about 1 minute or until the cheese is melted.

PER SERVING *¾ cup equals 244 cal., 19 g fat (12 g sat. fat), 53 mg chol., 747 mg sodium, 10 g carb., 3 g fiber, 10 g pro.*

CHEDDAR, CORN & POTATO CHOWDER

Just a little bit of curry adds a good amount of zip to my Cheddar, Corn & Potato Chowder without being overpowering. My kids always requested a big bowlful, even when they were young. I used to fix a double or triple batch so they'd have leftovers to enjoy the next day.
—**BECKY RUFF** MCGREGOR, IA

Cheddar, Corn & Potato Chowder

PREP: 15 MIN. • **COOK:** 35 MIN.
MAKES: 6 SERVINGS

- ¼ **cup butter, cubed**
- 2 **celery ribs, chopped**
- 2 **medium carrots, sliced**
- 1 **medium green pepper, finely chopped**
- 1 **medium onion, chopped**
- ¼ **cup all-purpose flour**
- 1 **teaspoon curry powder**
- ½ **teaspoon salt**
- ¼ **teaspoon pepper**
- 1 **cup 2% milk**
- 1 **carton (32 ounces) chicken broth**
- 1 **pound potatoes (about 2 medium), peeled and cubed**
- 1 **can (8¾ ounces) whole kernel corn, drained**
- 2 **cups (8 ounces) shredded cheddar cheese**
- 1 **tablespoon minced fresh parsley**

1. In a 6-qt. stockpot, heat the butter over medium heat. Add the celery, carrots, green pepper and onion; cook and stir 3-4 minutes or until onion is tender. Stir in flour and seasonings until blended.
2. Gradually stir in the milk. Add the broth, potatoes and corn; bring to a boil. Reduce the heat; simmer, covered, 15-20 minutes or until the potatoes are tender.
3. Stir in cheddar cheese until melted; remove from heat. Puree soup using an immersion blender. Or, cool slightly and puree in batches in a blender; return to the pot and heat through. Stir in parsley.
PER SERVING *1½ cups equals 366 cal., 22 g fat (13 g sat. fat), 66 mg chol., 1,311 mg sodium, 27 g carb., 3 g fiber, 14 g pro.*

EAT SMART ⑤ INGREDIENTS

Roasted Fresh Pumpkin Seeds

I learned how to roast pumpkin seeds from my mother, who learned it from her mother. It's a wholesome, healthy snack and fun to make after you finish carving Halloween jack-o'-lanterns.
—**MARGARET DRYE** PLAINFIELD, NH

PREP: 20 MIN. + SOAKING
BAKE: 1½ HOURS + COOLING
MAKES: 1½ CUPS

- 2 **cups fresh pumpkin seeds**
- 1 **teaspoon salt**
- 1 **tablespoon olive oil**
- ¾ **teaspoon kosher or fine sea salt**

1. Place pumpkin seeds in a 1-qt. bowl; cover with water. Stir in salt; let stand, covered, overnight.
2. Preheat the oven to 200°. Drain and rinse the pumpkin seeds; drain seeds again and pat dry. Transfer to a 15x10x1-in. baking pan. Toss with the olive oil and kosher salt; spread in a single layer.
3. Roast seeds 1½-1¾ hours or until crisp and lightly browned, stirring occasionally. Cool completely. Store in an airtight container.
PER SERVING *¼ cup equals 115 cal., 6 g fat (1 g sat. fat), 0 chol., 248 mg sodium, 11 g carb., 4 g fiber, 4 g pro.*
***Diabetic Exchanges:** 1 fat, ½ starch.*

ROASTED FRESH PUMPKIN SEEDS

HAM & MANDARIN SALAD

EAT SMART FAST FIX
Ham & Mandarin Salad

Tangy, sweet and spicy, this is a main-dish salad that satisfies all the big eaters in our family.
—**PATRICIA SWART**
GALLOWAY, NJ

START TO FINISH: 25 MIN.
MAKES: 4 SERVINGS

- ⅓ cup fat-free mayonnaise
- 2 tablespoons fat-free milk
- 1 tablespoon cider vinegar
- 1 garlic clove, minced
- ¼ teaspoon pepper
- 8 slices deli ham (about 6 ounces), cut into strips
- 1 can (11 ounces) mandarin oranges, drained
- 2 celery ribs, thinly sliced
- ⅓ cup chopped walnuts, toasted
- 2 green onions, chopped
- 6 cups torn romaine

In a large bowl, mix the first five ingredients. Stir in ham, mandarin oranges, celery, walnuts and green onions. Serve on romaine, tossing before serving if desired.
NOTE *To toast nuts, bake in a shallow pan in a 350° oven for 5-10 minutes or cook in a skillet over low heat until lightly browned, stirring occasionally.*
PER SERVING *2¼ cups equals 172 cal., 8 g fat (1 g sat. fat), 21 mg chol., 586 mg sodium, 17 g carb., 4 g fiber, 11 g pro.*
Diabetic Exchanges: 2 lean meat, 1 vegetable, 1 fat, ½ starch.

SLOW COOKER
Slow Cooker Spaghetti & Meatballs

Here's a mainstay I've relied on for years. The sauce works with nearly any pasta.
—**JANE WHITTAKER** PENSACOLA, FL

PREP: 50 MIN. • **COOK:** 5 HOURS
MAKES: 12 SERVINGS
(ABOUT 3½ QTS. SAUCE)

- 1 cup seasoned bread crumbs
- 2 tablespoons grated Parmesan and Romano cheese blend
- 1 teaspoon pepper
- ½ teaspoon salt
- 2 large eggs, lightly beaten
- 2 pounds ground beef

SAUCE

- 1 large onion, finely chopped
- 1 medium green pepper, finely chopped
- 3 cans (15 ounces each) tomato sauce
- 2 cans (14½ ounces each) diced tomatoes, undrained
- 1 can (6 ounces) tomato paste
- 6 garlic cloves, minced
- 2 bay leaves
- 1 teaspoon each dried basil, oregano and parsley flakes
- 1 teaspoon salt
- ½ teaspoon pepper
- ¼ teaspoon crushed red pepper flakes
  Hot cooked spaghetti

1. In a large bowl, mix bread crumbs, cheese, pepper and salt; stir in eggs. Add beef; mix lightly but thoroughly. Shape into 1½-in. meatballs. In a large skillet, brown the meatballs in batches over medium heat; drain.

2. Place the first five sauce ingredients in a 6-qt. slow cooker; stir in garlic and seasonings. Add the meatballs, stirring gently to coat. Cook, covered, on low 5-6 hours or until the meatballs are cooked through.

3. Remove the bay leaves. Serve with spaghetti.

PER SERVING *1 cup (calculated without spaghetti) equals 254 cal., 11 g fat (4 g sat. fat), 79 mg chol., 1,133 mg sodium, 20 g carb., 3 g fiber, 20 g pro.*

SLOW COOKER SPAGHETTI & MEATBALLS

EAT SMART

Black Bean & Pumpkin Chili

Feel free to try sweet potatoes or butternut squash in place of the pumpkin in this chili.

—**JEAN ECOS**
HARTLAND, WI

PREP: 20 MIN. • **COOK:** 1 HOUR
MAKES: 8 SERVINGS (2½ QUARTS)

- 1 tablespoon olive oil
- 1 medium sweet yellow pepper, chopped
- 1 medium onion, chopped
- 3 garlic cloves, minced
- 3 cups reduced-sodium chicken broth
- 1 can (15 ounces) solid-pack pumpkin
- 1 can (14½ ounces) diced tomatoes, undrained
- 2 teaspoons chili powder
- 1½ teaspoons ground cumin
- 1½ teaspoons dried oregano
- ½ teaspoon salt
- ½ teaspoon smoked paprika
- 2 cans (15 ounces each) black beans, rinsed and drained
- 1½ cups shredded cooked chicken
- ¼ cup chopped fresh cilantro or parsley

1. In a 6-qt. stockpot, heat the oil over medium heat. Add the pepper and onion; cook and stir 6-8 minutes or until tender. Stir in the garlic; cook 1 minute longer.

2. Stir in broth, pumpkin, tomatoes and seasonings. Mash one can of beans. Add mashed beans and remaining can of whole beans to pot; bring to a boil. Reduce the heat; simmer, covered, 45 minutes to allow flavors to blend, stirring occasionally. Stir in chicken and cilantro; heat through.

PER SERVING *1¼ cups equals 200 cal., 4 g fat (1 g sat. fat), 23 mg chol., 698 mg sodium, 26 g carb., 8 g fiber, 15 g pro.* **Diabetic Exchanges:** *2 lean meat, 1 starch, 1 vegetable.*

Bacon-Cheeseburger Chowder

A classic, all-American bacon cheeseburger is hard to beat—but this chowder just might!

—**KRISTIN STONE**
LITTLE ELM, TX

PREP: 15 MIN. • **COOK:** 30 MIN.
MAKES: 6 SERVINGS

- 1 pound ground beef
- 1 medium onion, chopped
- 1 medium sweet red pepper, chopped
- 1 garlic clove, minced
- 3 tablespoons all-purpose flour
- 2½ cups 2% milk
- 1 pound potatoes (about 2 medium), peeled and chopped
- 1½ cups water
- 1 tablespoon reduced-sodium beef bouillon granules
- 12 ounces process cheese (Velveeta), cubed (about 2¼ cups)
- 3 bacon strips, cooked and crumbled

1. In a 6-qt. stockpot, cook the beef, onion and pepper over medium heat 6-8 minutes or until beef is no longer pink and onion is tender, breaking up beef into crumbles; drain. Add garlic to beef mixture; cook 1 minute longer. Stir in flour until blended.

2. Gradually stir in the milk. Add the potatoes, water and bouillon; bring to a boil. Reduce the heat; simmer, covered, 15-20 minutes or until the potatoes are tender.

3. Add the cheese; stir until melted. Sprinkle servings with bacon.

PER SERVING *1⅓ cups equals 473 cal., 27 g fat (14 g sat. fat), 115 mg chol., 1,047 mg sodium, 27 g carb., 2 g fiber, 30 g pro.*

BLACK BEAN & PUMPKIN CHILI

Sweet and Sour Zucchini Pickles

Is your garden overflowing with zucchini? To put all those ripe-and-ready beauties to good use, make these unexpected pickles. At Christmastime, you'll have jars of them to share as holiday gifts from your kitchen.

—**TINA BUTLER** ROYSE CITY, TX

PREP: 1 HOUR + SOAKING
PROCESS: 10 MIN.
MAKES: ABOUT 6 PINTS

- 11 **cups thinly sliced zucchini (about 3 pounds)**
- 1 **large onion, halved and thinly sliced**
- ⅓ **cup canning salt**
- 4½ **cups white vinegar**
- 3 **cups sugar**
- 1 **tablespoon mustard seed**
- 1½ **teaspoons ground turmeric**

1. Place zucchini and onion in a large nonreactive bowl. Sprinkle with salt and toss to coat. Add water to cover; let stand at room temperature 2 hours. Drain; rinse and drain thoroughly.
2. In a 6-qt. stockpot, combine the remaining ingredients. Bring to a boil, stirring to dissolve the sugar. Reduce the heat; simmer 5 minutes to allow the flavors to blend. Add the zucchini mixture; return to a boil, stirring occasionally. Reduce heat; simmer, uncovered, 4-5 minutes or until heated through.
3. Carefully ladle hot mixture into six hot 1-pint jars, leaving ½-in. headspace. Remove air bubbles and, if necessary, adjust the headspace by adding hot pickling liquid. Wipe the rims. Center the lids on jars; screw on bands until fingertip tight.
4. Place the jars into the canner with simmering water, ensuring that they are completely submerged. Bring to a boil; process for 10 minutes. Remove jars and cool.
NOTE *The processing time listed is for altitudes of 1,000 feet or less. For altitudes up to 3,000 feet, add 5 minutes; 6,000 feet, add 10 minutes; 8,000 feet, add 15 minutes; 10,000 feet, add 20 minutes.*
PER SERVING *¼ cup equals 12 cal., trace fat (trace sat. fat), 0 chol., 87 mg sodium, 3 g carb., trace fiber, trace pro.*

CHOCOLATE CHIP RED VELVET WHOOPIE PIES

Chocolate Chip Red Velvet Whoopie Pies

Baking fun treats is a must when my four grandkids come to stay at "Grandma Camp."

—**LINDA SCHEND** KENOSHA, WI

PREP: 45 MIN.
BAKE: 10 MIN./BATCH + COOLING
MAKES: ABOUT 2 DOZEN

- 1 **package red velvet cake mix (regular size)**
- 3 **large eggs**
- ½ **cup canola oil**
- 2 **teaspoons vanilla extract**

FILLING
- 1 **package (8 ounces) cream cheese, softened**
- ½ **cup butter, softened**
- 2 **cups confectioners' sugar**
- 1 **cup (6 ounces) miniature semisweet chocolate chips**

1. Preheat oven to 350°. In a large bowl, combine cake mix, eggs, oil and extract; beat on low speed 30 seconds. Beat on medium 2 minutes.
2. Cut a ½-in. hole in the tip of a pastry bag or in a corner of a food-safe plastic bag. Transfer dough to bag. Pipe 1½x1-in. hearts onto parchment paper-lined baking sheets, spacing hearts 1 in. apart.
3. Bake 6-8 minutes or until edges are set. Cool on pans 2 minutes. Remove to wire racks to cool completely.
4. For filling, in a large bowl, beat cream cheese and butter until blended. Gradually beat in confectioners' sugar until smooth. Stir in chocolate chips. Spread filling on bottoms of half of the cookies. Top with remaining cookies. Refrigerate leftovers.
PER SERVING *1 whoopie pie equals 267 cal., 16 g fat (6 g sat. fat), 44 mg chol., 194 mg sodium, 30 g carb., 1 g fiber, 2 g pro.*

GRILLED PEPPER JACK CHICKEN SANDWICHES

FAST FIX ▶

Grilled Pepper Jack Chicken Sandwiches

With zesty cheese, bacon and grilled flavor, these sandwiches taste like specialties from a restaurant.

—**LINDA FOREMAN** LOCUST GROVE, OK

START TO FINISH: 25 MIN.
MAKES: 2 SERVINGS

- 2 **boneless skinless chicken breast halves (4 ounces each)**
- 1 **teaspoon poultry seasoning**
- 2 **center-cut bacon strips, cooked and halved**
- 2 **slices (½ ounce each) pepper jack cheese**
- 2 **hamburger buns, split**
- 2 **lettuce leaves**
- 1 **slice onion, separated into rings**
- 2 **slices tomato**
  Dill pickle slices, optional

1. Sprinkle the chicken with poultry seasoning. Moisten a paper towel with cooking oil; using long-handled tongs, lightly coat the grill rack.
2. Grill the chicken, covered, over medium heat or broil 4 in. from the heat for 4-7 minutes on each side or until a thermometer reads 165°. Top with the bacon and cheese; cover and cook 1-2 minutes longer or until the cheese is melted.
3. Serve on buns with lettuce, onion, tomato and pickles if desired.
PER SERVING *1 sandwich (calculated without pickles) equals 335 cal., 11 g fat (4 g sat. fat), 85 mg chol., 456 mg sodium, 25 g carb., 2 g fiber, 33 g pro.*
Diabetic Exchanges: *4 lean meat, 1½ starch.*

New England Pumpkin Walnut Bread

Pumpkin bread is best on cold days when you crave comfort. Pair a slice with coffee or tea.

—**KIM FORNI**
LACONIA, NH

PREP: 25 MIN. • **BAKE:** 1 HOUR + COOLING
MAKES: 2 LOAVES (16 SLICES EACH)

- ½ **cup old-fashioned oats**
- ¼ **teaspoon sugar**
- ⅛ **teaspoon ground cinnamon**

BREAD
- 1 **can (15 ounces) solid-pack pumpkin**
- 4 **large eggs**
- ¾ **cup canola oil**
- ⅔ **cup water**
- 2 **cups sugar**
- 1 **cup honey**
- 1½ **teaspoons vanilla extract**
- 3½ **cups all-purpose flour**
- 2 **teaspoons baking soda**
- 1½ **teaspoons salt**
- 1½ **teaspoons ground cinnamon**
- 1 **teaspoon ground nutmeg**
- ½ **teaspoon ground cloves**
- ½ **teaspoon ground ginger**
- 1 **cup coarsely chopped walnuts, toasted**

1. Preheat oven to 350°. In a small skillet, combine the oats, sugar and cinnamon; cook and stir over medium heat 4-6 minutes or until the oats are toasted. Remove from heat.
2. For the bread, in a large bowl, beat the pumpkin, eggs, oil, water, sugar, honey and vanilla until well blended. In another bowl, whisk flour, baking soda, salt and spices; gradually beat into the pumpkin mixture. Fold in the toasted walnuts.
3. Transfer to two greased 9x5-in. loaf pans. Sprinkle tops with oat mixture.
4. Bake 60-70 minutes or until a toothpick inserted in center comes out clean. Cool in the pan 10 minutes before removing to a wire rack to cool.
NOTE *To toast nuts, bake in a shallow pan in a 350° oven for 5-10 minutes or cook in a skillet over low heat until lightly browned, stirring occasionally.*
PER SERVING *1 slice equals 220 cal., 9 g fat (1 g sat. fat), 23 mg chol., 200 mg sodium, 34 g carb., 1 g fiber, 3 g pro.*

NEW ENGLAND PUMPKIN WALNUT BREAD

Chocolate-Raspberry Whoopie Pies

I saw the idea for a jam-filled whoopie pie in a newspaper years ago and still have the original recipe I clipped out. It's one of my grandson's favorite treats.

—**NANCY FOUST** STONEBORO, PA

PREP: 40 MIN.
BAKE: 10 MIN./BATCH + COOLING
MAKES: ABOUT 2½ DOZEN

- ½ cup butter, softened
- 1 cup sugar
- 1 large egg
- 1 teaspoon vanilla extract
- 2 cups all-purpose flour
- ½ cup baking cocoa
- 1½ teaspoons baking soda
- ½ teaspoon baking powder
- ½ teaspoon salt
- 1 cup 2% milk

FILLING

- 1 jar (7 ounces) marshmallow creme
- ½ cup shortening
- ⅓ cup seedless raspberry jam
- 1 teaspoon vanilla extract
- 2 cups confectioners' sugar

1. Preheat oven to 400°. In a large bowl, cream the butter and sugar until light and fluffy. Beat in the egg and vanilla. In another bowl, whisk flour, baking cocoa, baking soda, baking powder and salt; add to the creamed mixture alternately with milk, beating well after each addition.

2. Drop the dough by tablespoonfuls 2 in. apart onto greased baking sheets. Bake 6-8 minutes or until set and the tops spring back when lightly touched. Remove from the pans to wire racks to cool completely.

3. For the filling, in a large bowl, beat marshmallow creme and shortening until blended. Beat in jam and vanilla. Gradually beat in confectioners' sugar until smooth. Spread on the bottoms of half of the cookies; cover with the remaining cookies.

PER SERVING *1 whoopie pie equals 186 cal., 7 g fat (3 g sat. fat), 15 mg chol., 148 mg sodium, 30 g carb., trace fiber, 2 g pro.*

BLUEBERRY-PEACH SHORTCAKES

When I'm preparing Blueberry-Peach Shortcakes, I often freeze half of the cakes to enjoy later. Juicy fruit and fresh basil make this dessert perfect for summer.
—**SUE GRONHOLZ** BEAVER DAM, WI

Blueberry-Peach Shortcakes

PREP: 35 MIN. + STANDING • **BAKE:** 10 MIN.
MAKES: 8 SHORTCAKES

- ½ cup sugar
- ⅓ cup water
- ¾ cup loosely packed fresh basil leaves

FILLING

- 2 cups fresh or frozen unsweetened blueberries
- 3 tablespoons unsalted butter
- 3 cups sliced peeled fresh peaches or frozen sliced peaches, thawed

SHORTCAKES

- 2 cups all-purpose flour
- ¼ cup plus 4 teaspoons sugar, divided
- 1 teaspoon baking powder
- ½ teaspoon baking soda
- ¼ teaspoon salt
- ¼ cup cold unsalted butter, cubed
- 1 cup (8 ounces) sour cream
- ¼ cup 2% milk
  Vanilla ice cream or whipped topping, optional

1. In a large skillet, combine sugar, water and basil; bring to a boil over medium heat, stirring to dissolve the sugar. Remove from heat; let stand 30 minutes.

2. Strain syrup through a fine-mesh strainer; discard basil. Return syrup to skillet. Add berries and butter; bring just to a boil. Gently stir in the peaches; heat through. Cool 30 minutes.

3. Meanwhile, preheat oven to 450°. For the shortcakes, in a large bowl, whisk the flour, ¼ cup sugar, baking powder, baking soda and salt. Cut in butter until mixture resembles coarse crumbs. In a small bowl, whisk sour cream and milk until blended; stir into flour mixture just until moistened.

4. Drop dough by ⅓ cupfuls 2 in. apart onto a parchment paper-lined baking sheet. Sprinkle with remaining sugar. Bake 10-12 minutes or until lightly browned. Remove from pans to wire racks to cool slightly.

5. To serve, split cakes in half. Fill with fruit. If desired, serve with ice cream.

PER SERVING *1 shortcake with ⅓ cup filling (calculated without ice cream) equals 395 cal., 16 g fat (10 g sat. fat), 47 mg chol., 219 mg sodium, 58 g carb., 3 g fiber, 6 g pro.*

One of my favorite side dishes to serve for a buffet is Pea & Pepper Pasta Salad. If I have any leftovers, I stuff them into halved and cored plum tomatoes.
—ANN SHEEHY LAWRENCE, MA

PEA & PEPPER PASTA SALAD

Maple Whoopie Pies

My state of New York is a huge producer of maple syrup. I poured some into a batch of classic whoopie pies for a sweet twist.

—HOLLY HARZ MALONE, NY

PREP: 40 MIN.
BAKE: 10 MIN./BATCH + COOLING
MAKES: ABOUT 2 DOZEN

- ⅓ cup butter, softened
- ¾ cup sugar
- 1 large egg
- 1 teaspoon vanilla extract
- 1 teaspoon maple flavoring
- 2¼ cups all-purpose flour
- 1¼ teaspoons baking powder
- 1 teaspoon salt
- ½ cup heavy whipping cream
- ½ cup maple syrup
- ½ cup chopped pecans

FILLING
- ½ cup butter, softened
- ½ cup shortening
- 1 teaspoon maple flavoring
- 4 cups confectioners' sugar
- ¼ cup heavy whipping cream
- 2 tablespoons maple syrup

1. Preheat the oven to 375°. In a large bowl, cream the butter and sugar until light and fluffy. Beat in egg, vanilla and flavoring. In another bowl, whisk the flour, baking powder and salt; add to the creamed mixture alternately with the cream and syrup, beating well after each addition. Stir in pecans.
2. Drop the cookie dough by rounded tablespoonfuls 2 in. apart onto greased baking sheets. Bake 8-10 minutes or until edges are light brown and tops spring back when lightly touched. Remove from the pans to wire racks to cool completely.
3. For the filling, in a large bowl, beat butter, shortening and flavoring until creamy. Beat in confectioners' sugar alternately with cream and syrup until smooth. Spread on bottoms of half of the cookies; cover with remaining cookies. Store in airtight containers.
PER SERVING *1 whoopie pie equals 306 cal., 15 g fat (7 g sat. fat), 35 mg chol., 183 mg sodium, 41 g carb., 1 g fiber, 2 g pro.*

EAT SMART
Pea & Pepper Pasta Salad

PREP: 20 MIN. • **COOK:** 10 MIN. + STANDING
MAKES: 10 SERVINGS

- 1 package (16 ounces) acini di pepe pasta
- 1½ cups coarsely chopped Cubanelle peppers or miniature sweet peppers (in assorted colors)
- 1 cup loosely packed fresh Italian parsley leaves
- 4 radishes, trimmed and quartered
- ½ medium red onion, coarsely chopped
- 2 green onions, cut into 1-inch pieces
- 1¾ cups frozen petite peas (about 8 ounces), thawed
- ½ cup creamy Caesar salad dressing
- ¾ teaspoon salt
- ½ teaspoon freshly ground pepper
  Thinly sliced radishes, optional

1. Cook the acini di pepe pasta according to the package directions. Drain pasta; rinse with cold water and drain well.
2. Place peppers, parsley, radishes, red onion and green onions in a food processor; pulse until finely chopped, scraping the sides of food processor bowl as necessary.
3. In a large bowl, combine the pasta, chopped vegetables and peas. Add the Caesar salad dressing, salt and pepper; toss to coat. Let stand 15 minutes to allow the flavors to blend. If desired, top with sliced radishes.
PER SERVING *¾ cup equals 255 cal., 8 g fat (1 g sat. fat), 5 mg chol., 352 mg sodium, 39 g carb., 3 g fiber, 8 g pro.*

Chocolate Lover's Strawberry Shortcakes

As a mom of four, I appreciate quick ideas. My strawberry shortcakes take advantage of refrigerated biscuits, giving me time to add special touches such as homemade whipped cream and warm fudge topping.

—**MELISSA HAINES** VALPARAISO, IN

PREP: 20 MIN. • **BAKE:** 15 MIN.
MAKES: 8 SHORTCAKES

- ¼ cup confectioners' sugar
- 1 tablespoon baking cocoa
- 1 tube (16.3 ounces) large refrigerated buttermilk biscuits

ASSEMBLY

- 2 cups sliced fresh strawberries or frozen sliced strawberries, thawed and drained
- 1 tablespoon sugar
- 1 cup heavy whipping cream
- 2 tablespoons baking cocoa
- ⅓ cup confectioners' sugar
   Hot fudge ice cream topping, warmed

1. Preheat oven to 350°. In a shallow bowl, mix confectioners' sugar and cocoa until blended. Dip biscuits in cocoa mixture to coat; shake off excess.
2. Place 2 in. apart on an ungreased baking sheet. Bake 12-14 minutes or until lightly browned. Remove from pan to a wire rack to cool slightly.
3. In a small bowl, toss strawberries with sugar. In another bowl, beat the cream and cocoa until cream begins to thicken. Add confectioners' sugar; beat until soft peaks form.
4. To serve, split shortcakes in half. Fill with the strawberries and half of the whipped cream. Serve with the fudge ice cream topping and remaining whipped cream.

PER SERVING *1 serving (calculated without the fudge ice cream topping) equals 332 cal., 18 g fat (9 g sat. fat), 41 mg chol., 628 mg sodium, 40 g carb., 2 g fiber, 5 g pro.*

SLOW COOKER

Gingered Short Ribs with Green Rice

I love Korean cooking and converted this recipe to give it slow cooker convenience.

—**LILY JULOW** LAWRENCEVILLE, GA

PREP: 35 MIN. • **COOK:** 8 HOURS
MAKES: 6 SERVINGS

- ½ cup reduced-sodium beef broth
- ⅓ cup sherry or additional reduced-sodium beef broth
- ¼ cup reduced-sodium soy sauce
- 3 tablespoons honey
- 1 tablespoon rice vinegar
- 1 tablespoon minced fresh gingerroot
- 3 garlic cloves, minced
- 4 medium carrots, chopped
- 2 medium onions, chopped
- 3 pounds bone-in beef short ribs
- ½ teaspoon salt
- ½ teaspoon pepper
- 3 cups uncooked instant brown rice
- 3 green onions, thinly sliced
- 3 tablespoons minced fresh cilantro
- 2 tablespoons chopped pickled jalapenos
- ¾ teaspoon grated lime peel
- 1 tablespoon cornstarch
- 1 tablespoon cold water

1. In a small bowl, whisk the first seven ingredients until blended. Place the carrots and onions in a 5-qt. slow cooker. Sprinkle the ribs with salt and pepper; place over vegetables. Pour the broth mixture over the top. Cook, covered, on low 8-10 hours or until the meat is tender.
2. Just before serving, prepare the rice according to the package directions. Stir in the onions, cilantro, jalapenos and lime peel.
3. Remove the ribs to a serving plate; keep warm. Transfer the cooking juices to a small saucepan; skim the fat. Bring the cooking juices to a boil. In a small bowl, mix the cornstarch and cold water until smooth; stir into cooking juices. Return to a boil; cook and stir 2 minutes or until thickened. Serve with ribs and rice.

PER SERVING *1 serving equals 444 cal., 12 g fat (5 g sat. fat), 55 mg chol., 714 mg sodium, 56 g carb., 5 g fiber, 24 g pro.*

GINGERED SHORT RIBS WITH GREEN RICE

DEBBIE LIMAS'
AVOCADO QUESADILLAS
PAGE 229

Quick Fixes

Have a hectic schedule? **Busy cooks** rely on this chapter of recipes with **short prep times.** These scrumptious entrees, sides and more cut down the fuss but keep **all the great taste** you crave.

**MARTHA NETH'S
WARM TASTY GREENS
WITH GARLIC** *PAGE 231*

**GLORIA HUSE'S
SUPER FAST MEXICAN SOUP**
PAGE 233

**STACY MULLENS'
TURKEY-JALAPENO
SANDWICHES** *PAGE 234*

Cranberry-Walnut Brussels Sprouts

A Brussels sprout is one vegetable that picky eaters often resist. This recipe will change their minds! If you like, mix in a little garlic or additional dried fruits.

—JENNIFER ARMELLINO LAKE OSWEGO, OR

START TO FINISH: 20 MIN.
MAKES: 4 SERVINGS

- ¼ **cup olive oil**
- 1 **pound fresh Brussels sprouts, trimmed and halved lengthwise**
- ½ **cup dried cranberries**
- 2 **tablespoons water**
- ⅓ **cup chopped walnuts**
- 2 **tablespoons balsamic vinegar**

1. In a large skillet, heat the olive oil over medium heat. Place the Brussels sprouts in the pan, cut side down; cook 4-5 minutes or until the bottoms of sprouts are browned.

2. Add the dried cranberries and water; cook, covered, 1-2 minutes or until Brussels sprouts are crisp-tender. Stir in the walnuts; cook and stir until the water is evaporated. Stir in the balsamic vinegar.

PER SERVING ¾ cup equals 281 cal., 20 g fat (3 g sat. fat), 0 chol., 26 mg sodium, 25 g carb., 5 g fiber, 5 g pro.

CHICKEN & WILD RICE STRUDELS

> I wanted the buttery crunch of layered pastry without the typical sweet filling. Chicken & Wild Rice Strudels make a deliciously savory main course.
> **—JOHNNA JOHNSON** SCOTTSDALE, AZ

CRANBERRY-WALNUT BRUSSELS SPROUTS

Chicken & Wild Rice Strudels

START TO FINISH: 30 MIN.
MAKES: 6 SERVINGS

- 1 **package (8.8 ounces) ready-to-serve long grain and wild rice**
- 1½ **cups coarsely chopped rotisserie chicken**
- ½ **cup shredded Swiss cheese**
- ½ **teaspoon Italian seasoning**
- ¼ **teaspoon salt**
- ¼ **teaspoon pepper**
- 12 **sheets phyllo dough (14x9-inch size)**
- 6 **tablespoons butter, melted**

1. Preheat the oven to 400°. Place the first six ingredients in a large bowl; toss to combine.

2. Place one sheet of phyllo on a work surface; brush lightly with the melted butter. Layer with five additional sheets, brushing each layer. (Keep remaining phyllo covered with plastic wrap and a damp towel to prevent it from drying out.)

3. Spoon half of the rice mixture down the center of the phyllo to within 1 in. of the ends. Fold up the short sides to enclose filling. Roll up tightly, starting with a long side.

4. Transfer strudel to a parchment paper-lined 15x10x1-in. baking pan, seam side down. Brush with additional butter. Repeat with the remaining ingredients. Bake 20-25 minutes or until golden brown and heated through.

PER SERVING 1 serving equals 323 cal., 18 g fat (10 g sat. fat), 70 mg chol., 550 mg sodium, 25 g carb., 1 g fiber, 16 g pro.

Peanut Butter Oatmeal Cookies

These delightfully simple cookies really hit the spot with a glass of cold milk.

—MARILYN BLANKSCHIEN

CLINTONVILLE, WI

START TO FINISH: 20 MIN.
MAKES: 2 DOZEN

- ½ cup chunky peanut butter
- ½ cup packed brown sugar
- 1 large egg
- 1¼ cups quick-cooking oats
- ½ teaspoon baking soda

1. In a small bowl, cream peanut butter and brown sugar until fluffy. Beat in egg. Add oats and baking soda to creamed mixture; mix well.

2. Drop by tablespoonfuls 2 in. apart onto greased baking sheets; flatten slightly. Bake at 350° for 6-8 minutes. Remove to wire racks to cool. Store in an airtight container.

PER SERVING *1 cookie equals 67 cal., 3 g fat (1 g sat. fat), 9 mg chol., 57 mg sodium, 8 g carb., 1 g fiber, 2 g pro. Diabetic Exchanges: ½ starch, ½ fat.*

Avocado Quesadillas

Avocado slices give quesadillas a nutritional boost and, fortunately, my son likes them, too. Add chicken or beef for extra protein.

—DEBBIE LIMAS NORTH ANDOVER, MA

START TO FINISH: 20 MIN.
MAKES: 4 SERVINGS

- 1 tablespoon canola oil
- 16 corn tortillas (6 inches)
- 2 cups (8 ounces) shredded Mexican cheese blend
- 1 cup pico de gallo
- 1 large ripe avocado, peeled and thinly sliced
- 3 tablespoons minced fresh cilantro
  Additional pico de gallo

1. Grease a griddle with the oil; heat over medium heat. Lightly sprinkle tortillas with water to moisten.

2. Place eight tortillas on the griddle; sprinkle with cheese. After the cheese has melted slightly, top with 1 cup pico de gallo, avocado and cilantro. Top with remaining tortillas.

3. Cook 3-4 minutes on each side or until lightly browned and the cheese is melted. Serve with additional pico de gallo.

PER SERVING *2 quesadillas (calculated without additional pico de gallo) equals 611 cal., 37 g fat (15 g sat. fat), 50 mg chol., 455 mg sodium, 54 g carb., 12 g fiber, 20 g pro.*

Saucy Skillet Lasagna

Thanks to convenient no-cook noodles, this stovetop lasagna can turn even a busy-day meal into an Italian feast.

—MEGHAN CRIHFIELD RIPLEY, WV

START TO FINISH: 30 MIN.
MAKES: 8 SERVINGS

- 1 pound ground beef
- 1 can (14½ ounces) diced tomatoes, undrained
- 2 large egg, lightly beaten
- 1½ cups ricotta cheese
- 4 cups marinara sauce
- 1 package (9 ounces) no-cook lasagna noodles
- 1 cup (4 ounces) shredded part-skim mozzarella cheese, optional

1. In a large skillet, cook the beef over medium heat 6-8 minutes or until no longer pink, breaking into crumbles; drain. Transfer to a large bowl; stir in tomatoes. In a small bowl, combine eggs and ricotta cheese.

2. Return 1 cup meat mixture to the skillet; spread evenly. Layer with 1 cup ricotta mixture, 1½ cups marinara sauce and half of the noodles, breaking noodles to fit as necessary. Repeat the layers. Top with remaining sauce.

3. Bring to a boil. Reduce the heat; simmer, covered, 15-17 minutes or until the noodles are tender and a thermometer reads 160°. Remove from heat. If desired, sprinkle with mozzarella. Let stand 2 minutes or until cheese is melted.

PER SERVING *1 serving equals 430 cal., 18 g fat (8 g sat. fat), 108 mg chol., 750 mg sodium, 41 g carb., 4 g fiber, 27 g pro.*

Easy Ground Beef Taco Salad

Every time I need to take a dish to a party, people ask for my taco salad. It's so easy to prepare, I'm happy to oblige!

—LORI BUNTROCK WISCONSIN RAPIDS, WI

START TO FINISH: 30 MIN.
MAKES: 6 SERVINGS

- 1 pound ground beef
- 1 envelope reduced-sodium taco seasoning
- ¾ cup water
- 1 medium head iceberg lettuce, torn (about 8 cups)
- 2 cups (8 ounces) shredded cheddar cheese
- 2 cups lightly crushed nacho-flavored tortilla chips
- ¼ cup Catalina salad dressing

1. In a large skillet, cook the beef over medium heat 6-8 minutes or until no longer pink, breaking into crumbles; drain. Stir in the taco seasoning and water; bring to a boil. Reduce the heat; simmer, uncovered, 4-6 minutes or until thickened, stirring occasionally. Cool slightly.

2. In a large bowl, toss the lettuce with the cheddar cheese. Top with the beef mixture and tortilla chips; drizzle with the salad dressing and toss to combine. Serve immediately.

PER SERVING *1⅔ cups equals 416 cal., 27 g fat (12 g sat. fat), 86 mg chol., 830 mg sodium, 19 g carb., 2 g fiber, 25 g pro.*

EASY GROUND BEEF TACO SALAD

FAST PHILLY CHEESESTEAK PIZZA

⑤ INGREDIENTS FAST FIX

Fast Philly Cheesesteak Pizza

Cheesesteaks and pizza are such favorites, I just had to combine them. We pile the crust with beef, cheese and veggies for a hand-held feast.

—JACKIE HANNAHS CEDAR SPRINGS, MI

START TO FINISH: 30 MIN.
MAKES: 6 SLICES

- 1 tube (13.8 ounces) refrigerated pizza crust
- 2 cups frozen pepper and onion stir-fry blend
- 2 tablespoons Dijon-mayonnaise blend
- ½ pound thinly sliced deli roast beef, cut into wide strips
- 1½ cups (6 ounces) shredded cheddar cheese

1. Preheat the oven to 425°. Grease a 12-in. pizza pan. Unroll and press the pizza crust dough to fit the prepared pan. Pinch the edge of dough to form a rim. Bake 8-10 minutes or until the edge is lightly browned.
2. Meanwhile, place a large nonstick skillet coated with cooking spray over medium-high heat. Add the stir-fry blend; cook and stir 3-5 minutes or until heated through.
3. Spread the mayonnaise blend over the pizza crust; top with the deli roast beef and vegetables. Sprinkle with the cheddar cheese. Bake 10-15 minutes or until cheese is melted.
PER SERVING *1 slice equals 330 cal., 13 g fat (7 g sat. fat), 51 mg chol., 983 mg sodium, 34 g carb., 1 g fiber, 20 g pro.*

EAT SMART FAST FIX

Mahi Mahi & Veggie Skillet

Cooking mahi mahi with veggies may seem complex, but this recipe makes it easy.
—SOLOMON WANG ARLINGTON, TX

START TO FINISH: 30 MIN.
MAKES: 4 SERVINGS

- 3 tablespoons olive oil, divided
- 4 mahi mahi or salmon fillets (6 ounces each)
- 3 medium sweet red peppers, cut into thick strips
- ½ pound sliced baby portobello mushrooms
- 1 large sweet onion, cut into thick rings and separated
- ⅓ cup lemon juice
- ¾ teaspoon salt, divided
- ½ teaspoon pepper
- ¼ cup minced fresh chives
- ⅓ cup pine nuts, optional

1. In a large skillet, heat 2 tablespoons oil over medium-high heat. Add the fillets; cook 4-5 minutes on each side or until fish just begins to flake easily with a fork. Remove from pan.
2. Add the remaining oil, red peppers, baby portobello mushrooms, sweet onion, lemon juice and ¼ teaspoon salt. Cook, covered, over medium heat 6-8 minutes or until the vegetables are tender, stirring occasionally.
3. Place the fish over the vegetables; sprinkle with pepper and remaining salt. Cook, covered, 2 minutes longer or until heated through. Sprinkle with minced chives and, if desired, pine nuts before serving.
PER SERVING *1 serving (calculated without pine nuts) equals 307 cal., 12 g fat (2 g sat. fat), 124 mg chol., 606 mg sodium, 15 g carb., 3 g fiber, 35 g pro.* **Diabetic Exchanges:** *4 lean meat, 3 vegetable, 2 fat.*

MAHI MAHI & VEGGIE SKILLET

1 tablespoon lime juice
¼ teaspoon salt
⅛ teaspoon pepper
2 cups lump crabmeat (about 10 ounces)
  Sliced multigrain bread, optional
  Lime wedges, optional

In a small bowl, mix the first six ingredients; gently stir in the crab. If desired, spread over the bread. Serve with lime wedges if desired.
PER SERVING *½ cup (calculated without bread) equals 196 cal., 15 g fat (2 g sat. fat), 72 mg chol., 748 mg sodium, 2 g carb., trace fiber, 12 g pro.*

⑤ INGREDIENTS FAST FIX
Mushroom Bread
Mom's best party food included baked crescent dough she topped with buttery mushrooms and a sprinkling of Parmesan. Now I serve her yummy appetizer with garlicky butter or hot sauce.
—JENNY MIKULICH MONTICELLO, IL

START TO FINISH: 25 MIN.
MAKES: 12 SERVINGS

1 tube (8 ounces) refrigerated crescent rolls
2 cups thinly sliced fresh mushrooms
1 tablespoon butter, melted
½ cup grated Parmesan cheese
½ teaspoon Italian seasoning
⅛ teaspoon pepper

1. Preheat the oven to 350°. On an ungreased baking sheet, unroll the crescent roll dough into one long rectangle; press perforations to seal. Prick dough several times with a fork. Bake 5 minutes.
2. Meanwhile, in a bowl, toss the mushrooms with the melted butter; arrange on crust. Sprinkle with the Parmesan cheese, Italian seasoning and pepper. Bake 12-14 minutes longer or until the crust is golden brown. Cut into 12 pieces.
PER SERVING *1 piece equals 100 cal., 6 g fat (3 g sat. fat), 5 mg chol., 209 mg sodium, 8 g carb., trace fiber, 3 g pro.*

WARM TASTY GREENS WITH GARLIC

When I had kale and other ingredients I needed to use up, I created Warm Tasty Greens with Garlic. It's become one of the side dishes I rely on most.
—MARTHA NETH AURORA, CO

EAT SMART ⑤ INGREDIENTS FAST FIX
Warm Tasty Greens with Garlic

START TO FINISH: 30 MIN.
MAKES: 4 SERVINGS

1 pound kale, trimmed and torn (about 20 cups)
2 tablespoons olive oil
¼ cup chopped oil-packed sun-dried tomatoes
5 garlic cloves, minced
2 tablespoons minced fresh parsley
¼ teaspoon salt

1. In a 6-qt. stockpot, bring 1 in. of water to a boil. Add the kale; cook, covered, 10-15 minutes or until tender. Remove with a slotted spoon; discard the cooking liquid.
2. In same pot, heat oil over medium heat. Add tomatoes and garlic; cook and stir 1 minute. Add kale, parsley and salt; heat through, stirring occasionally.
PER SERVING *⅔ cup equals 137 cal., 9 g fat (1 g sat. fat), 0 chol., 216 mg sodium, 14 g carb., 3 g fiber, 4 g pro.*
Diabetic Exchanges: *2 vegetable, 2 fat.*

⑤ INGREDIENTS FAST FIX
Spicy Crab Salad
My creamy crab mixture gets a hint of heat from Sriracha and a tangy burst from lime juice. Spread the salad on slices of bread or crackers for a fast lunch or snack.
—PATTI LAVELL ISLAMORADA, FL

START TO FINISH: 10 MIN.
MAKES: 4 SERVINGS

⅓ cup mayonnaise
1 tablespoon minced fresh parsley or cilantro
3 to 4 teaspoons Sriracha Asian hot chili sauce

BRATWURST HASH

½ teaspoon vanilla extract
1 large egg
2 teaspoons egg yolk
½ cup confectioners' sugar
3 tablespoons all-purpose flour
⅛ teaspoon ground ginger
⅛ teaspoon ground cinnamon
Additional confectioners' sugar

1. In a microwave, melt butter and chocolate; stir until smooth. Stir in wine and vanilla.

2. In a small bowl, beat the egg, egg yolk and confectioners' sugar until thick and lemon-colored. Beat in the flour, ginger and cinnamon until well blended. Gradually beat in the butter mixture.

3. Transfer batter to two greased 6-oz. ramekins or custard cups. Place the ramekins on a baking sheet. Bake at 425° for 10-12 minutes or until a thermometer inserted near the center reads 160° and sides of cakes are set.

4. Remove from oven and let stand for 1 minute. Run a knife around edges of ramekins; invert onto dessert plates. Dust with additional confectioners' sugar. Serve immediately.

PER SERVING *1 serving (calculated without additional confectioners' sugar) equals 560 cal., 36 g fat (21 g sat. fat), 234 mg chol., 200 mg sodium, 56 g carb., 2 g fiber, 8 g pro.*

The next time you make brats, try skipping the buns. Bratwurst Hash is a fast skillet meal that really sticks to your ribs.

—**MARIE PARKER** MILWAUKEE, WI

Bratwurst Hash

START TO FINISH: 30 MIN.
MAKES: 4 SERVINGS

4 uncooked bratwurst links, casings removed
1 medium green pepper, chopped
1 package (20 ounces) refrigerated diced potatoes with onion
1 cup fresh or frozen corn, thawed
¼ cup chopped roasted sweet red pepper
¼ teaspoon salt or ½ teaspoon seasoned salt
¾ cup shredded Colby-Monterey Jack cheese

1. In a large nonstick skillet, cook the bratwurst and pepper over medium heat 4-6 minutes or just until sausage is no longer pink, breaking up sausage into large crumbles.

2. Stir in the potatoes, corn, roasted sweet red pepper and salt; spread evenly onto the bottom of the skillet. Cook 10 minutes without stirring. Turn mixture over; cook 7-8 minutes longer or until the potatoes are tender. Sprinkle with cheese.

PER SERVING *1½ cups equals 506 cal., 31 g fat (13 g sat. fat), 82 mg chol., 1,458 mg sodium, 35 g carb., 3 g fiber, 19 g pro.*

Spiced Chocolate Molten Cakes

What's better than a chocolate cake? One that has a warm, rich, melty center just waiting to ooze out!

—**DEB CARPENTER** HASTINGS, MI

START TO FINISH: 30 MIN.
MAKES: 2 SERVINGS

¼ cup butter, cubed
2 ounces semisweet chocolate, chopped
1½ teaspoons dry red wine

SPICED CHOCOLATE MOLTEN CAKES

BLUEBERRY
CRUMBLE TARTS

Super Fast Mexican Soup

We take this spicy soup to rodeos or sip it by a campfire. Add toppings such as jalapenos, sour cream, onions, avocado, cheese and salsa.

—**GLORIA HUSE** SIMPSONVILLE, SC

START TO FINISH: 25 MIN.
MAKES: 4 SERVINGS

- 2 **teaspoons olive oil**
- 1 **pound boneless skinless chicken thighs, cut into ¾-inch pieces**
- 1 **tablespoon reduced-sodium taco seasoning**
- 1 **cup frozen corn**
- 1 **cup salsa**
- 1 **carton (32 ounces) reduced-sodium chicken broth**

1. In a large saucepan, heat the olive oil over medium-high heat. Add the chicken; cook and stir 6-8 minutes or until no longer pink. Stir in the taco seasoning.

2. Add the remaining ingredients; bring to a boil. Reduce heat; simmer, uncovered, 5 minutes to allow flavors to blend. Skim fat before serving.

PER SERVING *1½ cups equals 254 cal., 11 g fat (3 g sat. fat), 76 mg chol., 998 mg sodium, 14 g carb., 1 g fiber, 25 g pro.*

Blueberry Crumble Tarts

Sometimes I prepare my blueberry tarts the day before, store them in the fridge overnight and pop them into the oven to bake while I'm fixing dinner.

—**CAROLE FRASER** NORTH YORK, ON

START TO FINISH: 30 MIN.
MAKES: 6 SERVINGS

- 2 **cups fresh blueberries**
- ¼ **cup sugar**
- 1 **tablespoon cornstarch**
- 1 **package (6 count) individual graham cracker tart shells**
- ¼ **cup all-purpose flour**
- ¼ **cup quick-cooking oats**
- ¼ **cup packed brown sugar**
- 2 **tablespoons cold butter**
  Ice cream or whipped cream, optional

1. Preheat the oven to 375°. In a bowl, toss the blueberries with the sugar and cornstarch; spoon into the graham cracker tart shells. In a small bowl, mix the flour, oats and brown sugar; cut in the butter until crumbly. Sprinkle over the blueberries.

2. Place the tarts on a baking sheet. Bake 20-25 minutes or until topping is golden brown and filling is bubbly. Serve warm or at room temperature. If desired, top with ice cream.

PER SERVING *1 tart (calculated without ice cream) equals 278 cal., 10 g fat (4 g sat. fat), 10 mg chol., 174 mg sodium, 47 g carb., 2 g fiber, 3 g pro.*

SUPER FAST MEXICAN SOUP

Sandwich Specialties

Skip a trip to the deli—**stack your own sammie** with sensational ingredients. The recipes here make a **satisfying lunch or dinner** anytime.

MINI PARTY BURGERS

FAST FIX ▷
Turkey-Jalapeno Sandwiches

When a turkey sandwich meets modern Thai, it's a delicious combination of the traditional and trendy. I love it when mixing and matching different dishes turns out so tasty!

—**STACY MULLENS** GRESHAM, OR

START TO FINISH: 15 MIN. • **MAKES:** 6 SERVINGS

- 6 **tablespoons mayonnaise**
- 6 **hoagie buns, split**
- 6 **tablespoons jalapeno pepper jelly**
- 12 **lettuce leaves**
- 1½ **pounds thinly sliced deli turkey**
  Fresh cilantro leaves
  Thinly sliced seeded jalapeno pepper, optional

Spread mayonnaise on bun bottoms; spread pepper jelly over mayonnaise. Layer with lettuce and turkey; top with cilantro and, if desired, jalapeno. Replace tops.

PER SERVING *1 sandwich equals 493 cal., 18 g fat (3 g sat. fat), 45 mg chol., 1,505 mg sodium, 53 g carb., 2 g fiber, 31 g pro.*

TURKEY-JALAPENO SANDWICHES

---

⑤ INGREDIENTS FAST FIX ▷
Mini Party Burgers

Finger foods are always fun for parties. I assemble my mini burgers in advance, then bake and serve them with assorted sauces.

—**MONICA FLATFORD** KNOXVILLE, TN

START TO FINISH: 30 MIN. • **MAKES:** 8 SERVINGS

- ½ **pound ground beef**
- 1 **envelope ranch salad dressing mix**
- 1 **large egg**
- 1 **teaspoon water**
- 1 **sheet frozen puff pastry, thawed**
- 4 **slices Havarti cheese (about 4 ounces), quartered**

1. Preheat oven to 400°. Place beef in a small bowl; sprinkle with dressing mix and mix lightly but thoroughly. Shape into eight ½-in. thick patties.

2. In a large nonstick skillet, cook burgers over medium heat 3-4 minutes on each side or until a thermometer reads 160°. Remove from heat.

3. Meanwhile, in a small bowl, whisk the egg with water. On a lightly floured surface, unfold puff pastry; roll into a 12-in. square. Cut pastry into four 6-in. squares; cut squares in half to make eight rectangles. Place a burger on one end of each rectangle; top with cheese. Brush edges of pastry with egg mixture. Fold pastry over burger to enclose; press edges with a fork to seal.

4. Transfer to a parchment paper-lined baking sheet. Brush tops with egg mixture. Bake 15-20 minutes or until golden brown.

PER SERVING *1 appetizer equals 271 cal., 16 g fat (6 g sat. fat), 54 mg chol., 488 mg sodium, 20 g carb., 2 g fiber, 11 g pro.*

Tuna & White Bean Lettuce Wraps

START TO FINISH: 20 MIN. • **MAKES:** 4 SERVINGS (3 WRAPS EACH)

- 1 can (12 ounces) light tuna in water, drained and flaked
- 1 can (15 ounces) cannellini beans, rinsed and drained
- ¼ cup chopped red onion
- 2 tablespoons olive oil
- 1 tablespoon minced fresh parsley
- ⅛ teaspoon salt
- ⅛ teaspoon pepper
- 12 Bibb or Boston lettuce leaves (about 1 medium head)
- 1 medium ripe avocado, peeled and sliced

In a small bowl, combine the first seven ingredients; toss lightly to combine. Serve in lettuce leaves; top with avocado.

PER SERVING *3 wraps equals 279 cal., 13 g fat (2 g sat. fat), 31 mg chol., 421 mg sodium, 19 g carb., 7 g fiber, 22 g pro.* ***Diabetic Exchanges:*** *3 lean meat, 2 fat, 1 starch.*

HAM & BRIE MELTS

> Tuna & White Bean Lettuce Wraps are great when you want to break away from the ordinary.
> —**HEATHER SENGER** MADISON, WI

TUNA & WHITE BEAN
LETTUCE WRAPS

---

5 INGREDIENTS **FAST FIX**
Ham & Brie Melts

Give classic grilled cheese a simple but scrumptious makeover with layers of sliced Brie, ham and apricot preserves. These quick and crispy melts taste like a special treat.

—**BONNIE BAHLER** ELLINGTON, CT

START TO FINISH: 20 MIN. • **MAKES:** 4 SERVINGS

- 8 slices multigrain bread
- ¼ cup apricot preserves, divided
- ½ pound sliced deli ham
- 1 round (8 ounces) Brie cheese, rind removed, sliced
- 3 tablespoons butter, softened

1. Spread four bread slices with half of apricot preserves. Layer with ham and cheese. Spread remaining bread with remaining preserves; place over cheese, preserves side down. Spread outsides of sandwiches with butter.

2. In a large skillet, toast the sandwiches over medium heat 2-3 minutes on each side or until golden brown and cheese is melted.

PER SERVING *1 sandwich equals 500 cal., 27 g fat (16 g sat. fat), 104 mg chol., 1,208 mg sodium, 39 g carb., 3 g fiber, 27 g pro.*

CHEESY ONION CHICKEN SKILLET

Parmesan-Butternut Squash

Squash sprinkled with panko bread crumbs and Parmesan makes a superb side dish.

—JACKIE O'CALLAGHAN
WEST LAFAYETTE, IN

START TO FINISH: 25 MIN.
MAKES: 8 SERVINGS

- 1 **medium butternut squash (about 3 pounds), peeled and cut into 1-inch cubes**
- 2 **tablespoons water**
- ½ **cup panko (Japanese) bread crumbs**
- ½ **cup grated Parmesan cheese**
- ¼ **teaspoon salt**
- ⅛ **teaspoon pepper**

1. Place squash and water in a large microwave-safe bowl. Microwave, covered, on high 15-17 minutes or until tender; drain.
2. Preheat broiler. Transfer squash to a greased 15x10x1-in. baking pan. Toss bread crumbs with cheese, salt and pepper; sprinkle over squash. Broil 3-4 in. from heat 1-2 minutes or until topping is golden brown.
NOTE *This recipe was tested in a 1,100-watt microwave.*
PER SERVING *¾ cup equals 112 cal., 2 g fat (1 g sat. fat), 4 mg chol., 168 mg sodium, 23 g carb., 6 g fiber, 4 g pro. Diabetic Exchange: 1½ starch.*

Cheesy Onion Chicken Skillet

This zesty chicken with green peppers and onions is not only tasty, but also versatile. It's a complete meal when you serve it on a bed of rice, mashed potatoes or noodles. Or, scoop it into hoagie buns for hot and hearty dinner sandwiches.

—KIM JOHNSON SIBLEY, IA

START TO FINISH: 20 MIN.
MAKES: 4 SERVINGS

- 1 **pound boneless skinless chicken breasts, cubed**
- 2 **teaspoons Mrs. Dash Garlic & Herb seasoning blend**
- 2 **tablespoons olive oil, divided**
- 1 **medium green pepper, cut into strips**
- ½ **medium onion, sliced**
- 1 **cup (4 ounces) shredded Colby-Monterey Jack cheese**

1. Toss the chicken with seasoning blend. In a large nonstick skillet, heat 1 tablespoon oil over medium-high heat. Add the chicken; cook and stir 5-7 minutes or until no longer pink. Remove from the pan. In same pan, add the remaining oil, pepper and onion; cook and stir 3-4 minutes or until crisp-tender.
2. Stir in the chicken; sprinkle with the shredded cheese. Remove from the heat; let stand, covered, until the cheese is melted.
PER SERVING *1¼ cups equals 293 cal., 17 g fat (8 g sat. fat), 88 mg chol., 226 mg sodium, 4 g carb., 1 g fiber, 29 g pro.*

PARMESAN-BUTTERNUT SQUASH

ITALIAN OMELET *Omit chives and cheddar. Cook and stir ¾ cup sliced fresh mushrooms and 2 tablespoons chopped onion in 2 teaspoons olive oil until tender. Fill omelet with mushroom mixture; sprinkle with ¼ cup shredded mozzarella. Serve with spaghetti sauce.*
PER SERVING *½ cheddar omelet equals 216 cal., 18 g fat (9 g sat. fat), 309 mg chol., 392 mg sodium, 1 g carb., trace fiber, 13 g pro.*

⑤ INGREDIENTS **FAST FIX**

Chicken & Cheese Tortilla Pie

As quickly as my baked chicken tortilla pie goes together, it disappears even more quickly!

—**KAREN KUEBLER**
DALLAS, TX

START TO FINISH: 25 MIN.
MAKES: 4 SERVINGS

- 1 can (10 ounces) green enchilada sauce
- 8 corn tortillas (6 inches)
- 2 cups coarsely shredded rotisserie chicken
- 2 cups (8 ounces) shredded cheddar cheese
- ¼ cup sliced ripe olives
   Salsa, optional

1. Preheat oven to 375°. In a small skillet, warm the enchilada sauce over medium heat. Dip four corn tortillas, one at a time, in the warmed enchilada sauce to coat both sides; arrange on the bottom of a greased 9-in. pie plate, overlapping to fit.
2. Layer with 1 cup chicken, 1 cup cheese and 2 tablespoons ripe olives. Repeat the tortilla and chicken layers. Pour the remaining enchilada sauce over top. Sprinkle with the remaining cheese and olives.
3. Bake 10-15 minutes or until heated through and the cheese is melted. If desired, serve with salsa.
PER SERVING *1 piece equals 498 cal., 27 g fat (14 g sat. fat), 122 mg chol., 889 mg sodium, 26 g carb., 3 g fiber, 37 g pro.*

⑤ INGREDIENTS **FAST FIX**

Cheesy Chive Omelet

Fuel up for the day with eggs for breakfast. When you want a change, try the other omelet ideas at the end of the recipe.
—**NAOMI GIDDIS** TWO BUTTES, CO

START TO FINISH: 15 MIN.
MAKES: 2 SERVINGS

- 3 large eggs
- 2 tablespoons water
- ⅛ teaspoon salt
   Dash pepper
- 1 tablespoon minced fresh chives
- 1 tablespoon butter
- ¼ to ½ cup shredded cheddar cheese

1. In a small bowl, whisk eggs, water, salt and pepper. Stir in chives.
2. In a small nonstick skillet, heat the butter over medium-high heat. Pour in the egg mixture. The mixture should set immediately at the edges. As the eggs set, push cooked portions toward the center, letting the uncooked eggs flow underneath.
3. When the eggs are thickened and no liquid egg remains, sprinkle the cheddar cheese on one side; fold the omelet in half. Cut the omelet in half; slide onto plates.

HAM & SWISS OMELET *Omit chives and cheddar. Increase the pepper to ⅛ teaspoon. Sprinkle the egg mixture with ½ cup cubed cooked ham and ¼ cup shredded Swiss cheese.*
MEXICAN OMELET *Omit chives and cheddar. Fill omelet with ¼ cup cooked chorizo or sausage and 2 tablespoons chunky salsa.*

CHICKEN & CHEESE TORTILLA PIE

⑤ INGREDIENTS | FAST FIX

Beefy Tortellini Skillet

From browning the beef to cooking the pasta and melting the cheese, everything here happens in one pan. I love that!

—JULI MEYERS HINESVILLE, GA

START TO FINISH: 20 MIN.
MAKES: 4 SERVINGS

- 1 **pound ground beef**
- ½ **teaspoon Montreal steak seasoning**
- 1 **cup water**
- 1 **teaspoon beef bouillon granules**
- 1 **package (19 ounces) frozen cheese tortellini**
- 1 **cup (4 ounces) shredded Italian cheese blend**
  Thinly sliced fresh basil, optional

1. In a large skillet, cook the beef over medium heat 5-6 minutes or until no longer pink, breaking into crumbles; drain. Stir in steak seasoning. Add the water and bouillon; bring to a boil. Stir in tortellini; return to a boil. Reduce heat; simmer, covered, 3-4 minutes or until tortellini are tender.

2. Remove from heat; sprinkle with cheese. Let stand, covered, until cheese is melted. If desired, sprinkle with basil.

PER SERVING *1½ cups equals 566 cal., 28 g fat (13 g sat. fat), 111 mg chol., 899 mg sodium, 37 g carb., 2 g fiber, 39 g pro.*

EAT SMART | FAST FIX

Broccoli & Apple Salad

This creamy spin on veggie salad makes a cool, crunchy side for a variety of entrees.

—LYNN CLUFF LITTLEFIELD, AZ

START TO FINISH: 15 MIN.
MAKES: 6 SERVINGS

- 3 **cups small fresh broccoli florets**
- 3 **medium apples, chopped**
- ½ **cup chopped mixed dried fruit**
- 1 **tablespoon chopped red onion**
- ½ **cup reduced-fat plain yogurt**
- 4 **bacon strips, cooked and crumbled**

In a large bowl, combine broccoli, apples, dried fruit and onion. Add yogurt; toss to coat. Sprinkle with bacon. Refrigerate until serving.

PER SERVING *1 cup equals 124 cal., 3 g fat (1 g sat. fat), 7 mg chol., 134 mg sodium, 22 g carb., 3 g fiber, 4 g pro.* **Diabetic Exchanges:** *1½ starch, ½ fat.*

FAST FIX

Quick Pepperoni Calzones

Take your calzones to the next level by adding Parmesan and herbs on top.

—SHANNON ROUM WAUKESHA, WI

START TO FINISH: 30 MIN.
MAKES: 4 SERVINGS

- 1 **cup chopped pepperoni**
- ½ **cup pasta sauce with meat**
- ¼ **cup shredded part-skim mozzarella cheese**
- 1 **loaf (1 pound) frozen bread dough, thawed**
- 1 **to 2 tablespoons 2% milk**
- 1 **tablespoon grated Parmesan cheese**
- ½ **teaspoon Italian seasoning, optional**

1. Preheat oven to 350°. In a small bowl, mix pepperoni, sauce and mozzarella cheese.

2. On a lightly floured surface, divide dough into four portions. Roll each into a 6-in. circle; top each with a scant ⅓ cup pepperoni mixture. Fold dough over filling; pinch edges to seal. Place on a greased baking sheet.

3. Brush milk over tops; sprinkle with Parmesan cheese and, if desired, Italian seasoning. Bake 20-25 minutes or until golden brown.

PER SERVING *1 calzone equals 540 cal., 23 g fat (8 g sat. fat), 36 mg chol., 1,573 mg sodium, 59 g carb., 5 g fiber, 21 g pro.*

DID YOU KNOW?

Out of Italian seasoning? You can combine ¼ teaspoon each of basil, oregano, rosemary and thyme as a substitute for each teaspoon of Italian seasoning used in a recipe.

BEEFY TORTELLINI SKILLET

Mashed Cauliflower with Parmesan

I couldn't shake my mashed potato habit until I tried cauliflower mashed to a similar consistency. I started preparing my own, and now my family enjoys it, too.
—**MEREDITH HOWARD** FRANKLIN, KY

START TO FINISH: 30 MIN.
MAKES: 6 SERVINGS

- 1 large head cauliflower (about 2½ pounds), broken into florets
- 1 cup shredded Parmesan cheese, divided
- ⅓ cup heavy whipping cream or half-and-half cream
- 1 tablespoon butter
- ½ teaspoon pepper
  Minced fresh parsley, optional

1. Place 1 in. of water and cauliflower in a large saucepan; bring to a boil. Cook, covered, 10-12 minutes or until soft. Drain.
2. Mash the cauliflower to desired consistency. Stir in ½ cup Parmesan cheese, heavy whipping cream, butter and pepper. Sprinkle with remaining cheese and, if desired, parsley.
PER SERVING *⅔ cup equals 154 cal., 11 g fat (7 g sat. fat), 33 mg chol., 290 mg sodium, 8 g carb., 3 g fiber, 8 g pro.*

Spaghetti with Eggs and Bacon

Most people are surprised to see this combination of ingredients. Then they taste it—and it's gone in a flash!
—**GAIL JENNER** ETNA, CA

START TO FINISH: 25 MIN.
MAKES: 4 SERVINGS

- 8 ounces uncooked spaghetti
- 4 large eggs
- ¾ cup half-and-half cream
- ½ cup grated Parmesan cheese
- ½ pound bacon strips, cooked and crumbled
  Additional grated Parmesan cheese, optional

1. Cook the spaghetti according to package directions in a 6-qt. stockpot. In a small saucepan, whisk the eggs

At a truck stand in Hawaii, we sampled a specialty similar to Quick Tacos al Pastor. My husband, who's a high school football referee, said my version scores big-time.
—**LORI MCLAIN** DENTON, TX

QUICK TACOS AL PASTOR

and cream until blended. Cook over low heat until a thermometer reads 160°, stirring constantly (do not allow to simmer). Remove from the heat; stir in Parmesan cheese.
2. Drain the spaghetti; return to the stockpot. Add Parmesan cheese sauce and crumbled bacon; toss to combine. Serve immediately. If desired, sprinkle with additional cheese.
PER SERVING *1 serving (calculated without additional cheese) equals 486 cal., 21 g fat (9 g sat. fat), 238 mg chol., 611 mg sodium, 45 g carb., 2 g fiber, 26 g pro.*

Quick Tacos al Pastor

START TO FINISH: 25 MIN.
MAKES: 4 SERVINGS

- 1 package (15 ounces) refrigerated pork roast au jus
- 1 cup well-drained unsweetened pineapple chunks, divided
- 1 tablespoon canola oil
- ½ cup enchilada sauce
- 8 corn tortillas (6 inches), warmed
- ½ cup finely chopped onion
- ¼ cup chopped fresh cilantro
  Optional ingredients: crumbled queso fresco, salsa verde and lime wedges

1. Coarsely shred the pork, reserving juices. In a small bowl, crush half of the pineapple with a fork.
2. In a large nonstick skillet, heat oil over medium-high heat. Add whole pineapple chunks; cook 2-3 minutes or until lightly browned, turning occasionally. Remove from pan.
3. Add enchilada sauce and crushed pineapple to the same skillet; stir in the pork and reserved juices. Cook over medium-high heat 4-6 minutes or until the liquid is evaporated, stirring occasionally.
4. Serve in tortillas with pineapple chunks, onion and cilantro. If desired, top with cheese and salsa and serve with lime wedges.
PER SERVING *2 tacos (calculated without optional ingredients) equals 317 cal., 11 g fat (3 g sat. fat), 57 mg chol., 573 mg sodium, 36 g carb., 5 g fiber, 24 g pro.* **Diabetic Exchanges:** *3 lean meat, 2 starch, 1 fat.*

LYNN PRICE'S
SOUTHWEST-STYLE
SHEPHERD'S PIE *PAGE 243*

Cooking Lighter

You can serve these entrees **with confidence** to family, friends, guests…everyone you cook for. Each slimmed-down dish is not only lower in fat and calories, but also **absolutely delicious!**

**DEB PERRY'S
FISH TACOS WITH
GUACAMOLE** *PAGE 242*

**JENNIFER KENT'S
TURKEY-THYME STUFFED PEPPERS**
PAGE 246

**KATHLEEN SPECHT'S
PORK & MANGO STIR-FRY**
PAGE 249

EAT SMART
Italian Burritos

My family has its share of picky eaters, and it can be a challenge to satisfy everyone at the dinner table. I've found that these tasty hand-held burritos do the trick.

—DONNA HOLTER CENTENNIAL, CO

PREP: 20 MIN. • **BAKE:** 20 MIN.
MAKES: 8 SERVINGS

- 1 **pound lean ground beef (90% lean)**
- 1 **cup marinara sauce**
- ½ **cup shredded part-skim mozzarella cheese**
- ¼ **cup grated Parmesan cheese**
- ¼ **teaspoon garlic powder**
- 8 **whole wheat tortillas (8 inches)**

1. Preheat oven to 375°. In a large skillet, cook beef over medium heat 6-8 minutes or until no longer pink, breaking into crumbles; drain. Stir in marinara sauce, mozzarella cheese, Parmesan cheese and garlic powder.
2. Spoon ⅓ cup filling near the center of each tortilla. Fold bottom and sides of tortilla over filling and roll up. Place on a baking sheet coated with cooking spray. Bake 18-20 minutes or until bottoms are light brown.

PER SERVING *1 burrito equals 275 cal., 10 g fat (3 g sat. fat), 42 mg chol., 326 mg sodium, 26 g carb., 3 g fiber, 18 g pro. Diabetic Exchanges: 2 starch, 2 lean meat.*

FISH TACOS WITH GUACAMOLE

Fish Tacos with Guacamole is my new favorite recipe—lighter than beef tacos smothered in cheese. Try hot sauce, onions, tomatoes or jalapenos on top.

—DEB PERRY TRAVERSE CITY, MI

ITALIAN BURRITOS

EAT SMART
Fish Tacos with Guacamole

PREP: 25 MIN. • **COOK:** 10 MIN.
MAKES: 4 SERVINGS

- 2 **cups angel hair coleslaw mix**
- 1½ **teaspoons canola oil**
- 1½ **teaspoons lime juice**

GUACAMOLE
- 1 **medium ripe avocado, peeled and quartered**
- 2 **tablespoons fat-free sour cream**
- 1 **tablespoon finely chopped onion**
- 1 **tablespoon minced fresh cilantro**
- ⅛ **teaspoon salt**
  Dash pepper

TACOS
- 1 **pound tilapia fillets, cut into 1-inch pieces**
- ¼ **teaspoon salt**
- ⅛ **teaspoon pepper**
- 2 **teaspoons canola oil**
- 8 **corn tortillas (6 inches), warmed**

Optional toppings: hot pepper sauce and chopped tomatoes, green onions and jalapeno pepper

1. In a small bowl, toss the coleslaw mix with oil and lime juice; refrigerate until serving. In another bowl, mash avocado with a fork; stir in sour cream, onion, cilantro, salt and pepper.
2. Sprinkle the tilapia with the salt and pepper. In a large nonstick skillet coated with cooking spray, heat oil over medium-high heat. Add tilapia; cook 3-4 minutes on each side or until fish just begins to flake easily with a fork. Serve in tortillas with coleslaw, guacamole and toppings as desired.

PER SERVING *2 tacos (calculated without optional toppings) equals 308 cal., 12 g fat (2 g sat. fat), 56 mg chol., 299 mg sodium, 28 g carb., 6 g fiber, 25 g pro. Diabetic Exchanges: 3 lean meat, 2 starch, 2 fat.*

Southwest-Style Shepherd's Pie

Now a resident of New England, I was born in Montreal and have lived in the Southwest, too. All of these regions have influenced my cooking, inspiring dishes such as this Tex-Mex shepherd's pie.

—LYNN PRICE MILLVILLE, MA

PREP: 20 MIN. • **BAKE:** 25 MIN.
MAKES: 6 SERVINGS

- 1¼ pounds lean ground turkey
- 1 small onion, chopped
- 2 garlic cloves, minced
- ½ teaspoon salt, divided
- 1 can (14¾ ounces) cream-style corn
- 1 can (4 ounces) chopped green chilies
- 1 to 2 tablespoons chipotle hot pepper sauce, optional
- 2⅔ cups water
- 2 tablespoons butter
- 2 tablespoons half-and-half cream
- ½ teaspoon pepper
- 2 cups mashed potato flakes

1. Preheat oven to 425°. In a large skillet, cook the turkey, onion, garlic and ¼ teaspoon salt over medium heat 8-10 minutes or until turkey is no longer pink and onion is tender, breaking up turkey into crumbles. Stir in the corn, green chilies and, if desired, chipotle hot pepper sauce. Transfer to a greased 8-in.-square baking dish.

2. Meanwhile, in a saucepan, bring water, butter, half-and-half cream, pepper and remaining salt to a boil. Remove from the heat. Stir in the mashed potato flakes. Spoon over turkey mixture, spreading to cover. Bake 25-30 minutes or until bubbly and potatoes are light brown.

PER SERVING *1 cup equals 312 cal., 12 g fat (5 g sat. fat), 78 mg chol., 583 mg sodium, 31 g carb., 3 g fiber, 22 g pro.* **Diabetic Exchanges:** *3 lean meat, 2 starch, 1 fat.*

Chicken Cordon Bleu Stroganoff

I like classic Stroganoff but wanted a version with chicken instead. For a little French flair, I added ham, Swiss and Dijon. The recipe has become one of our mainstays.

—JEANNE HOLT MENDOTA HEIGHTS, MN

PREP: 15 MIN. • **COOK:** 25 MIN.
MAKES: 6 SERVINGS

- 1 tablespoon canola oil
- ½ pound sliced fresh mushrooms
- 1 large onion, chopped
- 2 tablespoons all-purpose flour
- 3 cups reduced-sodium chicken broth
- ⅓ cup white wine or additional chicken broth
- 1 tablespoon Dijon mustard
- 4 cups uncooked whole wheat egg noodles
- 2 cups cubed cooked chicken breast
- ¾ cup cubed fully cooked ham
- ½ cup shredded Swiss cheese, divided
- ½ cup reduced-fat sour cream
- ¼ teaspoon salt
- ¼ teaspoon pepper
- 1 green onion, thinly sliced

1. In a 6-qt. stockpot, heat oil over medium-high heat. Add mushrooms and onion; cook and stir 6-8 minutes or until tender. Stir in the flour until blended; gradually stir in broth, wine and mustard. Bring to a boil.

2. Add the egg noodles; return to a boil. Reduce heat; simmer, uncovered, 10-12 minutes or until the noodles are tender, stirring occasionally. Stir in the chicken, ham and ¼ cup cheese until cheese is melted.

3. Remove from heat; stir in the sour cream, salt and pepper. Sprinkle with green onion and remaining cheese.

PER SERVING *1⅓ cups equals 308 cal., 9 g fat (3 g sat. fat), 61 mg chol., 732 mg sodium, 29 g carb., 4 g fiber, 28 g pro.* **Diabetic Exchanges:** *3 lean meat, 1½ starch, 1 vegetable, ½ fat.*

CHICKEN CORDON BLEU STROGANOFF

EAT SMART **FAST FIX**
Oven Chicken Cordon Bleu

To please my son, who craves chicken Cordon Bleu, I created this quick meal.

—RONDA EAGLE GOOSE CREEK, SC

START TO FINISH: 30 MIN.
MAKES: 6 SERVINGS

- 6 boneless skinless chicken breast halves (4 ounces each)
- ¼ teaspoon salt
- ¼ teaspoon pepper
- 6 slices deli ham
- 3 slices aged Swiss cheese, halved
- 1 cup panko (Japanese) bread crumbs
  Cooking spray

SAUCE
- 2 tablespoons all-purpose flour
- 1 cup 2% milk
- ½ cup dry white wine
- ⅓ cup finely shredded Swiss cheese
- ¼ teaspoon salt
- ⅛ teaspoon pepper

1. Preheat the oven to 375°. Sprinkle the chicken breasts with the salt and pepper; arrange chicken in a greased 13x9-in. baking dish.
2. Top each with 1 slice deli ham and ½ slice cheese, folding ham in half and covering chicken as much as possible. Sprinkle with bread crumbs. Carefully spritz the bread crumbs with cooking spray, keeping the crumbs in place. Bake 15-20 minutes or until golden brown and a thermometer inserted in chicken reads 165°.
3. For the sauce, in a small saucepan, whisk the flour and milk until smooth. Bring to a boil, stirring constantly; cook and stir 1-2 minutes or until thickened.
4. Reduce to medium heat. Stir in the wine and Swiss cheese; cook and stir 2-3 minutes or until cheese is melted and sauce is thickened and bubbly. Stir in salt and pepper. Keep warm over low heat until ready to serve. Serve with chicken.

PER SERVING *1 chicken breast half with 3 tablespoons sauce equals 285 cal., 9 g fat (4 g sat. fat), 89 mg chol., 490 mg sodium, 12 g carb., trace fiber, 33 g pro.* **Diabetic Exchanges:** *4 lean meat, 1 starch.*

EAT SMART **FAST FIX**
Mom's Spanish Rice

My mom is famous for her Spanish rice. I think it's the ultimate comfort food.

—JOAN HALLFORD
NORTH RICHLAND HILLS, TX

START TO FINISH: 20 MIN.
MAKES: 4 SERVINGS

- 1 pound lean ground beef (90% lean)
- 1 large onion, chopped
- 1 medium green pepper, chopped
- 1 can (15 ounces) tomato sauce
- 1 can (14½ ounces) no-salt-added diced tomatoes, drained
- 1 teaspoon ground cumin
- 1 teaspoon chili powder
- ½ teaspoon garlic powder
- ¼ teaspoon salt
- 2⅔ cups cooked brown rice

1. In a large skillet, cook the beef, onion and pepper over medium heat 6-8 minutes or until beef is no longer pink and onion is tender, breaking up beef into crumbles; drain.
2. Stir in the tomato sauce, diced tomatoes and seasonings; bring to a boil. Add brown rice; heat through, stirring occasionally.

PER SERVING *1½ cups equals 395 cal., 11 g fat (4 g sat. fat), 71 mg chol., 757 mg sodium, 46 g carb., 6 g fiber, 29 g pro.* **Diabetic Exchanges:** *3 lean meat, 2 starch, 2 vegetable.*

MOM'S SPANISH RICE

MUSHROOM BOLOGNESE WITH WHOLE WHEAT PASTA

EAT SMART

Mushroom Bolognese with Whole Wheat Pasta

PREP: 10 MIN. • **COOK:** 50 MIN.
MAKES: 6 SERVINGS

- 1 tablespoon olive oil
- 1 large sweet onion, finely chopped
- 2 medium carrots, finely chopped
- 1 large zucchini, finely chopped
- ½ pound baby portobello mushrooms, finely chopped
- 3 garlic cloves, minced
- ½ cup dry red wine or reduced-sodium chicken broth
- 1 can (28 ounces) crushed tomatoes, undrained
- 1 can (14½ ounces) diced tomatoes, undrained
- ½ cup grated Parmesan cheese
- ½ teaspoon dried oregano
- ½ teaspoon pepper
- ⅛ teaspoon crushed red pepper flakes
  Dash ground nutmeg
- 4½ cups uncooked whole wheat rigatoni

1. In a 6-qt. stockpot coated with cooking spray, heat the olive oil over medium-high heat. Add the onion and carrots; cook and stir until tender. Add the zucchini, mushrooms and garlic; cook and stir until tender. Stir in the wine; bring to a boil; cook until liquid is almost evaporated.

2. Stir in crushed and diced tomatoes, Parmesan cheese and seasonings; bring to a boil. Reduce heat; simmer, covered, 25-30 minutes or until slightly thickened.

3. Cook rigatoni according to package directions; drain. Serve with sauce.

PER SERVING *1⅓ cups sauce with 1 cup pasta equals 369 cal., 6 g fat (2 g sat. fat), 6 mg chol., 483 mg sodium, 65 g carb., 12 g fiber, 17 g pro.*

Pecan-Orange Salmon

This nutty, citrusy baked salmon is a favorite I've prepared for family and guests many times.

—**KARI KELLEY**
PLAINS, MT

START TO FINISH: 25 MIN.
MAKES: 4 SERVINGS

- 1 tablespoon grated orange peel
- ⅓ cup orange juice
- 1 tablespoon Dijon mustard
- 1 tablespoon honey
- 2 teaspoons olive oil
- ½ teaspoon salt
- ¼ teaspoon pepper
- 4 salmon fillets (5 ounces each)
- 2 tablespoons finely chopped pecans

1. Preheat the oven to 425°. In a small bowl, whisk the first seven ingredients until blended.

2. Place the salmon fillets in a greased 11x7-in. baking dish. Pour sauce over salmon; sprinkle with pecans. Bake, uncovered, 15-18 minutes or until fish just begins to flake easily with a fork.

PER SERVING *1 salmon fillet equals 297 cal., 18 g fat (3 g sat. fat), 71 mg chol., 456 mg sodium, 8 g carb., 1 g fiber, 24 g pro.* **Diabetic Exchanges:** *4 lean meat, 1½ fat, ½ starch.*

PECAN-ORANGE SALMON

I think my young daughter may be the biggest fan of Turkey-Thyme Stuffed Peppers. She always wants to help me prepare and mix the ingredients.
—**JENNIFER KENT** PHILADELPHIA, PA

TURKEY-THYME STUFFED PEPPERS

Dijon Pork Medallions

My husband loves Dijon mustard, so this pork is a sure bet whenever I put it on the table.
—**JOYCE MOYNIHAN**
LAKEVILLE, MN

START TO FINISH: 20 MIN.
MAKES: 4 SERVINGS

- 1 pork tenderloin (1 pound)
- 1½ teaspoons lemon-pepper seasoning
- 2 tablespoons butter
- 2 tablespoons lemon juice
- 1 tablespoon Worcestershire sauce
- 1 teaspoon Dijon mustard
- 1 tablespoon minced fresh parsley

1. Cut the pork tenderloin into eight slices; lightly pound with a meat mallet to 1-in. thickness. Sprinkle with the lemon-pepper seasoning.
2. In a large nonstick skillet, heat the butter over medium heat. Add pork; cook 3-4 minutes on each side or until a thermometer reads 145°. Remove from pan; keep warm.
3. Add lemon juice, Worcestershire sauce and Dijon mustard to skillet; cook 3-4 minutes, stirring to loosen browned bits from the pan. Serve with pork; sprinkle with parsley.
PER SERVING *2 pork slices with about 2 teaspoons sauce equals 189 cal., 10 g fat (5 g sat. fat), 78 mg chol., 330 mg sodium, 2 g carb., trace fiber, 23 g pro.* **Diabetic Exchanges:** *3 lean meat, 1 fat.*

Turkey-Thyme Stuffed Peppers

PREP: 30 MIN. • **COOK:** 10 MIN.
MAKES: 4 SERVINGS

- 1 pound lean ground turkey
- 1 medium onion, finely chopped
- 3 garlic cloves, minced
- ½ teaspoon dried thyme
- ¼ teaspoon salt
- ¼ teaspoon dried rosemary, crushed
- ⅛ teaspoon pepper
- 1 can (14½ ounces) diced tomatoes, undrained
- 1 package (8.8 ounces) ready-to-serve brown rice
- ½ cup seasoned bread crumbs
- 4 medium sweet yellow or orange peppers
- ¼ cup shredded part-skim mozzarella cheese

1. In a large skillet, cook turkey and onion over medium heat 8-10 minutes or until the turkey is no longer pink and onion is tender, breaking up the turkey into crumbles. Add garlic and seasonings; cook 1 minute longer. Stir in tomatoes, rice and bread crumbs.
2. Cut sweet peppers lengthwise in half; remove seeds. Arrange pepper halves in a 13x9-in. microwave-safe dish; fill with turkey mixture. Sprinkle with cheese. Microwave, covered, on high for 7-9 minutes or until peppers are crisp-tender.
NOTE *This recipe was tested in a full-size 1,100-watt microwave. If your microwave does not accommodate a 13x9-in. dish, microwave stuffed pepper halves, half at a time, in an 8-in.-square dish for 6-8 minutes or until peppers are crisp-tender.*
PER SERVING *2 stuffed pepper halves equals 423 cal., 13 g fat (3 g sat. fat), 82 mg chol., 670 mg sodium, 43 g carb., 6 g fiber, 31 g pro.* **Diabetic Exchanges:** *3 medium-fat meat, 2 starch, 2 vegetable.*

DIJON PORK MEDALLIONS

BBQ Beef & Vegetable Stir-Fry

Sometimes a little spur-of-the-moment experimenting ends with a happy surprise, like my beef stir-fry. I created it when I had no plan for supper but had steak, peppers and an onion on hand. Now the recipe is a regular on our menus.

—ROCHELLE DICKSON POTWIN, KS

START TO FINISH: 25 MIN.
MAKES: 4 SERVINGS

- 1 **beef top sirloin steak (1 pound), cut into thin strips**
- 3 **tablespoons reduced-sodium soy sauce**
- 1 **garlic clove, minced**
- ¼ **teaspoon pepper**
- 1 **large sweet onion, halved and sliced**
- 1 **medium green pepper, cut into thin strips**
- 1 **medium sweet red pepper, cut into thin strips**
- ¼ **cup barbecue sauce**
- 3 **cups hot cooked brown rice**

1. Toss the beef strips with the soy sauce, garlic and pepper. Place a large nonstick skillet coated with cooking spray over medium-high heat. Add the beef mixture; stir-fry 2-3 minutes or until beef is no longer pink. Remove from the pan.

2. Add vegetables; stir-fry 3-4 minutes or until crisp-tender. Return the beef to pan; stir in barbecue sauce and heat through. Serve with rice.

PER SERVING *1 cup beef mixture with ¾ cup rice equals 387 cal., 6 g fat (2 g sat. fat), 46 mg chol., 673 mg sodium, 51 g carb., 5 g fiber, 30 g pro. Diabetic Exchanges: 3 starch, 3 lean meat, 1 vegetable.*

TOP TIP

A soft flour tortilla can do wonders for a leftover stir-fry and rice. Simply reheat the stir-fry and rice together with a little soy sauce. Then just tuck the mixture into a warm tortilla, fold it up burrito-style and enjoy.

—LAURA P. RICHMOND, VA

CREAMY TUNA-NOODLE CASSEROLE

Creamy Tuna-Noodle Casserole

This comforting casserole makes a super one-dish dinner. Have cooked chicken breast? Use that instead of tuna.

—EDIE DESPAIN LOGAN, UT

PREP: 20 MIN. • **BAKE:** 25 MIN.
MAKES: 6 SERVINGS

- 5 **cups uncooked egg noodles**
- 1 **cup frozen peas**
- 1 **can (10¾ ounces) reduced-fat reduced-sodium condensed cream of mushroom soup, undiluted**
- 1 **cup (8 ounces) fat-free sour cream**
- ⅔ **cup grated Parmesan cheese**
- ⅓ **cup 2% milk**
- ¼ **teaspoon salt**
- 2 **cans (5 ounces each) light tuna in water, drained and flaked**
- ¼ **cup finely chopped onion**
- ¼ **cup finely chopped green pepper**

TOPPING

- ½ **cup soft bread crumbs**
- 1 **tablespoon butter, melted**

1. Preheat oven to 350°. Cook noodles according to the package directions for al dente, adding the peas during the last minute of cooking; drain.

2. Meanwhile, in a large bowl, combine the cream of mushroom soup, sour cream, Parmesan cheese, milk and salt; stir in the tuna, onion and green pepper. Add the noodles and peas; toss to combine.

3. Transfer to an 11x7-in. baking dish coated with cooking spray. In a small bowl, toss the soft bread crumbs with the melted butter; sprinkle over the top. Bake, uncovered, 25-30 minutes or until bubbly.

NOTE *To make soft bread crumbs, tear bread into pieces and place in a food processor or blender. Cover and pulse until crumbs form. One slice of bread yields ½-¾ cup crumbs.*

PER SERVING *1⅓ cups equals 340 cal., 8 g fat (4 g sat. fat), 63 mg chol., 699 mg sodium, 41 g carb., 3 g fiber, 25 g pro. Diabetic Exchanges: 3 starch, 2 lean meat, ½ fat.*

EAT SMART

Turkey Marsala

For lighter fare, I substituted turkey for the beef that was originally used in this dish.

—DEBORAH WILLIAMS PEORIA, AZ

PREP: 10 MIN. • **COOK:** 30 MIN.
MAKES: 4 SERVINGS

- 1 package (20 ounces) turkey breast tenderloins
- ¼ cup all-purpose flour
- ½ teaspoon salt, divided
- ½ teaspoon pepper, divided
- 1 tablespoon olive oil
- 1 tablespoon butter
- ½ pound sliced fresh mushrooms
- ½ cup reduced-sodium chicken broth
- ½ cup Marsala wine
- 1 teaspoon lemon juice

1. Cut turkey tenderloins crosswise in half; pound with a meat mallet to ¾-in. thickness. In a shallow bowl, mix the flour and ¼ teaspoon each salt and pepper. Dip turkey in flour mixture to coat both sides; shake off excess.

2. In a large nonstick skillet, heat the oil over medium heat. Add the turkey; cook 6-8 minutes on each side or until a thermometer reads 165°. Remove from pan; keep warm.

3. In same skillet, heat butter over medium-high heat. Add mushrooms; cook and stir 3-4 minutes or until tender. Stir in broth and wine. Bring to a boil; cook until liquid is reduced by half, about 12 minutes. Stir in the lemon juice and the remaining salt and pepper. Serve with turkey.

VEAL MARSALA *Substitute 1¼ pounds veal cutlets for the turkey tenderloins. Cook for 1-2 minutes on each side. Proceed as directed.*

PER SERVING *1 serving equals 295 cal., 8 g fat (3 g sat. fat), 77 mg chol., 482 mg sodium, 12 g carb., 1 g fiber, 36 g pro.* **Diabetic Exchanges:** *4 lean meat, 1½ fat, 1 starch.*

EAT SMART

Salisbury Steak Supreme

One night when I was running late, I thought of Mom's Salisbury steak dinner. It saved the day!

—PATRICIA SWART
GALLOWAY, NJ

PREP: 20 MIN. • **COOK:** 15 MIN.
MAKES: 4 SERVINGS

- 2 medium red onions, divided
- ½ cup soft bread crumbs
- ¾ teaspoon salt-free seasoning blend
- ½ teaspoon pepper
  Dash ground nutmeg
- 1 pound lean ground beef (90% lean)
- 1 teaspoon cornstarch
- 1 teaspoon reduced-sodium beef bouillon granules
- ½ cup cold water
- 2 teaspoons butter
- 1½ cups sliced fresh mushrooms

1. Thinly slice 1½ red onions; finely chop remaining half. In a large bowl, toss the bread crumbs with chopped onion and seasonings. Add beef; mix lightly but thoroughly. Shape into four ½-in.-thick oval patties.

2. Place a large nonstick skillet coated with cooking spray over medium heat. Add patties; cook 5-6 minutes on each side or until a thermometer reads 160°. Remove from pan. Discard drippings from pan.

3. In a small bowl, mix cornstarch, bouillon and water until smooth. In same skillet, heat butter over medium-high heat. Add mushrooms and sliced onions; cook and stir 5-7 minutes or until onions are tender.

4. Stir in cornstarch mixture. Bring to a boil; cook and stir 1-2 minutes or until thickened. Return the patties to the pan. Turn to coat with the sauce; heat through.

NOTE *To make soft bread crumbs, tear bread into pieces and place in a food processor or blender. Cover and pulse until crumbs form. One slice of bread yields ½-¾ cup crumbs.*

PER SERVING *244 cal., 12 g fat (5 g sat. fat), 76 mg chol., 192 mg sodium, 10 g carb., 1 g fiber, 24 g pro.* **Diabetic Exchanges:** *3 lean meat, 1 starch, ½ fat.*

TURKEY MARSALA

A recipe is special when everyone in your family raves about it and the requests just keep coming in. Pork & Mango Stir-Fry definitely falls into that category.
—**KATHLEEN SPECHT** CLINTON, MT

PORK & MANGO STIR-FRY

Poached Salmon with Dill & Turmeric

This moist, tender, juicy salmon is among my husband's favorites. The turmeric is robust but doesn't overpower the fish.
—**EVELYN BANKER** ELMHURST, NY

START TO FINISH: 30 MIN.
MAKES: 4 SERVINGS

- 1 tablespoon canola oil
- ¼ teaspoon cumin seeds
- 1 pound Yukon Gold potatoes (about 2 medium), finely chopped
- 1¼ teaspoons salt, divided
- ⅛ teaspoon plus ¼ teaspoon ground turmeric, divided
- 2 tablespoons chopped fresh dill, divided
- 4 salmon fillets (1 inch thick and 4 ounces each)
- 8 fresh dill sprigs
- 2 teaspoons grated lemon peel
- 2 tablespoons lemon juice
- 1 cup (8 ounces) reduced-fat plain yogurt
- ¼ teaspoon pepper

1. In a large skillet, heat oil and cumin over medium heat 1-2 minutes or until seeds are toasted, stirring occasionally. Stir in potatoes, ½ teaspoon salt and ⅛ teaspoon turmeric. Cook, covered, on medium-low 10-12 minutes or until tender. Stir in 1 tablespoon chopped dill; cook, uncovered, 1 minute. Remove from the heat.

2. Meanwhile, in a large skillet with high sides, place the salmon fillets, skin side down. Add the dill sprigs, lemon peel, lemon juice, ½ teaspoon salt, remaining turmeric and enough water to cover salmon. Bring just to a boil. Adjust heat to maintain a gentle simmer. Cook, uncovered, 7-9 minutes or until fish just begins to flake easily with a fork.

3. In a small bowl, mix the yogurt, pepper and remaining 1 tablespoon chopped dill and ¼ teaspoon salt. Serve with salmon and potatoes.

PER SERVING *3 ounces cooked salmon with ½ cup potatoes and ¼ cup sauce equals 350 cal., 15 g fat (3 g sat. fat), 61 mg chol., 704 mg sodium, 27 g carb., 2 g fiber, 25 g pro.* **Diabetic Exchanges:** *3 lean meat, 2 starch, 1 fat.*

Pork & Mango Stir-Fry

START TO FINISH: 25 MIN.
MAKES: 4 SERVINGS

- 1 pork tenderloin (1 pound)
- 1 tablespoon plus 2 teaspoons canola oil, divided
- ¼ teaspoon salt
- ½ teaspoon crushed red pepper flakes, optional
- 6 ounces uncooked multigrain angel hair pasta
- 1 package (8 ounces) fresh sugar snap peas
- 1 medium sweet red pepper, cut into thin strips
- ⅓ cup reduced-sugar orange marmalade
- ¼ cup reduced-sodium teriyaki sauce
- 1 tablespoon packed brown sugar
- 2 garlic cloves, minced
- 1 cup chopped peeled mango
- ¼ cup lightly salted cashews, coarsely chopped

1. Cut pork tenderloin lengthwise in half; cut each half crosswise into thin slices. Toss pork with 1 tablespoon oil, salt and, if desired, pepper flakes. Cook the angel hair pasta according to the package directions.

2. Place a large nonstick skillet over medium-high heat. Add half of the pork mixture; stir-fry 2-3 minutes or just until browned. Remove from pan; repeat with remaining pork mixture.

3. Stir-fry the sugar snap peas and sweet red pepper in the remaining oil 2-3 minutes or just until crisp-tender. Stir in the orange marmalade, teriyaki sauce, brown sugar and garlic; cook 1-2 minutes longer. Return the pork to pan and add mango and cashews; heat through, stirring to combine. Serve with pasta.

PER SERVING *1½ cups pork mixture with ¾ cup angel hair pasta equals 515 cal., 16 g fat (3 g sat. fat), 64 mg chol., 553 mg sodium, 58 g carb., 6 g fiber, 36 g pro.*

My mother inspired me to create a pasta sauce of my own. Quick Chicken Parmesan uses the one I developed. The longer it simmers, the better it gets—so keep that in mind if you have a little extra time to spare.
—DANIELLE GROCHOWSKI
MILWAUKEE, WI

EAT SMART

Quick Chicken Parmesan

PREP: 35 MIN. • **MAKES:** 4 SERVINGS

- 12 ounces frozen grilled chicken breast strips (about 3 cups)
- 1 can (14½ ounces) diced tomatoes, undrained
- 1 can (6 ounces) tomato paste
- 2 tablespoons dry red wine or chicken broth
- 1 tablespoon olive oil
- 1½ teaspoons Italian seasoning
- 1 garlic clove, minced
- ½ teaspoon sugar
- ⅓ cup shredded Parmesan cheese
- ⅓ cup shredded part-skim mozzarella cheese
  Hot cooked pasta

1. Heat a large skillet over medium heat. Add the grilled chicken breast strips; cook and stir 5-8 minutes or until heated through. Remove from the pan.
2. In the same skillet, combine the diced tomatoes, tomato paste, wine, oil, Italian seasoning, garlic and sugar; bring to a boil, stirring occasionally. Reduce the heat; simmer, uncovered, 10-15 minutes to allow flavors to blend, stirring occasionally.
3. Stir in the chicken. Sprinkle with Parmesan cheese and mozzarella cheese; cook, covered, 1-2 minutes longer or until the cheese is melted. Serve with pasta.

PER SERVING *1 cup (calculated without pasta) equals 248 cal., 9 g fat (3 g sat. fat), 86 mg chol., 739 mg sodium, 15 g carb., 3 g fiber, 28 g pro. Diabetic Exchanges: 3 lean meat, 2 vegetable, 2 fat.*

EAT SMART **FAST FIX**
Peanut Ginger Pasta
Love Thai cuisine? Combine fresh ginger, basil, lime, peanut butter and linguine for a restaurant-worthy specialty.
—ALLIL BINDER SPOKANE, WA

START TO FINISH: 30 MIN.
MAKES: 4 SERVINGS

- 2½ teaspoons grated lime peel
- ¼ cup lime juice
- 2 tablespoons reduced-sodium soy sauce
- 2 teaspoons water
- 1 teaspoon sesame oil
- ⅓ cup creamy peanut butter
- 2½ teaspoons minced fresh gingerroot
- 2 garlic cloves, minced
- ¼ teaspoon salt
- ¼ teaspoon pepper
- 8 ounces uncooked whole wheat linguine
- 2 cups small fresh broccoli florets
- 2 medium carrots, grated
- 1 medium sweet red pepper, julienned
- 2 green onions, chopped
- 2 tablespoons minced fresh basil

1. Place the first 10 ingredients in a blender; cover and process until blended. Cook the linguine according to the package directions, adding the broccoli during the last 5 minutes of cooking; drain.
2. Transfer linguine and broccoli to a large bowl. Add remaining ingredients. Add the peanut butter mixture and toss to combine.

PER SERVING *2 cups equals 365 cal., 13 g fat (2 g sat. fat), 0 chol., 567 mg sodium, 57 g carb., 10 g fiber, 14 g pro.*

PEANUT GINGER PASTA

Hearty Beef Ravioli

This family-friendly supper adds popular taco fixings to ready-made beef ravioli. It's easy for children to customize their plates by choosing their toppings.

—*TASTE OF HOME* TEST KITCHEN

START TO FINISH: 25 MIN.
MAKES: 6 SERVINGS

- 1 package (25 ounces) frozen beef ravioli
- ½ pound extra-lean ground beef (95% lean)
- 1 medium green pepper, chopped
- 1 can (14½ ounces) no-salt-added diced tomatoes, undrained
- 1 can (8 ounces) no-salt-added tomato sauce
- 2 tablespoons reduced-sodium taco seasoning
- ¾ cup shredded reduced-fat cheddar cheese
- 1 can (2¼ ounces) sliced ripe olives, drained

1. Cook ravioli according to package directions; drain.
2. Meanwhile, in a large nonstick skillet, cook the beef and green pepper over medium heat 4-6 minutes or until the beef is no longer pink, breaking up the beef into crumbles. Stir in the diced tomatoes, tomato sauce and taco seasoning. Bring to a boil. Reduce the heat; simmer, uncovered, 5-7 minutes or until slightly thickened.
3. Serve with ravioli. Top with cheese and olives.

PER SERVING *1 serving equals 375 cal., 10 g fat (5 g sat. fat), 44 mg chol., 695 mg sodium, 49 g carb., 4 g fiber, 21 g pro.*

TOP TIP

Want to cut down on the amount of ground beef in your family's diet? For recipes like tacos, sloppy joes or soups, I eliminate some of the beef the recipe calls for and combine the remaining cooked meat with cooked brown rice. You could also experiment with replacing some of the beef with refried beans.
—**KRISTA F.** RHODODENDRON, OR

SPINACH & ARTICHOKE PIZZA

Spinach & Artichoke Pizza

My from-scratch pie has a whole wheat crust flavored with beer. To make a meaty version, pile on some cooked ham or chicken.

—**RAYMONDE BOURGEOIS** SWASTIKA, ON

PREP: 25 MIN. • **BAKE:** 20 MIN.
MAKES: 6 SLICES

- 1½ to 1¾ cups white whole wheat flour
- 1½ teaspoons baking powder
- ¼ teaspoon salt
- ¼ teaspoon each dried basil, oregano and parsley flakes
- ¾ cup beer or nonalcoholic beer

TOPPINGS

- 1½ teaspoons olive oil
- 1 garlic clove, minced
- 2 cups (8 ounces) shredded Italian cheese blend, divided
- 2 cups fresh baby spinach
- 1 can (14 ounces) water-packed quartered artichoke hearts, drained and coarsely chopped
- 2 medium tomatoes, seeded and coarsely chopped
- 2 tablespoons thinly sliced fresh basil

1. Preheat oven to 425°. In a large bowl, whisk 1½ cups flour, baking powder, salt and dried herbs until blended. Add the beer, stirring just until moistened.
2. Turn the dough onto a well-floured surface; knead gently 6-8 times, adding additional flour if needed. Press dough to fit a greased 12-in. pizza pan. Pinch the edge to form a rim. Bake 8 minutes or until edge is lightly browned.
3. Mix the oil and garlic; spread over the pizza crust. Sprinkle with ½ cup cheese; layer with spinach, artichoke hearts and tomatoes. Sprinkle with remaining cheese. Bake 8-10 minutes or until crust is golden and cheese is melted. Sprinkle with fresh basil.

PER SERVING *1 slice equals 290 cal., 10 g fat (6 g sat. fat), 27 mg chol., 654 mg sodium, 32 g carb., 5 g fiber, 14 g pro.* **Diabetic Exchanges:** *2 starch, 1 medium-fat meat, 1 vegetable.*

SKILLET PORK CHOPS
WITH APPLES & ONION

Fish & Fries

Dine like you're in a traditional British pub. These moist fish fillets from the oven have a fuss-free coating that's healthier but just as crunchy and golden as the deep-fried kind. Simply seasoned and baked, the crispy fries are perfect on the side.

—**JANICE MITCHELL** AURORA, CO

PREP: 10 MIN. • **BAKE:** 35 MIN.
MAKES: 4 SERVINGS

- 1 **pound potatoes (about 2 medium)**
- 2 **tablespoons olive oil**
- ¼ **teaspoon pepper**

FISH

- ⅓ **cup all-purpose flour**
- ¼ **teaspoon pepper**
- 1 **large egg**
- 2 **tablespoons water**
- ⅔ **cup crushed cornflakes**
- 1 **tablespoon grated Parmesan cheese**
- ⅛ **teaspoon cayenne pepper**
- 1 **pound haddock or cod fillets**
   Tartar sauce, optional

1. Preheat oven to 425°. Peel and cut potatoes lengthwise into ½-in.-thick slices; cut slices into ½-in.-thick sticks.
2. In a large bowl, toss the potatoes with olive oil and pepper. Transfer to a 15x10x1-in. baking pan coated with cooking spray. Bake, uncovered, 25-30 minutes or until golden brown and crisp, stirring once.
3. Meanwhile, in a shallow bowl, mix flour and pepper. In another shallow bowl, whisk the egg with the water. In a third bowl, toss the cornflakes with the grated Parmesan cheese and cayenne pepper.
4. Dip fish fillets in the flour mixture to coat both sides; shake off the excess. Dip in the egg mixture, then in the cornflake mixture, patting to help the coating adhere.
5. Place on a baking sheet coated with cooking spray. Bake 10-12 minutes or until the fish just begins to flake easily with a fork. Serve with potatoes and, if desired, tartar sauce.
PER SERVING *376 cal., 9 g fat (2 g sat. fat), 120 mg chol., 228 mg sodium, 44 g carb., 2 g fiber, 28 g pro.* **Diabetic Exchanges:** *3 starch, 3 lean meat, 1½ fat.*

Skillet Pork Chops with Apples & Onion

Fast dinners are a lifesaver for busy cooks. I fix pork chops with veggies and, when my husband lobbies for it, corn bread stuffing.

—**TRACEY KARST** PONDERAY, ID

START TO FINISH: 20 MIN.
MAKES: 4 SERVINGS

- 4 **boneless pork loin chops (6 ounces each)**
- 3 **medium apples, cut into wedges**
- 1 **large onion, cut into thin wedges**
- ¼ **cup water**
- ⅓ **cup balsamic vinaigrette**
- ½ **teaspoon salt**
- ¼ **teaspoon pepper**

1. Place a large nonstick skillet over medium heat; brown pork chops on both sides, about 4 minutes. Remove from the pan.
2. In the same skillet, add the apples, onion and water. Place the pork chops over apple mixture; drizzle the chops with the balsamic vinaigrette. Sprinkle with the salt and pepper. Reduce the heat; simmer, covered, 3-5 minutes or until a thermometer inserted in chops reads 145°.
PER SERVING *1 pork chop with ¾ cup apple mixture equals 360 cal., 15 g fat (4 g sat. fat), 82 mg chol., 545 mg sodium, 22 g carb., 3 g fiber, 33 g pro.* **Diabetic Exchanges:** *5 lean meat, 1 fruit, 1 fat.*

Stovetop Tarragon Chicken

My oldest daughter can never get enough of the tarragon sauce in this main course. She likes to use biscuits to soak up every last drop. My husband and I prefer ours served over mashed potatoes.

—**TINA WESTOVER** LA MESA, CA

PREP: 10 MIN. • **COOK:** 30 MIN.
MAKES: 4 SERVINGS

- 4 **boneless skinless chicken breast halves (5 ounces each)**
- 2 **teaspoons paprika**
- 1 **tablespoon olive oil**
- 1 **package (10 ounces) julienned carrots**
- ½ **pound sliced fresh mushrooms**
- 2 **cans (10¾ ounces each) reduced-fat reduced-sodium condensed cream of chicken soup, undiluted**
- 3 **teaspoons dried tarragon**
- 1 **tablespoon lemon juice**
- 3 **small zucchini, thinly sliced**

1. Sprinkle the chicken with paprika. In a Dutch oven, heat oil over medium heat. Cook chicken 2 minutes on each side or until lightly browned; remove from the pan.

2. Add the carrots and mushrooms to same pan; cook, covered, 6-8 minutes or until the carrots are crisp-tender, stirring occasionally.

3. In a small bowl, mix soup, tarragon and lemon juice until blended; pour over vegetables. Return chicken to pan. Bring to a boil; reduce the heat to low. Cook, covered, 8 minutes. Top with zucchini; cook, covered, 6-8 minutes longer or until a thermometer inserted in chicken reads 165° and vegetables are tender.

PER SERVING *1 chicken breast with 1 cup vegetables equals 345 cal., 11 g fat (3 g sat. fat), 85 mg chol., 649 mg sodium, 28 g carb., 5 g fiber, 35 g pro.* **Diabetic Exchanges:** *4 lean meat, 2 vegetable, 1 starch, 1 fat.*

Light & Lemony Scampi

PREP: 20 MIN. • **COOK:** 15 MIN.
MAKES: 4 SERVINGS

- 1 **pound uncooked shrimp (26-30 per pound)**
- 8 **ounces uncooked multigrain angel hair pasta**
- 1 **tablespoon butter**
- 1 **tablespoon olive oil**
- 2 **green onions, thinly sliced**
- 4 **garlic cloves, minced**
- ½ **cup reduced-sodium chicken broth**
- 2 **teaspoons grated lemon peel**
- 3 **tablespoons lemon juice**
- ½ **teaspoon freshly ground pepper**
- ¼ **teaspoon salt**
- ¼ **teaspoon crushed red pepper flakes**
- ¼ **cup minced fresh parsley**
   Grated Parmesan cheese, optional

1. Peel and devein shrimp, removing the tails. Cut each shrimp lengthwise in half. Cook the pasta according to the package directions.

2. In a large nonstick skillet, heat the butter and oil over medium-high heat. Add shrimp, green onions and garlic; cook and stir 2-3 minutes or until the shrimp turn pink. Remove from pan with a slotted spoon.

3. Add the chicken broth, lemon peel, lemon juice, pepper, salt and pepper flakes to the same pan. Bring to a boil; cook until the liquid is slightly reduced, about 1 minute. Return the shrimp to the pan; heat through. Remove from the heat.

4. Drain the pasta; divide among four bowls. Top with the shrimp mixture; sprinkle with parsley. If desired, serve with cheese.

PER SERVING *1 serving (calculated without cheese) equals 378 cal., 10 g fat (3 g sat. fat), 146 mg chol., 405 mg sodium, 42 g carb., 5 g fiber, 29 g pro.* **Diabetic Exchanges:** *3 very lean meat, 2½ starch, 1½ fat.*

A touch of citrus flavor helped me trim the calories in our favorite shrimp entree. The result was Light & Lemony Scampi. Want to indulge? Add a little Parmesan.
—**ANN SHEEHY** LAWRENCE, MA

LIGHT & LEMONY SCAMPI

I think my Skillet Pork Chops with Apples recipe is a good example of how you can brighten savory foods with fruit. We love this homey main course.

—**AMANDA JOBE** OLATHE, KS

Skillet Pork Chops with Apples

PREP: 15 MIN. • **COOK:** 20 MIN.
MAKES: 4 SERVINGS

- 4 boneless pork loin chops (4 ounces each and ¾ inch thick)
- 1 teaspoon dried oregano, divided
- ½ teaspoon salt
- ¼ teaspoon coarsely ground pepper
- 1½ teaspoons canola oil
- 2 small apples, cut into ½-inch slices
- 1 cup sliced sweet onion (¼ inch thick)
- ⅓ cup unsweetened applesauce
- ¼ cup cider vinegar

1. Sprinkle the pork chops with ½ teaspoon oregano, salt and pepper. Place a large nonstick skillet coated with cooking spray over medium-high heat. Add the pork chops; brown 3 minutes on each side. Remove from the pan.

2. In the same pan, heat the oil over medium-high heat. Add the apples, onion and remaining oregano; cook and stir 6-8 minutes or until the apples are tender.

3. Reduce the heat to medium; stir in the applesauce and cider vinegar. Return the pork chops to the pan; cook, covered, 4-6 minutes or until the pork chops are tender. Let stand 5 minutes before serving.

PER SERVING *1 pork chop with ½ cup apple mixture equals 215 cal., 8 g fat (2 g sat. fat), 55 mg chol., 329 mg sodium, 12 g carb., 2 g fiber, 22 g pro. Diabetic Exchanges: 3 lean meat, ½ fruit, ½ fat.*

Quick Chicken & Broccoli Stir-Fry

Here's a spicy stir-fry sauce that works not only with chicken, but also with seafood and other meats. Feel free to experiment with different vegetables, too.

—**KRISTIN RIMKUS** SNOHOMISH, WA

START TO FINISH: 25 MIN.
MAKES: 4 SERVINGS

- 2 tablespoons rice vinegar
- 2 tablespoons mirin (sweet rice wine)
- 2 tablespoons chili garlic sauce
- 1 tablespoon cornstarch
- 1 tablespoon reduced-sodium soy sauce
- 2 teaspoons fish sauce or additional soy sauce
- ½ cup reduced-sodium chicken broth, divided
- 2 cups instant brown rice
- 2 teaspoons sesame oil
- 4 cups fresh broccoli florets
- 2 cups cubed cooked chicken
- 2 green onions, sliced

1. In a small bowl, mix the first six ingredients and ¼ cup chicken broth until smooth. Cook the rice according to package directions.

2. Meanwhile, in a large skillet, heat the oil over medium-high heat. Add the broccoli; stir-fry 2 minutes. Add the remaining broth; cook 1-2 minutes or until broccoli is crisp-tender. Stir sauce mixture and add to pan. Bring to a boil; cook and stir 1-2 minutes or until sauce is thickened.

3. Stir in chicken and green onions; heat through. Serve with rice.

PER SERVING *1 cup chicken mixture with ½ cup rice equals 387 cal., 9 g fat (2 g sat. fat), 62 mg chol., 765 mg sodium, 45 g carb., 4 g fiber, 28 g pro. Diabetic Exchanges: 3 lean meat, 2½ starch, 1 vegetable, ½ fat.*

QUICK CHICKEN & BROCCOLI STIR-FRY

LIGHT LINGUINE CARBONARA

2. Grill the kabobs, covered, over medium heat or broil 4 in. from the heat 2-4 minutes on each side or until the beef reaches the desired doneness. Add the peanuts to sauce; serve with kabobs and rice.

PER SERVING *1 kabob with ¾ cup rice and 1 tablespoon sauce equals 352 cal., 8 g fat (2 g sat. fat), 46 mg chol., 502 mg sodium, 39 g carb., 3 g fiber, 29 g pro.* **Diabetic Exchanges:** *3 lean meat, 2½ starch.*

EAT SMART FAST FIX▸
Quick Italian Veggie Skillet

When you don't know what to serve, Italian flavors are always a safe bet. We mix cannellini and garbanzo beans for a meatless main dish.
—**SONYA LABBE** WEST HOLLYWOOD, CA

START TO FINISH: 25 MIN.
MAKES: 4 SERVINGS

- 1 **can (15 ounces) no-salt-added garbanzo beans, rinsed and drained**
- 1 **can (15 ounces) no-salt-added cannellini or white kidney beans, rinsed and drained**
- 1 **can (14½ ounces) no-salt-added stewed tomatoes, undrained**
- 1 **cup vegetable broth**
- ¾ **cup uncooked instant rice**
- 1 **teaspoon Italian seasoning**
- ¼ **teaspoon crushed red pepper flakes, optional**
- 1 **cup marinara sauce**
- ¼ **cup grated Parmesan cheese**
  Minced fresh basil

In a large skillet, combine the first six ingredients and, if desired, red pepper flakes; bring to a boil. Reduce the heat; simmer, covered, 7-9 minutes or until rice is tender. Stir in marinara sauce; heat through, stirring occasionally. Top with cheese and basil.

PER SERVING *1⅓ cups equals 342 cal., 4 g fat (1 g sat. fat), 6 mg chol., 660 mg sodium, 59 g carb., 11 g fiber, 16 g pro.*

EAT SMART FAST FIX▸
Light Linguine Carbonara

On busy nights, I rely on my speedy pasta. Pair it with breadsticks or garlic toast.
—**MARY JO MILLER** MANSFIELD, OH

START TO FINISH: 25 MIN.
MAKES: 4 SERVINGS

- 8 **ounces uncooked linguine**
- ½ **cup frozen peas**
- 1 **large egg**
- 1 **cup fat-free evaporated milk**
- ¼ **cup finely chopped sweet red pepper**
- ⅛ **teaspoon crushed red pepper flakes**
- ⅛ **teaspoon pepper**
- ½ **cup grated Parmesan cheese, divided**
- 2 **bacon strips, cooked and crumbled**

1. In a 6-qt. stockpot, cook linguine according to the package directions, adding peas during the last 2 minutes of cooking. Meanwhile, in a small saucepan, whisk the egg, evaporated milk, red pepper, pepper flakes and pepper until blended; cook and stir over medium-low heat until mixture is just thick enough to coat a spoon and a thermometer reads at least 160°. Stir in ¼ cup Parmesan cheese and bacon; remove from heat.

2. Drain the linguine; return to pot. Add sauce and toss to coat. Serve with remaining cheese.
PER SERVING *1 cup equals 352 cal., 7 g fat (3 g sat. fat), 66 mg chol., 349 mg sodium, 52 g carb., 3 g fiber, 20 g pro.*

EAT SMART FAST FIX▸
Sublime Lime Beef

It's fun to see the reactions of guests when they sample these citrusy grilled skewers for the first time. The kabobs and rice are so delicious, it's hard not to smile!
—**DIEP NGUYEN** HANFORD, CA

START TO FINISH: 25 MIN.
MAKES: 4 SERVINGS

- ⅓ **cup lime juice**
- 2 **teaspoons sugar**
- 2 **garlic cloves, minced**
- 1 **beef top sirloin steak (1 inch thick and 1 pound)**
- 1½ **teaspoons pepper**
- ¾ **teaspoon salt**
- 2 **tablespoons unsalted dry roasted peanuts, chopped**
- 3 **cups hot cooked brown rice**

1. In a small bowl, mix the lime juice, sugar and garlic until blended; set aside. Cut steak into 2x1x¾-in. pieces; toss with the pepper and salt. Thread the beef onto four metal or soaked wooden skewers.

PARMESAN PORK CHOPS
WITH SPINACH SALAD

EAT SMART FAST FIX ▶
Parmesan Pork Chops with Spinach Salad

I came across an idea for pan-fried chops. After a few tweaks, I had both an entree and a spinach salad on the side.
—**LAUREL DALZELL** MANTECA, CA

START TO FINISH: 30 MIN.
MAKES: 4 SERVINGS

- 3 **medium tomatoes, seeded and chopped**
- 1 **tablespoon olive oil**
- 1 **tablespoon lemon juice**
- 1 **small garlic clove, minced**
- ½ **teaspoon salt, divided**
- ¼ **teaspoon pepper, divided**
- 2 **large egg whites**
- 1 **tablespoon Dijon mustard**
- ½ **teaspoon dried oregano**
- ½ **cup dry bread crumbs**
- 3 **tablespoons grated Parmesan cheese**
- 4 **thin boneless pork loin chops (½ inch thick and 3 ounces each)**
- 4 **cups fresh baby spinach**

1. In a large bowl, combine tomatoes, oil, lemon juice, garlic, ¼ teaspoon salt and ⅛ teaspoon pepper; toss to combine.

2. In a shallow bowl, whisk the egg whites, Dijon mustard, oregano and the remaining salt and pepper until blended. In another shallow bowl, mix the dry bread crumbs with Parmesan cheese. Dip the pork chops in the egg white mixture, then coat with the bread crumb mixture.

3. Place a large nonstick skillet coated with cooking spray over medium heat. Add the pork chops; cook 2-3 minutes on each side or until golden brown and pork is tender.

4. Add the spinach to the tomato mixture; toss to combine. Serve with the pork chops.

PER SERVING *1 pork chop with 1 cup spinach salad equals 223 cal., 10 g fat (3 g sat. fat), 43 mg chol., 444 mg sodium, 12 g carb., 2 g fiber, 22 g pro.* *Diabetic Exchanges: 3 lean meat, 2 vegetable, 1 fat.*

EAT SMART
Rustic Summer Vegetable Pasta

Bursting with summery vegetables and herbs, this pasta proves you can't have too much of a good thing!
—**BRYN NAMAVARI** CHICAGO, IL

PREP: 15 MIN. • **COOK:** 30 MIN.
MAKES: 8 SERVINGS

- 3 **tablespoons olive oil, divided**
- 1 **medium zucchini, cut into ¾-inch pieces**
- 1 **medium yellow summer squash, cut into ¾-inch pieces**
- 1 **medium onion, chopped**
- 1 **medium eggplant, peeled and cut into ¾-inch pieces**
- 2 **cups sliced fresh mushrooms**
- 2 **garlic cloves, minced**
- ¾ **teaspoon crushed red pepper flakes**
- 1 **can (28 ounces) crushed tomatoes**
- ½ **teaspoon salt**
- ½ **teaspoon pepper**
- 1 **tablespoon minced fresh oregano or 1 teaspoon dried oregano**
- 1 **tablespoon minced fresh parsley**
- 3 **tablespoons minced fresh basil or 1 tablespoon dried basil, divided**
- 1 **package (14½ ounces) uncooked multigrain spaghetti**
- ½ **cup shredded Parmesan cheese**

1. In a 6-qt. stockpot, heat 1 tablespoon oil over medium-high heat. Add the zucchini and yellow squash; cook and stir until tender. Remove from pan.

2. In same pot, heat 1 tablespoon oil over medium-high heat. Add onion, eggplant and mushrooms; cook and stir until tender. Add the garlic and pepper flakes; cook 1 minute longer. Add the tomatoes, salt and pepper; stir in the oregano, parsley and half of the basil; bring to a boil. Reduce the heat; simmer, uncovered, 15 minutes, stirring occasionally.

3. Meanwhile, cook the spaghetti according to the package directions. Drain; add to the vegetable mixture. Drizzle with the remaining oil; toss to combine. Top with Parmesan cheese and remaining basil.

PER SERVING *2 cups equals 315 cal., 8 g fat (2 g sat. fat), 4 mg chol., 445 mg sodium, 50 g carb., 8 g fiber, 15 g pro.*

EAT SMART **FAST FIX** ▸
Israeli Couscous & Chicken Sausage Skillet

START TO FINISH: 30 MIN.
MAKES: 4 SERVINGS

- 2 teaspoons olive oil
- 1 package (12 ounces) fully cooked spinach and feta chicken sausage links or flavor of your choice, sliced
- 1 small onion, finely chopped
- 1 celery rib, finely chopped
- 1 garlic clove, minced
- 1 cup reduced-sodium chicken broth
- 1 cup water
- ¼ teaspoon crushed red pepper flakes
- 1¼ cups uncooked pearl (Israeli) couscous
- 2 tablespoons minced fresh parsley
- ¼ cup crumbled feta cheese, optional

1. In a large nonstick skillet, heat the olive oil over medium-high heat. Add the chicken sausage, onion and celery; cook and stir 6-8 minutes or until the sausage is browned. Add garlic; cook 1 minute longer.

2. Stir in broth, water and pepper flakes; bring to a boil. Stir in couscous. Reduce the heat; simmer, covered, 10-12 minutes or until the liquid is absorbed. Remove from the heat; let stand, covered, 5 minutes. Stir in the parsley. If desired, sprinkle with cheese.

PER SERVING *1 cup (calculated without cheese) equals 343 cal., 10 g fat (3 g sat. fat), 65 mg chol., 694 mg sodium, 41 g carb., 1 g fiber, 22 g pro.* ***Diabetic Exchanges:*** *3 starch, 3 lean meat, ½ fat.*

EAT SMART
Pork with Sweet Potatoes

With sweet potatoes, dried cranberries and apple slices, this pork dish is especially popular during fall and winter. Your family will love not only the taste, but also the colorful medley of ingredients.

—**MARY RELYEA** CANASTOTA, NY

PREP: 20 MIN. • **COOK:** 20 MIN.
MAKES: 4 SERVINGS

- ½ cup all-purpose flour
- ½ teaspoon salt
- ¼ teaspoon pepper
- 1 pork tenderloin (about 1 pound)
- 1 tablespoon canola oil
- 2 medium sweet potatoes (about 1 pound), peeled and cubed
- ½ cup dried cranberries
- 1 can (14½ ounces) reduced-sodium chicken broth
- 1 tablespoon Dijon mustard
- 1 medium apple, sliced
- 4 green onions, chopped

1. In a shallow bowl, mix flour, salt and pepper. Cut the pork tenderloin into 12 slices; pound each with a meat mallet to ¼-in. thickness. Dip pork in the flour mixture to coat both sides; shake off excess.

2. In a large nonstick skillet coated with cooking spray, heat the oil over medium-high heat; brown the pork in batches. Remove from pan.

3. Add the sweet potatoes, cranberries and chicken broth to the same pan. Bring to a boil. Reduce heat; simmer, covered, 4-6 minutes or until potatoes are almost tender. Stir in mustard.

4. Return pork to pan; add apple and onions. Return to a boil. Reduce heat; simmer, covered, 4-6 minutes or until pork and sweet potatoes are tender.

PER SERVING *3 slices pork with 1 cup potato mixture equals 315 cal., 8 g fat (2 g sat. fat), 63 mg chol., 513 mg sodium, 36 g carb., 4 g fiber, 26 g pro.* ***Diabetic Exchanges:*** *3 lean meat, 2½ starch, ½ fat.*

PORK WITH SWEET POTATOES

SUZANNE CLARK'S
**SLITHERING SNAKEWICH WITH
SPICY VENOM SAUCE** *PAGE 261*

Kid-Friendly Foods

When these **child-pleasing choices** are on the menu, you won't need to coax kids to eat. Toddlers, teens and everyone in between will dig right in to these **fun and tasty treats.**

**BRENDA LOVELESS'
BANANA BOATS**
PAGE 260

**HELENA GEORGETTE MANN'S
PEANUT BUTTER & JELLY WAFFLES**
PAGE 264

**ARLENE PICKARD'S
STRAWBERRY MALLOW POPS**
PAGE 271

CHILI CONEY DOGS

<5 INGREDIENTS> <FAST FIX>

Banana Boats

Years ago, a friend gave me her recipe for chocolaty banana desserts on the grill. Try them the next time you go camping or host a backyard barbecue.

—**BRENDA LOVELESS** GARLAND, TX

START TO FINISH: 20 MIN.
MAKES: 4 SERVINGS

4	**medium unpeeled ripe bananas**
4	**teaspoons miniature chocolate chips**
4	**tablespoons miniature marshmallows**

1. Cut banana peel lengthwise about ½ in. deep, leaving ½ in. at both ends. Open the peel wider to form a pocket. Fill each with 1 teaspoon miniature chocolate chips and 1 tablespoon miniature marshmallows. Crimp and shape four pieces of heavy-duty foil (about 12 in. square) around bananas, forming boats.

2. Grill, covered, over medium heat for 5-10 minutes or until marshmallows melt and are golden brown.

PER SERVING *136 cal., 2 g fat (1 g sat. fat), 0 chol., 3 mg sodium, 32 g carb., 3 g fiber, 1 g pro.*

BANANA BOATS

<SLOW COOKER>

Chili Coney Dogs

Everyone in our family, from the smallest children to the oldest adults, loves these dogs. They're so easy to throw together in the slow cooker, and everyone can pile on whatever toppings they want.

—**MICHELE HARRIS** VICKSBURG, MI

PREP: 20 MIN. • **COOK:** 4 HOURS
MAKES: 8 SERVINGS

1	**pound lean ground beef (90% lean)**
1	**can (15 ounces) tomato sauce**
½	**cup water**
2	**tablespoons Worcestershire sauce**
1	**tablespoon dried minced onion**
½	**teaspoon garlic powder**
½	**teaspoon ground mustard**
½	**teaspoon chili powder**
½	**teaspoon pepper**
	Dash cayenne pepper
8	**hot dogs**
8	**hot dog buns, split**
	Optional toppings: shredded cheddar cheese, relish and chopped onion

1. In a large skillet, cook the beef over medium heat 6-8 minutes or until no longer pink, breaking into crumbles; drain. Stir in the tomato sauce, water, Worcestershire sauce, minced onion and seasonings.

2. Place the hot dogs in a 3-qt. slow cooker; top with the beef mixture. Cook, covered, on low 4-5 hours or until heated through.

3. Serve on hot dog buns with toppings as desired.

PER SERVING *(calculated without optional ingredients) 371 cal., 20 g fat (8 g sat. fat), 53 mg chol., 992 mg sodium, 26 g carb., 2 g fiber, 21 g pro.*

For a kids' party on Halloween or anytime, scare up a Slithering Snakewich with Spicy Venom Sauce. It's so fun, the grown-ups will want a slice, too!

—SUZANNE CLARK PHOENIX, AZ

Slithering Snakewich with Spicy Venom Sauce

PREP: 45 MIN. + RISING
BAKE: 20 MIN. + COOLING
MAKES: 20 SERVINGS

- 2 loaves (1 pound each) frozen bread dough
- 3 tablespoons butter, melted
- 2 tablespoons sesame seeds or poppy seeds
- ¾ cup roasted sweet red peppers, drained
- 1 cup mayonnaise
- ½ cup finely chopped pepperoncini
- 2 garlic cloves, minced
- 1 pound sliced deli smoked turkey
- 1 pound sliced deli ham
- ¾ pound sliced provolone cheese
- 2 large tomatoes, thinly sliced
- 1 medium head iceberg lettuce, thinly sliced
- 2 pretzel sticks or toothpicks
- 2 pickle slices
- 2 ripe olive slices

1. Thaw the bread dough according to package directions. Roll dough from each loaf into a 2-in.-thick log, shaping the end of one log to resemble a snake head and the end of the second log to resemble a rattle.
2. Transfer to greased baking sheets, curving slightly to resemble a snake. Cover with kitchen towels; let rise in a warm place until doubled, about 45 minutes. Preheat oven to 350°.
3. Brush dough with melted butter; sprinkle with sesame seeds. Bake 20-25 minutes or until golden brown. Remove from the pans to wire racks to cool completely.

4. Cut a roasted red pepper into a 3-in.-long strip to make snake tongue; set aside. Finely chop the remaining peppers and place in a bowl; stir in the mayonnaise, pepperoncini and garlic.
5. On a large cutting board, trim off the plain end of each loaf of bread, leaving the head and rattle ends intact. Cut each loaf horizontally in half. Connect the bottom halves to make a snake; layer with the turkey, ham, provolone cheese, tomatoes and 4 cups lettuce. Spread the top halves with 1 cup sauce; place over lettuce. Insert snake tongue.
6. For the grass, arrange remaining lettuce around the sandwich. Insert the pretzel sticks to attach the pickle slices and ripe olive slices for the eyes. Using a serrated knife, cut the sandwich into 20 slices; serve with remaining sauce.
PER SERVING *1 slice equals 346 cal., 18 g fat (5 g sat. fat), 39 mg chol., 897 mg sodium, 25 g carb., 2 g fiber, 18 g pro.*

FAST FIX
Crunchy Peanut Butter Apple Dip
Mom made this for us each fall. Now I carry on the tradition with my own children.
—JULI MEYERS HINESVILLE, GA

START TO FINISH: 10 MIN.
MAKES: 2½ CUPS

- 1 carton (8 ounces) reduced-fat spreadable cream cheese
- 1 cup creamy peanut butter
- ¼ cup fat-free milk
- 1 tablespoon brown sugar
- 1 teaspoon vanilla extract
- ½ cup chopped unsalted peanuts
  Apple slices

In a small bowl, beat the first five ingredients until blended. Stir in the peanuts. Serve with the apple slices. Refrigerate leftovers.
PER SERVING *2 tablespoons dip (calculated without apples) equals 126 cal., 10 g fat (3 g sat. fat), 5 mg chol., 115 mg sodium, 5 g carb., 1 g fiber, 5 g pro.*

CRUNCHY PEANUT BUTTER APPLE DIP

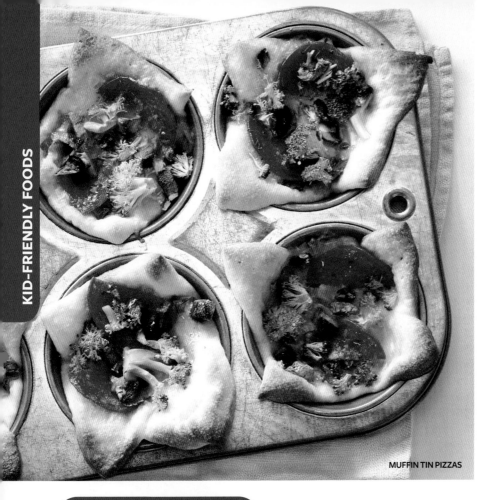

MUFFIN TIN PIZZAS

EAT SMART FAST FIX ▶

Homemade Fish Sticks

Moist inside and crunchy outside, these fish sticks are perfect with oven fries or roasted veggies and tartar sauce.

—**JENNIFER ROWLAND** ELIZABETHTOWN, KY

START TO FINISH: 25 MIN.
MAKES: 2 SERVINGS

- ½ **cup dry bread crumbs**
- ½ **teaspoon salt**
- ½ **teaspoon paprika**
- ½ **teaspoon lemon-pepper seasoning**
- ½ **cup all-purpose flour**
- 1 **large egg, beaten**
- ¾ **pound cod fillets, cut into 1-inch strips**
  Butter-flavored cooking spray

1. Preheat oven to 400°. In a shallow bowl, mix the crumbs and seasonings. Place flour and egg in separate shallow bowls. Dip the fish in flour to coat both sides; shake off excess. Dip in egg, then in the crumb mixture, patting to help coating adhere.

2. Place fish sticks on a baking sheet coated with cooking spray; spritz with butter-flavored cooking spray. Bake 10-12 minutes or until fish just begins to flake easily with a fork, turning once.

PER SERVING *1 serving equals 278 cal., 4 g fat (1 g sat. fat), 129 mg chol., 718 mg sodium, 25 g carb., 1 g fiber, 33 g pro.* **Diabetic Exchanges:** *4 lean meat, 1½ starch.*

HOMEMADE FISH STICKS

Soon after I first fixed a batch of Muffin Tin Pizzas, my kids were asking for more. The no-cook sauce and refrigerated dough make this meal so easy.

—**MELISSA HAINES** VALPARAISO, IN

Muffin Tin Pizzas

PREP: 25 MIN. • **BAKE:** 10 MIN.
MAKES: 8 SERVINGS

- 1 **can (15 ounces) tomato sauce**
- 1 **can (6 ounces) tomato paste**
- 1 **teaspoon dried basil**
- ½ **teaspoon garlic salt**
- ¼ **teaspoon onion powder**
- ¼ **teaspoon sugar**
- 1 **tube (11 ounces) refrigerated thin pizza crust**
- 1½ **cups (6 ounces) shredded part-skim mozzarella cheese**
- ½ **cup finely chopped fresh mushrooms**
- ½ **cup finely chopped fresh broccoli**
- 16 **slices pepperoni, halved**

1. Preheat oven to 425°. In a small bowl, mix the first six ingredients.
2. Unroll the pizza crust; cut into 16 squares. Press the squares onto bottom and up sides of 16 ungreased muffin cups, allowing the corners to hang over the edge.
3. Spoon 1 tablespoon pizza sauce mixture into each muffin cup. Top with shredded mozzarella cheese, mushrooms, broccoli and pepperoni. Bake 10-12 minutes or until pizza crust is golden brown. Serve the remaining sauce mixture, warmed if desired, with pizzas.
FREEZE OPTION *Freeze cooled baked pizzas in a resealable plastic freezer bag. To use, reheat pizzas on a baking sheet in a preheated 425° oven until heated through.*
PER SERVING *2 pizzas with 2 tablespoons sauce equals 233 cal., 9 g fat (4 g sat. fat), 16 mg chol., 755 mg sodium, 26 g carb., 2 g fiber, 12 g pro.*

PEANUT BUTTER
BROWNIE CUPCAKES

Peanut Butter Brownie Cupcakes

Just about everyone loves brownies and cupcakes, so why not combine them?

—**CAROL GILLESPIE** CHAMBERSBURG, PA

PREP: 15 MIN. • **BAKE:** 15 MIN. + COOLING
MAKES: 1 DOZEN

- 1 package fudge brownie mix
  (8-inch-square pan size)
- ½ cup miniature semisweet
  chocolate chips
- ⅓ cup creamy peanut butter
- 3 tablespoons cream cheese,
  softened
- 1 large egg
- ¼ cup sugar
  Confectioners' sugar

1. Preheat oven to 350°. Prepare the fudge brownie batter according to the package directions; stir in miniature semisweet chocolate chips. For the filling, in a small bowl, beat the peanut butter, cream cheese, egg and sugar until smooth.
2. Fill paper-lined muffin cups one-third full with batter. Drop filling by teaspoonfuls into the center of each cupcake. Cover with remaining batter.
3. Bake 15-20 minutes or until a toothpick inserted in brownie portion comes out clean. Cool the cupcakes 10 minutes before removing from the pan to a wire rack to cool completely. Dust the tops with confectioners' sugar. Store in the refrigerator.
PER SERVING *1 cupcake equals 328 cal., 18 g fat (5 g sat. fat), 40 mg chol., 201 mg sodium, 39 g carb., 2 g fiber, 5 g pro.*

⑤ INGREDIENTS FAST FIX

Raspberry Ice Cream in a Bag

Making homemade ice cream is fun for the whole family. Children can shake the bags until the liquid changes to a frosty treat and then savor the reward!

—**ERIN HOFFMAN** CANBY, MN

START TO FINISH: 15 MIN.
MAKES: 1 CUP

- 1 cup half-and-half cream
- ½ cup fresh raspberries
- ¼ cup sugar
- 2 tablespoons evaporated milk
- 1 teaspoon vanilla extract
- 4 cups coarsely crushed ice
- ¾ cup salt

1. Using two quart-size resealable plastic bags, place one plastic bag inside the other. Place the first five ingredients inside the inner bag. Seal both bags, pressing out as much air as possible.
2. Place the two bags in a gallon-size resealable plastic freezer bag. Add ice and salt. Seal bag, again pressing out as much air as possible.
3. Shake and knead cream mixture until thickened, about 5 minutes. (If desired, wear mittens or wrap bags in a kitchen towel while shaking to protect hands from the cold ice.)
PER SERVING *½ cup equals 299 cal., 13 g fat (9 g sat. fat), 65 mg chol., 76 mg sodium, 35 g carb., 2 g fiber, 5 g pro.*

RASPBRRY ICE CREAM IN A BAG

Yay for Breakfast!

Children will cheer for their morning meal when you serve up these **sunny sensations,** from fruity beverages to egg-filled tortillas.

PEANUT BUTTER & JELLY WAFFLES

---

⑤INGREDIENTS FAST FIX

Mango-Peach Smoothies

Here is my toddler's absolute favorite breakfast. He'll choose a smoothie over pancakes any day! The blend of mango and peach is one of our regular flavor combinations, but it's fun to experiment with different fruits and yogurts.
—**DANA HERRA** DEKALB, IL

START TO FINISH: 5 MIN. • **MAKES:** 4 SERVINGS

- 1 **cup fat-free milk**
- 12 **ounces peach yogurt (about 1¼ cups)**
- 2½ **cups frozen mango chunks**

Place all ingredients in a blender; cover and process until smooth. Serve immediately.

PER SERVING *1 cup equals 180 cal., 1 g fat (1 g sat. fat), 5 mg chol., 71 mg sodium, 39 g carb., 3 g fiber, 6 g pro.*

MANGO-PEACH SMOOTHIES

FAST FIX

Peanut Butter & Jelly Waffles

You might find that the adults you know crave these homemade peanut butter waffles just as much as youngsters do. What's the perfect finishing touch on top? Of course, jelly!
—**HELENA GEORGETTE MANN** SACRAMENTO, CA

START TO FINISH: 25 MIN. • **MAKES:** 10 WAFFLES

- 1¼ **cups all-purpose flour**
- 3 **tablespoons sugar**
- 1 **tablespoon baking powder**
- ¼ **teaspoon baking soda**
- ¼ **teaspoon ground cinnamon**
- 2 **large eggs, separated**
- 1¼ **cups milk**
- ⅓ **cup peanut butter**
- 3 **tablespoons butter, melted**
  Jelly of your choice

1. In a large bowl, combine the flour, sugar, baking powder, baking soda and cinnamon. In another bowl, whisk the egg yolks, milk, peanut butter and butter; stir mixture into dry ingredients just until moistened.

2. In a small bowl, beat the egg whites until stiff peaks form; fold into batter. Bake in a preheated waffle iron according to the manufacturer's directions until golden brown. Serve waffles with jelly.

FREEZE OPTION *Arrange the waffles in a single layer on sheet pans. Freeze overnight or until frozen. Transfer to a resealable plastic freezer bag. Waffles may be frozen for up to 2 months. Reheat the frozen waffles in a toaster. Serve with jelly.*

PER SERVING *2 waffles (calculated without jelly) equals 370 cal., 20 g fat (8 g sat. fat), 109 mg chol., 484 mg sodium, 38 g carb., 2 g fiber, 12 g pro.*

Nacho Hash Brown Casserole

Toss packaged cubed potatoes in a slow cooker with a few other ingredients and you'll get the best hash browns ever. The creamy side dish is great for breakfast and dinner, too.
—**PAT HABIGER** SPEARVILLE, KS

PREP: 15 MIN. • **COOK:** 3¼ HOURS • **MAKES:** 8 SERVINGS

- 1 **package (32 ounces) frozen cubed hash brown potatoes, thawed**
- 1 **can (10¾ ounces) condensed cream of celery soup, undiluted**
- 1 **can (10¾ ounces) condensed nacho cheese soup, undiluted**
- 1 **large onion, finely chopped**
- ⅓ **cup butter, melted**
- 1 **cup (8 ounces) reduced-fat sour cream**

1. In a greased 3-qt. slow cooker, combine the first five ingredients. Cover and cook on low for 3-4 hours or until potatoes are tender.

2. Stir in the sour cream. Cover and cook 15-30 minutes longer or until heated through.

PER SERVING *¾ cup equals 259 cal., 14 g fat (7 g sat. fat), 32 mg chol., 640 mg sodium, 31 g carb., 3 g fiber, 5 g pro.*

BREAKFAST QUESADILLAS

NACHO HASH BROWN CASSEROLE

⑤ INGREDIENTS **FAST FIX** ▶

Breakfast Quesadillas

Kids find it fun to eat these mild-flavored tortilla wedges filled with scrambled eggs, cheese, bacon and onion. If it suits your family's tastes, serve the quesadillas with salsa and sour cream.
—**JENNIFER EVANS** OCEANSIDE, CA

START TO FINISH: 20 MIN. • **MAKES:** 2 SERVINGS

- 3 **large eggs**
- 2 **flour tortillas (8 inches)**
- ½ **cup shredded fontina cheese**
- 2 **bacon strips, cooked and crumbled**
- 1 **green onion, thinly sliced**
  Sour cream and salsa, optional

1. In a small bowl, whisk the eggs. Coat a large skillet with cooking spray. Add eggs; cook and stir over medium heat until completely set.

2. Place tortillas on a griddle. Spoon eggs over half of each tortilla; sprinkle with cheese, bacon and onion. Fold over and cook over low heat for 1-2 minutes on each side or until cheese is melted. Serve with sour cream and salsa.

PER SERVING *1 quesadilla (calculated without sour cream and salsa) equals 401 cal., 22 g fat (9 g sat. fat), 357 mg chol., 728 mg sodium, 27 g carb., trace fiber, 24 g pro.*

SCOOTER SNACKS

On-the-Go Granola Bars

I take these perennial favorites to many school functions. The homemade granola bars make great hand-held goodies for little ones. Feel free to change the flavor a bit by substituting different preserves or by swapping in other dried fruits.

—SUZANNE MCKINLEY LYONS, GA

PREP: 20 MIN. + CHILLING
MAKES: 16 BARS

- 7 tablespoons butter, softened, divided
- 1½ cups miniature marshmallows
- ½ cup apricot or peach preserves
- ¼ cup packed brown sugar
- 4 cups reduced-fat granola with raisins
- 1⅓ cups diced dried mixed fruit

1. Line an 8-in.-square pan with waxed paper. Grease the paper with 1 tablespoon butter; set aside.
2. In a large heavy saucepan, combine the marshmallows, preserves, brown sugar and remaining butter; cook and stir over medium heat until blended. Remove from the heat.
3. Stir in granola and mixed fruit; toss to coat. Press firmly into prepared pan. Cover and refrigerate for 1½ hours or until firm. Invert and remove waxed paper. Cut into bars.
PER SERVING *1 bar equals 208 cal., 6 g fat (4 g sat. fat), 13 mg chol., 105 mg sodium, 38 g carb., 2 g fiber, 2 g pro.*

FAST FIX ▸
Scooter Snacks

Ready, set, go! Whimsical scooters will have your children happily nibbling on a wholesome snack of vegetables, string cheese and more. It's a fun way to tide over hungry tots before dinner.

—DIDI DESJARDINS DARTMOUTH, MA

START TO FINISH: 30 MIN.
MAKES: 2 SCOOTERS

- 8 slices zucchini (¼ inch thick)
- 6 pretzel sticks, divided
- 2 pieces string cheese (1 ounce each)
- 2 pretzel rods, cut into 3-inch pieces
- 2 tablespoons spreadable garden vegetable cream cheese
- 4 cherry tomatoes, halved
- 2 pimiento-stuffed olives, halved

1. For each of four axles, thread two zucchini slices through a pretzel stick, leaving a 1-in. space in the center. For each scooter, position string cheese between two axles.
2. Attach a pretzel rod with cream cheese to each scooter; top each with a pretzel stick for the handlebars. Add tomato hubcaps and olive headlights and taillights with cream cheese.
PER SERVING *1 scooter equals 201 cal., 13 g fat (8 g sat. fat), 35 mg chol., 591 mg sodium, 13 g carb., 1 g fiber, 9 g pro.*

ON-THE-GO GRANOLA BARS

LASAGNA ROLLS

⑤ INGREDIENTS

Root Beer Float Cake

Slice up this soda-licious cake for a bunch of hungry kids, and it'll disappear in a snap! I pour root beer into both the batter and the fluffy whipped topping.

—**KAT THOMPSON** PRINEVILLE, OR

PREP: 15 MIN. • **BAKE:** 30 MIN. + COOLING
MAKES: 12-15 SERVINGS

- 1 **package white cake mix (regular size)**
- 1¾ **cups cold root beer, divided**
- ¼ **cup canola oil**
- 2 **large eggs**
- 1 **envelope whipped topping mix (Dream Whip)**

1. In a large bowl, combine cake mix, 1¼ cups root beer, oil and eggs. Beat on low speed for 2 minutes or stir by hand for 3 minutes.

2. Pour into a greased 13x9-in. baking pan. Bake at 350° for 30-35 minutes or until a toothpick inserted near center comes out clean. Cool completely on a wire rack.

3. For the frosting, in a small bowl, combine whipped topping mix and remaining root beer. Beat until soft peaks form. Frost cake. Store in the refrigerator.

PER SERVING *1 piece equals 203 cal., 8 g fat (2 g sat. fat), 27 mg chol., 216 mg sodium, 31 g carb., trace fiber, 2 g pro.*

⑤ INGREDIENTS

Lasagna Rolls

My Italian roll-ups require just five basic ingredients to assemble. Using prepared spaghetti sauce, I can save time and get dinner on the table sooner.

—**MARY LEE THOMAS** LOGANSPORT, IN

PREP: 25 MIN. • **BAKE:** 10 MIN.
MAKES: 6 SERVINGS

- 6 **lasagna noodles**
- 1 **pound ground beef**
- 1 **jar (14 ounces) spaghetti sauce**
- 1 **teaspoon fennel seed, optional**
- 2 **cups (8 ounces) shredded part-skim mozzarella cheese, divided**

1. Cook lasagna noodles according to package directions. Meanwhile, in a large skillet, cook the beef over medium heat until no longer pink, breaking into crumbles; drain. Stir in the spaghetti sauce and, if desired, fennel seed; heat through.

2. Drain noodles. Spread ¼ cup meat sauce over each noodle; sprinkle with 2 tablespoons cheese. Carefully roll up noodles and place seam side down in an 8-in.-square baking dish. Top with remaining sauce and cheese.

3. Bake rolls, uncovered, at 400° for 10-15 minutes or until heated through and the cheese is melted.

PER SERVING *1 each equals 377 cal., 18 g fat (8 g sat. fat), 70 mg chol., 549 mg sodium, 26 g carb., 2 g fiber, 28 g pro.*

ROOT BEER FLOAT CAKE

FUN FISH PASTRIES

1. In a small bowl, combine crab, egg yolk, onion powder, garlic powder and salt. Stir in cheddar cheese; set aside.

2. For pastry, in a large bowl, combine the flour and salt. Cut in shortening until the mixture resembles coarse crumbs. Combine tomato juice and Worcestershire sauce; stir into dry ingredients just until moistened. Turn onto a lightly floured surface; knead 8-10 times.

3. Divide dough into 22 equal pieces. Pat or roll each piece into a 4-in. circle, ¼-in. thick.

4. Place eight pastry circles among two greased baking sheets. Place a heaping tablespoonful of filling in the center of each circle.

5. For the fins and tails, cut six circles into fourths. Cut lines on each curved side. Place two fins and a tail on each uncut circle on baking sheets, attaching with water. Press onto circles.

6. In the remaining eight circles, cut scale shapes into bodies using the small end of a pastry bag coupler. Brush the edges with water and place over filling; press to seal. Brush the tops of pastries with egg white.

7. Bake at 400° for 10-15 minutes or until golden brown. For eyes, cut small circles out of mozzarella using coupler; place on hot pastries with a piece of olive in center for pupils. Garnish plates with endive and berries if desired.

8. In a small saucepan, combine the sauce ingredients. Cook and stir over medium heat until cheese is melted. Serve with pastries.

PER SERVING *1 fish pastry with 5 tablespoons sauce equals 537 cal., 34 g fat (11 g sat. fat), 66 mg chol., 836 mg sodium, 41 g carb., 2 g fiber, 16 g pro.*

Fun Fish Pastries

Everyone will be hooked on these pastries paired with cheese sauce. For extra fun, add endive and blueberries to each plate for the seaweed and bubbles.

—**MARY BALKAVICH** TYRONE, PA

PREP: 1 HOUR • **BAKE:** 15 MIN.
MAKES: 8 SERVINGS (2½ CUPS SAUCE)

- 1 can (6 ounces) lump crabmeat, drained or light tuna in water
- 1 large egg yolk
- ⅛ teaspoon onion powder
- ⅛ teaspoon garlic powder
- ⅛ teaspoon salt
- 2 tablespoons shredded cheddar cheese

PASTRY
- 3 cups all-purpose flour
- 1 teaspoon salt
- 1 cup shortening
- ⅓ cup tomato juice
- 1 teaspoon Worcestershire sauce

ASSEMBLY
- 1 egg white, beaten
- 1 slice part-skim mozzarella cheese
- 1 pitted ripe olive, chopped
  Curly endive and fresh blueberries, optional

SAUCE
- 1 can (10¾ ounces) condensed cream of celery soup or cream of mushroom soup, undiluted
- 1 cup (4 ounces) shredded cheddar cheese
- ¾ cup 2% milk
- 1 jar (2 ounces) diced pimientos, drained

Crescent Dough Crackers

Serve leaf-shaped crackers, cheese and salami—you'll rake in the compliments! Just unroll 1 sheet of crescent roll dough and flatten it slightly. Sprinkle on poppy seeds, sesame seeds, coarse salt and Italian seasoning before cutting with leaf-shaped cookie cutters. Bake at 375° for 10-12 minutes or until golden brown.

—**TASTE OF HOME** TEST KITCHEN

CRESCENT DOUGH CRACKERS

SLOW-COOKED SLOPPY JOES

1. Arrange the kettle-cooked potato chips in a single layer on a waxed paper-lined baking sheet.
2. In a microwave, melt semisweet chocolate chips and shortening; stir until smooth. Drizzle over potato chips. Refrigerate 5 minutes or until set.
PER SERVING *½ cup equals 140 cal., 9 g fat (4 g sat. fat), 0 chol., 75 mg sodium, 16 g carb., 1 g fiber, 1 g pro.*

(5) INGREDIENTS **FAST FIX**
Easy Homemade Chunky Applesauce
Here's a comforting, home-style treat that never loses its appeal. Dish up big bowlfuls and wait for the smiles!
—**MARILEE CARDINAL** BURLINGTON, NJ

START TO FINISH: 30 MIN.
MAKES: 5 CUPS

- 7 medium McIntosh, Empire or other apples (about 3 pounds)
- ½ cup sugar
- ½ cup water
- 1 tablespoon lemon juice
- ¼ teaspoon almond or vanilla extract

1. Peel, core and cut each apple into eight wedges. Cut each apple wedge crosswise in half; place in a large saucepan. Add remaining ingredients.
2. Bring to a boil. Reduce the heat; simmer, covered, 15-20 minutes or until desired consistency, stirring occasionally.
PER SERVING *¾ cup equals 139 cal., trace fat (trace sat. fat), 0 chol., trace sodium, 36 g carb., 2 g fiber, trace pro.*

SLOW COOKER
Slow-Cooked Sloppy Joes
On hot summer days, this sloppy joe meat cooks without heating up the kitchen and gives me time to prepare the rest of our meal, too. The recipe is also easy to double or triple when I'm serving a crowd.
—**CAROL LOSIER** BALDWINSVILLE, NY

PREP: 20 MIN. • **COOK:** 3 HOURS
MAKES: 8 SERVINGS

- 1½ pounds ground beef
- 2 celery ribs, chopped
- 1 small onion, chopped
- 1 bottle (12 ounces) chili sauce
- 2 tablespoons brown sugar
- 2 tablespoons sweet pickle relish
- 1 tablespoon Worcestershire sauce
- 1 teaspoon salt
- ⅛ teaspoon pepper
- 8 hamburger buns, split

1. In a large skillet, cook beef, celery and onion over medium-high heat 8-10 minutes or until beef is no longer pink, breaking up beef into crumbles; drain. Transfer to a 3-qt. slow cooker.

2. Stir in the chili sauce, brown sugar, pickle relish, Worcestershire sauce, salt and pepper. Cook, covered, on low 3-4 hours or until heated through and the flavors are blended.
3. Spoon the meat mixture onto the bottoms of hamburger buns. Replace the tops.
PER SERVING *1 sandwich equals 324 cal., 10 g fat (4 g sat. fat), 42 mg chol., 1,313 mg sodium, 40 g carb., 1 g fiber, 19 g pro.*

(5) INGREDIENTS **FAST FIX**
Chocolaty Chips
My two young sons can't get enough of this sweet-and-salty snack, which uses just three ingredients and is ready to eat in 15 minutes. The boys like to drizzle on the melted chocolate, too. Sometimes we replace the potato chips with apple slices.
—**JAMI GEITTMANN** GREENDALE, WI

START TO FINISH: 15 MIN.
MAKES: 6 SERVINGS

- 3 cups kettle-cooked potato chips
- ½ cup semisweet chocolate chips
- 1 teaspoon shortening

EASY HOMEMADE CHUNKY APPLESAUCE

(5) INGREDIENTS FAST FIX ▶

Cinnamon Roll Bunnies

A tube of purchased cinnamon roll dough and a little imagination make these adorable bunnies almost too cute to eat. They're sure to appeal to "somebunny" at your house.

—**JENNI SHARP** MILWAUKEE, WI

START TO FINISH: 30 MIN.
MAKES: 4 SERVINGS

- 1 **tube (12.4 ounces) refrigerated cinnamon rolls with icing**
  Optional decorations: red food coloring, assorted candies and decorating gel

1. Preheat oven to 400°. Separate the dough into eight rolls. Place four rolls on a greased baking sheet.
2. Using a 2-in. biscuit cutter, cut ¾ in. into each side of the remaining rolls, forming the ears and bow ties. Add ears and bow ties to cinnamon rolls, pinching to attach; press slightly to flatten. Bake 8-10 minutes or until golden brown.
3. Spread the cinnamon roll icing over the bunnies, tinting a portion of icing pink with red food coloring if desired. Decorate as desired with candies and decorating gel.

PER SERVING *290 cal., 10 g fat (3 g sat. fat), 0 chol., 685 mg sodium, 47 g carb., 1 g fiber, 4 g pro.*

WEEKNIGHT RAVIOLI LASAGNA

CINNAMON ROLL BUNNIES

(5) INGREDIENTS

Weeknight Ravioli Lasagna

We love lasagna, but many recipes are time-consuming to assemble or leave us with a large pan full of leftovers. Using frozen ravioli to make a shortcut version solves everything! This quick dish is saucy, cheesy and delicious.

—**PAMELA NICHOLSON** FESTUS, MO

PREP: 15 MIN. • **BAKE:** 45 MIN.
MAKES: 6 SERVINGS

- 1 **jar (24 ounces) pasta sauce**
- 1 **package (25 ounces) frozen meat or cheese ravioli**
- 1½ **cups (6 ounces) shredded part-skim mozzarella cheese**
- 3 **cups fresh baby spinach**

1. Preheat the oven to 350°. In a small saucepan, heat sauce 5-7 minutes over medium heat or just until simmering, stirring occasionally.
2. Spread ½ cup sauce into a greased 11x7-in. baking dish. Layer with half of the ravioli, 1½ cups spinach, ½ cup mozzarella and half of the remaining sauce; repeat the layers. Sprinkle with remaining cheese.
3. Bake, uncovered, 45-50 minutes or until the edges are bubbly and the cheese is melted. Let stand 5 minutes before serving.

PER SERVING *1 cup equals 344 cal., 10 g fat (5 g sat. fat), 26 mg chol., 850 mg sodium, 45 g carb., 5 g fiber, 17 g pro.* **Diabetic Exchanges:** *3 starch, 2 medium-fat meat.*

Taco Biscuit Bake

Bored with the usual tacos? Spice up your dinner routine by putting all the fixings into a hot, hearty casserole.

—SARA MARTIN WHITEFISH, MT

PREP: 20 MIN. • **BAKE:** 25 MIN.
MAKES: 8 SERVINGS

- 1 **pound lean ground beef (90% lean)**
- ⅔ **cup water**
- 1 **envelope taco seasoning**
- 2 **tubes (12 ounces each) refrigerated buttermilk biscuits**
- 1 **can (15 ounces) chili con carne**
- 1 **cup (4 ounces) shredded reduced-fat cheddar cheese**
   Salsa and sour cream, optional

1. In a large skillet, cook beef over medium heat until no longer pink, breaking into crumbles; drain. Stir in the water and taco seasoning. Bring to a boil; cook and stir for 2 minutes or until thickened.

2. Meanwhile, quarter the biscuits; place in a greased 13x9-in. baking dish. Layer with the beef mixture, chili and cheddar cheese.

3. Bake, uncovered, at 375° for 25-30 minutes or until the cheese is melted and the biscuits are golden brown. Serve with salsa and sour cream if desired.

PER SERVING *1 serving (calculated without salsa and sour cream) equals 422 cal., 14 g fat (6 g sat. fat), 62 mg chol., 1,439 mg sodium, 49 g carb., 1 g fiber, 26 g pro.*

TACO BISCUIT BAKE

STRAWBERRY MALLOW POPS

Strawberry Mallow Pops

Dotted with bits of strawberries and fluffy marshmallows, these creamy pink pops are always in demand. I keep a cache in the freezer for scorching summer days because I know everybody in my family, young and old alike, will be craving one. And that includes me!

—ARLENE PICKARD REDVERS, SK

PREP: 20 MIN. + FREEZING
MAKES: 2 DOZEN

- 1 **package (8 ounces) cream cheese, softened**
- ¼ **cup honey**
- 2 **packages (10 ounces each) frozen sweetened sliced strawberries, thawed**
- 3 **cups miniature marshmallows**
- 1 **cup heavy whipping cream, whipped**
- 24 **freezer pop molds or 24 paper cups (3 ounces each) and wooden pop sticks**

1. In a small bowl, beat cream cheese and honey until smooth. Add sliced strawberries with juice; beat until blended. Fold in the marshmallows and whipped cream.

2. Pour ¼ cupfuls into molds or cups. Top molds with holders. If using cups, top with foil and insert sticks through foil. Freeze until firm.

PER SERVING *1 pop equals 99 cal., 5 g fat (3 g sat. fat), 17 mg chol., 34 mg sodium, 13 g carb., trace fiber, 1 g pro.*

TOP TIP

Short on time? For a super-easy pop, push a wooden pop stick through the foil cover of a small yogurt. (Remove the plastic lid first if there is one.) Put it in the freezer until frozen, remove the plastic container and enjoy.

—DIANNE M. LAKEMOOR, IL

Campfire Bundles

I'd brought a hodgepodge of ingredients along on a camping trip and threw them together in a foil packet. It worked!
—**LAURI KRAUSE** JACKSON, NE

PREP: 15 MIN. • **GRILL:** 1 HOUR
MAKES: 6 SERVINGS

- 1 large sweet onion, sliced
- 1 each large green, sweet red and yellow pepper
- 4 medium potatoes, cut into ¼-inch slices
- 6 medium carrots, cut into ¼-inch slices
- 1 small head cabbage, sliced
- 2 medium tomatoes, chopped
- 1 to 1½ pounds smoked Polish sausage, cut into ½-inch slices
- ½ cup butter, cubed
- 1 teaspoon salt
- ½ teaspoon pepper

1. Place vegetables on three pieces of double-layered heavy-duty foil (about 18 in. square). Top with the sausage; dot with butter. Sprinkle with salt and pepper. Fold the foil around mixture and seal tightly.

2. Grill, covered, over medium heat for 30 minutes. Turn; grill 30 minutes longer or until vegetables are tender. Open the foil carefully to allow steam to escape.

PER SERVING *1 serving (1 each) equals 582 cal., 36 g fat (18 g sat. fat), 95 mg chol., 1,247 mg sodium, 50 g carb., 9 g fiber, 16 g pro.*

AFTER-SCHOOL TAMALE CAKES

After-School Tamale Cakes

When the kids get home and clamor for a snack, go beyond the usual peanut butter and jelly with these savory bites flavored with enchilada sauce. Skewers of fresh fruit are nice on the side.
—**SUZANNE CLARK** PHOENIX, AZ

PREP: 25 MIN. • **BAKE:** 20 MIN.
MAKES: 2 DOZEN

- 2 packages (8½ ounces each) corn bread/muffin mix
- 1 can (14¾ ounces) cream-style corn
- 2 large eggs, lightly beaten
- 1½ cups (6 ounces) shredded reduced-fat Mexican cheese blend, divided
- 1½ cups chopped cooked chicken breast
- ¾ cup red enchilada sauce

1. Preheat the oven to 400°. In a large bowl, combine muffin mix, corn and eggs; stir just until moistened. Stir in 1 cup cheese. In another bowl, toss the chicken with the enchilada sauce.

2. Fill each of 24 foil-lined muffin cups with 2 tablespoons batter. Place 1 tablespoon chicken mixture into the center of each; cover with about 1 tablespoon batter.

3. Bake 13-15 minutes or until golden brown. Sprinkle the tops with the remaining cheese. Bake 3-5 minutes longer or until the cheese is melted. Cool 5 minutes before removing from the pan to wire racks. Serve warm. Refrigerate leftovers.

PER SERVING *1 muffin equals 137 cal., 5 g fat (2 g sat. fat), 28 mg chol., 313 mg sodium, 18 g carb., 2 g fiber, 7 g pro.* **Diabetic Exchanges:** *1 starch, 1 lean meat.*

CAMPFIRE BUNDLES

BACON CREAM CHEESE PINWHEELS

Crispy Chicken Fingers

My children just love to eat these crispy yet tender strips. My husband and I cut up the chicken and toss it in a main-dish salad with lettuce, eggs, tomatoes and other fixings. Everybody's happy!

—**RACHEL FIZEL** WOODBURY, MN

PREP: 20 MIN. • **COOK:** 5 MIN./BATCH
MAKES: 7 SERVINGS

- 1 cup all-purpose flour
- 1 cup dry bread crumbs
- 2 tablespoons grated Parmesan cheese
- 1 teaspoon salt
- ¾ teaspoon garlic powder
- ½ teaspoon baking powder
- 1 large egg
- 1 cup buttermilk
- 1¾ pounds boneless skinless chicken breasts, cut into strips
  Oil for deep-fat frying

1. In a large resealable plastic bag, combine the first six ingredients. In a shallow bowl, whisk the egg and buttermilk. Dip a few pieces of chicken at a time in buttermilk mixture, then place in bag; seal and shake to coat.
2. In an electric skillet, heat the oil to 375°. Fry the chicken, a few strips at a time, for 2-3 minutes on each side or until the chicken is no longer pink. Drain on paper towels.
PER SERVING *4 ounces cooked chicken equals 341 cal., 16 g fat (2 g sat. fat), 80 mg chol., 485 mg sodium, 21 g carb., 1 g fiber, 28 g pro.*

Bacon Cream Cheese Pinwheels

With bacon, cream cheese and onion all rolled into one, these crescent pinwheels are impossible to resist. People scarf them down, so I make sure to double the recipe when we're having a party.

—**KRISTA MUNSON** SHARPSBURG, KY

START TO FINISH: 30 MIN.
MAKES: 2 DOZEN

- 3 ounces cream cheese, softened
- 2 tablespoons finely chopped onion
- 1 teaspoon 2% milk
- 1 tube (8 ounces) refrigerated crescent rolls
- 5 bacon strips, cooked and finely chopped

1. Preheat oven to 375°. In a small bowl, mix the cream cheese, onion and milk until blended. On a lightly floured surface, unroll the crescent roll dough into one long rectangle; press the perforations to seal.
2. Spread with cream cheese mixture; sprinkle with bacon. Roll up jelly-roll style, starting with a long side; pinch the seam to seal. Using a serrated knife, cut the roll crosswise into twenty-four (½-inch) slices. Place on ungreased baking sheets, cut side down.
3. Bake 12-15 minutes or until golden brown. Refrigerate leftovers.
PER SERVING *1 appetizer equals 58 cal., 4 g fat (2 g sat. fat), 6 mg chol., 116 mg sodium, 4 g carb., trace fiber, 1 g pro.*

CRISPY CHICKEN FINGERS

DEBORAH LOOP'S CANNELLONI-STYLE LASAGNA *PAGE 285*

Table Traditions

Sit down to a meal full of love. In this chapter, *Taste of Home* fans serve up some of their **favorite stories and recipes.** Enjoy these specialties with your own family and friends.

**COURTNEY STULTZ'S
SLOW COOKER ROAST CHICKEN**
PAGE 279

**ANTHONY BOLTON'S
EDDIE'S FAVORITE FIESTA CORN**
PAGE 281

**LIZ BELLVILLE'S
RAINBOW VEGGIE SALAD**
PAGE 282

At the Table Together

For this avid cook, dinner's always been about a big, cozy table. Just **surround it with family,** then load it up with bowls and plates of comfy **Southern dishes.**

RECIPES & STORY BY **JUDY BATSON** | TAMPA, FL

The heart of our military family's various homes was always the dining room table, as it was in my grandmother's house, too. Like her, I strive to make it a place full of love—and great food.

Southern cooking is all about comfort, warmth and fabulous flavor. One of our family's favorite menus features Beef Short Ribs in Burgundy Sauce, complemented by Spinach-Parm Casserole and Brown Sugar-Glazed Sweet Potatoes on the side.

As an Army general, my stepfather got the recipe for saucy beef ribs from his aide, who said it was his mother's best Sunday meal. Gathering together all the ingredients is so worth it!

For those who just won't eat spinach, I find that Spinach-Parm Casserole helps change their minds. The greens are delicious dressed up with garlicky butter and cheese.

Our family cherishes sweet potatoes with apples and raisins. If I suggest something other than the usual Brown Sugar-Glazed Sweet Potatoes, they say, "Oh *no,* that's part of the love!"

BEEF SHORT RIBS IN BURGUNDY SAUCE

Beef Short Ribs in Burgundy Sauce

PREP: 35 MIN. • **COOK:** 2¼ HOURS
MAKES: 6 SERVINGS

- 3 **pounds bone-in beef short ribs**
- 3 **tablespoons butter**
- 1 **large sweet onion, halved and sliced**
- 2 **celery ribs, thinly sliced**
- 1 **medium carrot, thinly sliced**
- 1 **garlic clove, minced**
  Dash dried thyme
- 2 **tablespoons all-purpose flour**
- 1 **cup water**
- 1 **cup dry red wine or beef broth**
- 1 **beef bouillon cube or 1 teaspoon beef bouillon granules**
- 2 **tablespoons minced fresh parsley**
- ½ **teaspoon Worcestershire sauce**
- ¼ **teaspoon salt**
- ¼ **teaspoon browning sauce, optional**
- ⅛ **teaspoon pepper**

1. Preheat oven to 450°. Place short ribs on a rack in a shallow roasting pan. Roast 30-40 minutes or until browned, turning once.

2. Meanwhile, in a Dutch oven, heat the butter over medium heat. Add onion, celery and carrot; cook and stir 10-12 minutes or until tender. Add garlic and thyme; cook 1 minute longer. Stir in flour until blended; gradually stir in water and wine. Add bouillon and parsley, stirring to dissolve bouillon.

3. Transfer the ribs to Dutch oven; bring to a boil. Reduce heat; simmer, covered, 2-2½ hours or until meat is tender.

4. Remove short ribs; keep warm. Skim fat from sauce; stir in remaining ingredients. Serve with ribs.

PER SERVING *1 serving equals 264 cal., 17 g fat (8 g sat. fat), 70 mg chol., 355 mg sodium, 8 g carb., 1 g fiber, 19 g pro.*

Spinach-Parm Casserole

START TO FINISH: 25 MIN. • **MAKES:** 6 SERVINGS

- 2 pounds fresh baby spinach
- 5 tablespoons butter
- 3 tablespoons olive oil
- 3 garlic cloves, minced
- 1 tablespoon Italian seasoning
- ¾ teaspoon salt
- 1 cup grated Parmesan cheese

1. Preheat oven to 400°. In a stockpot, bring 5 cups water to a boil. Add spinach; cook, covered, 1 minute or just until wilted. Drain well.

2. In a small skillet, heat butter and oil over medium-low heat. Add garlic, Italian seasoning and salt; cook and stir 1-2 minutes or until garlic is tender.

3. Spread the spinach in a greased 1½-qt. baking dish. Drizzle with the butter mixture; sprinkle with Parmesan cheese. Bake, uncovered, 10-15 minutes or until the cheese is lightly browned.

PER SERVING ⅔ cup equals 239 cal., 21 g fat (9 g sat. fat), 37 mg chol., 703 mg sodium, 7 g carb., 3 g fiber, 10 g pro.

BROWN SUGAR-GLAZED SWEET POTATOES

SPINACH-PARM CASSEROLE

Brown Sugar-Glazed Sweet Potatoes

PREP: 25 MIN. • **BAKE:** 25 MIN.
MAKES: 6 SERVINGS

- 2¼ pounds sweet potatoes (about 4 medium), peeled and cut into 1-inch pieces
- 2 tablespoons butter
- ⅔ cup packed brown sugar
- ¼ cup unsweetened apple juice
- ½ cup finely chopped peeled apple
- ¼ cup raisins
- ¼ cup brandy, optional

1. Preheat oven to 350°. Place sweet potatoes in a 6-qt. stockpot; add water to cover. Bring to a boil. Reduce heat; cook, uncovered, 5 minutes. Drain.

2. Meanwhile, in a small saucepan, combine butter, brown sugar, apple juice, apple and raisins; bring to a boil, stirring frequently. Remove from heat. If desired, stir in brandy.

3. Transfer potatoes to a greased 8-in.-square baking dish; top with apple mixture. Bake, uncovered, 25-30 minutes or until bubbly and the potatoes are tender, basting occasionally with sauce.

PER SERVING ¾ cup equals 330 cal., 4 g fat (2 g sat. fat), 10 mg chol., 59 mg sodium, 72 g carb., 5 g fiber, 3 g pro.

Fresh Take on Menus

When this Kansas cook discovered she had food allergies, she **worked a little magic** to update a recipe box full of scrumptious favorites to **share with her family.**

RECIPES & STORY BY **COURTNEY STULTZ** | COLUMBUS, KS

A s I see it, there's a definite upside to having food allergies: discovering creative new ways to whip up tasty, good-for-you food the whole family can enjoy together.

When I learned that my health issues stemmed from celiac disease and other food sensitivities, I got busy tweaking our favorite recipes to produce homemade dishes my family and I would still like. They eat what I make, and I make what I can eat, so we've all had to adjust.

The result? Change never tasted so good! We've learned that a gluten-free diet and scrumptious home-cooked food can go hand in hand.

Early on, I scored a hit with slow cooker chicken. I often fix it on Sundays, then use it in salads and enchiladas throughout the week.

I also streamline sides, experimenting with herbs and spices and substituting fresh ingredients for canned and boxed ones. These days, rather than scanning labels for gluten and other things I can't have, I scour the farmers market for just-picked seasonal veggies and fruits.

Everyone in our family now eats dinner together daily. We're all healthier and happier, with more energy. And the kids have even started to request broccoli—so I call that a win!

EAT SMART
Fresh Sugar Snap Pea Salad

PREP: 15 MIN. + CHILLING
MAKES: 6 SERVINGS

- 2 tablespoons olive oil
- 2 tablespoons white wine vinegar
- 2 teaspoons honey
- ½ teaspoon salt
- ½ teaspoon pepper
- ¼ teaspoon dried thyme
- ½ cup chopped onion
- ½ teaspoon poppy seeds
- 1 pound fresh sugar snap peas, trimmed and halved (about 4 cups)

FRESH SUGAR SNAP PEA SALAD

1. Place the first seven ingredients in a blender; cover and process until blended. Transfer to a large bowl; stir in the poppy seeds.

2. Add the peas to the dressing and toss to coat. Refrigerate, covered, 30 minutes before serving.

PER SERVING ⅔ cup equals 86 cal., 5 g fat (1 g sat. fat), 0 chol., 201 mg sodium, 9 g carb., 2 g fiber, 3 g pro. **Diabetic Exchanges:** 1 vegetable, 1 fat.

Slow Cooker Roast Chicken

PREP: 20 MIN. • **COOK:** 4 HOURS + STANDING
MAKES: 6 SERVINGS

- 2 medium carrots, cut into 1-inch pieces
- 1 medium onion, cut into 1-inch pieces
- 2 garlic cloves, minced
- 2 teaspoons olive oil
- 1 teaspoon dried parsley flakes
- 1 teaspoon pepper
- ¾ teaspoon salt
- ½ teaspoon dried oregano
- ½ teaspoon rubbed sage
- ½ teaspoon chili powder
- 1 broiler/fryer chicken (4 to 5 pounds)

1. Place the carrots and onion in a 6-qt. slow cooker. In a small bowl, mix the garlic and oil. In another bowl, mix the dry seasonings.

2. Tuck the wings under chicken; tie drumsticks together. With fingers, carefully loosen the skin from chicken breast; rub garlic mixture under the skin. Secure skin to underside of breast with toothpicks.

3. Place chicken in slow cooker over vegetables, breast side up; sprinkle with seasoning mixture. Cook, covered, on low 4-5 hours (a thermometer inserted in thigh should read at least 170°).

4. Remove the chicken from the slow cooker; tent with foil. Let chicken stand 15 minutes before carving.

PER SERVING *5 ounces cooked chicken equals 423 cal., 24 g fat (6 g sat. fat), 139 mg chol., 439 mg sodium, 4 g carb., 1 g fiber, 45 g pro.*

SCALLOPED POTATOES
WITH MUSHROOMS

Scalloped Potatoes with Mushrooms

PREP: 40 MIN. • **BAKE:** 15 MIN. + STANDING
MAKES: 8 SERVINGS

- 2 pounds potatoes (about 4 medium), peeled and sliced
- 1 tablespoon butter
- ½ pound sliced fresh mushrooms
- 1 small onion, chopped
- 1 garlic clove, minced
- ¼ cup all-purpose flour
- 1 cup chicken broth
- 1 teaspoon salt
- ½ teaspoon dried oregano
- ½ teaspoon pepper
- 1 cup (8 ounces) sour cream
- 1 cup coarsely chopped fresh spinach
- 2 cups (8 ounces) shredded Swiss cheese

1. Preheat the oven to 375°. Place the potatoes in a large saucepan; add water to cover. Bring to a boil. Reduce heat; cook, uncovered, 8-12 minutes or until tender. Drain.

2. Meanwhile, in another saucepan, heat the butter over medium-high heat. Add the mushrooms and onion; cook and stir 6-8 minutes or until tender. Stir in the garlic; cook 1 minute longer.

3. In a small bowl, whisk the flour, broth and seasonings until smooth; stir into mushroom mixture. Bring to a boil, stirring constantly; cook and stir 1-2 minutes or until sauce is thickened. Remove from heat; stir in sour cream.

4. Arrange half of the potatoes in a greased 1½-qt. or 8-in.-square baking dish; top with spinach. Spread half of the hot mushroom sauce over top; sprinkle with 1 cup cheese. Layer with remaining potatoes, sauce and cheese.

5. Bake, uncovered, 12-15 minutes or until heated through and cheese is melted. Let stand 10 minutes before serving.

PER SERVING *1 cup equals 269 cal., 14 g fat (9 g sat. fat), 49 mg chol., 471 mg sodium, 23 g carb., 2 g fiber, 11 g pro.*

SLOW COOKER ROAST CHICKEN

Tex-Mex Night

This Nebraska cook's easygoing fiesta is made with pantry staples, zesty spices and a whole lotta love.

RECIPES & STORY BY **ANTHONY BOLTON** | BELLEVUE, NE

I grew up in Texas and Iowa in a big family of bakers. My Grandma Edna Shimon was a phenomenal baker who made doughnuts, pies, cakes—you name it—and so did my mom, Cathy Moya.

I call my cooking style "entertaining," because my partner, Eddie Bolton, and I love to throw big parties and barbecues with at least 10 people—and I never plan what I'm going to serve guests very far in advance.

I work full time, and enchiladas are my go-to recipe because I usually have the ingredients on hand, including the caramelized onions. I fix those veggies several times a week to add to all kinds of dishes. I use sweet onions or Vidalias in season—they're what make the enchiladas stand out. I usually make them meatless, but they're good with cooked chicken, too.

I'm also a fan of Penzeys spices. Try their salt-free Arizona Dreaming seasoning instead of low-sodium taco seasoning when you make the enchiladas.

I add just as much of a kick to chili, too. Spicy Pork & Green Chili Verde is brimming with sweet red peppers and poblanos. Serve it with sour cream, Monterey Jack and tortilla chips.

We recently opened up a wine bar in Papillion, outside Omaha—that's where my cooking really comes into play. Hands down, the enchiladas with a side of creamy, spicy corn are everyone's favorite.

ONION & GREEN CHILI ENCHILADAS

Onion & Green Chili Enchiladas

PREP: 20 MIN. • **BAKE:** 20 MIN.
MAKES: 6 SERVINGS

- 2 **tablespoons butter**
- 3 **large onions, sliced (about 6 cups)**
- 2 **cups (8 ounces) shredded cheddar cheese, divided**
- 1 **cup sour cream**
- ⅓ **cup salsa**
- 2 **tablespoons reduced-sodium taco seasoning**
- 12 **flour tortillas (6 inches)**
- 2 **cans (10 ounces each) green enchilada sauce**
  Minced fresh cilantro

1. Preheat oven to 350°. In a large skillet, heat butter over medium heat. Add onions; cook and stir 8-10 minutes or until tender and golden brown. Cool slightly.

2. Meanwhile, in a large bowl, combine 1 cup shredded cheddar cheese, sour cream, salsa and taco seasoning. Stir in the cooled onions.

3. Place 2 tablespoons mixture off center on each tortilla. Roll up and place in a well-greased 13x9-in. baking dish, seam side down. Top with enchilada sauce; sprinkle with remaining cheese.

4. Bake, uncovered, 20-25 minutes or until heated through and cheese is melted. Sprinkle with cilantro.

PER SERVING *2 enchiladas equals 561 cal., 32 g fat (18 g sat. fat), 76 mg chol., 1,466 mg sodium, 50 g carb., 4 g fiber, 17 g pro.*

Eddie's Favorite Fiesta Corn

PREP: 15 MIN. • **COOK:** 25 MIN.
MAKES: 8 SERVINGS

- ½ pound bacon strips, chopped
- 5 cups fresh or frozen super sweet corn
- 1 medium sweet red pepper, finely chopped
- 1 medium sweet yellow pepper, finely chopped
- 1 package (8 ounces) reduced-fat cream cheese
- ½ cup half-and-half cream
- 1 can (4 ounces) chopped green chilies, optional
- 2 teaspoons sugar
- 1 teaspoon pepper
- ¼ teaspoon salt

1. In a 6-qt. stockpot, cook bacon over medium heat until crisp, stirring occasionally. Remove with a slotted spoon; drain on paper towels. Discard bacon drippings, reserving 1 tablespoon in pan.
2. Add the corn and sweet peppers to bacon drippings; cook and stir over medium-high heat 5-6 minutes or until tender.
3. Stir in the remaining ingredients until blended; bring to a boil. Reduce heat; simmer, covered, 8-10 minutes or until thickened.

PER SERVING *⅔ cup equals 249 cal., 14 g fat (7 g sat. fat), 39 mg chol., 399 mg sodium, 22 g carb., 2 g fiber, 10 g pro.*

EDDIE'S FAVORITE FIESTA CORN

SPICY PORK & GREEN CHILI VERDE

Spicy Pork & Green Chili Verde

PREP: 35 MIN. • **COOK:** 25 MIN.
MAKES: 6 SERVINGS

- 6 poblano peppers
- 2 tablespoons butter
- 1½ pounds pork tenderloin, cut into 1-inch pieces
- 2 medium sweet red or yellow peppers, coarsely chopped
- 1 large sweet onion, coarsely chopped
- 1 jalapeno pepper, seeded and finely chopped
- 2 garlic cloves, minced
- 2 tablespoons chili powder
- 1 teaspoon salt
- ¼ teaspoon ground nutmeg
- 2 cups chicken broth
  Optional toppings: sour cream, shredded Monterey Jack cheese, tortilla chips and lime wedges, optional

1. Place the poblano peppers on a foil-lined baking sheet. Broil 4 in. from the heat until skins blister, about 10 minutes. With tongs, rotate peppers a quarter turn. Broil and rotate until all sides are blistered and blackened. Immediately place peppers in a large bowl; let stand, covered, 10 minutes.
2. Peel off and discard the charred skin. Remove stems and seeds. Finely chop peppers.
3. In a 6-qt. stockpot, heat the butter over medium heat. Brown the pork in batches. Remove with a slotted spoon.
4. In same pan, add red peppers, onion and jalapeno; cook, covered, over medium heat 8-10 minutes or until tender, stirring occasionally. Stir in the garlic, chili powder, salt and nutmeg. Add the broth, roasted peppers and pork; bring to a boil. Reduce heat; simmer, uncovered, 10-15 minutes or until pork is tender. Serve with toppings as desired.

PER SERVING *1 cup (calculated without optional toppings) equals 235 cal., 9 g fat (4 g sat. fat), 75 mg chol., 913 mg sodium, 14 g carb., 4 g fiber, 25 g pro.*

Home for Dinner

This **Marine wife and mom** combines her love of veggies with her family's hankering for **down-home cooking.**

RECIPES & STORY BY **LIZ BELLVILLE** | JACKSONVILLE, NC

I am proud of my humongous family—it's one where being related isn't required! My husband is a Marine, and we've crisscrossed the United States together. While Stephen serves our country, I enjoy serving up food to our close-knit group of neighbors and friends.

Quite simply, I love to cook. I'm a vegetarian, but I happily feed meat eaters, too—I just make a little bit extra for me without meat. My Mediterranean pasta is just as good without chicken!

When Stephen comes home from time away, I fix something he craves. And we always have a party.

Wherever we're stationed, I get cooking on base, too, sharing cupcakes at the USO or serving waffle breakfasts. I also help teach cooking classes at the Wounded Warrior Battalion at Camp Lejeune.

My dream is to go to culinary school—maybe when Stephen retires. Until then, I'll keep spreading a little home-cooked love, one base at a time.

EAT SMART
Rainbow Veggie Salad

PREP: 35 MIN. • **MAKES:** 8 SERVINGS

- ⅔ **cup buttermilk**
- ½ **cup fat-free plain Greek yogurt**
- ½ **cup prepared pesto**
- ¼ **cup shredded Parmesan cheese**
- 1 **tablespoon white wine vinegar**
- 1 **tablespoon grated lemon peel**
- 1 **garlic clove, minced**
- ½ **teaspoon coarsely ground pepper**
- ⅛ **teaspoon salt**

SALAD
- ½ **English cucumber, cut lengthwise in half and sliced**
- 2 **medium carrots, thinly sliced**
- 1 **cup each red and yellow cherry tomatoes, halved**
- ¾ **cup pitted ripe olives, halved**
- 1 **celery rib, thinly sliced**
- ¼ **cup each chopped sweet yellow, orange and red pepper**
- ¼ **cup thinly sliced red onion**
- ⅛ **teaspoon garlic salt**
  - **Dash coarsely ground pepper**
- 1 **package (5 ounces) spring mix salad greens**

RAINBOW VEGGIE SALAD

1. Place the first nine ingredients in a jar with a tight-fitting lid; shake well. Refrigerate 1 hour.

2. Place cucumber, carrots, tomatoes, olives, celery, sweet peppers, onion, garlic salt and pepper in a large bowl; toss to combine.

3. To serve, add salad greens. Drizzle with ⅔ cup dressing; toss to combine. Reserve remaining dressing for another use.

PER SERVING *1 cup equals 64 cal., 3 g fat (1 g sat. fat), trace chol., 232 mg sodium, 7 g carb., 2 g fiber, 2 g pro.*
***Diabetic Exchanges:** 1 vegetable, ½ fat.*

Mediterranean Chicken Pasta

START TO FINISH: 25 MIN. • **COOK:** 20 MIN.
MAKES: 8 SERVINGS

- 1 package (12 ounces) uncooked tricolor spiral pasta
- 2 tablespoons olive oil, divided
- 1 pound boneless skinless chicken breasts, cut into ½-inch pieces
- 1 large sweet red pepper, chopped
- 1 medium onion, chopped
- 3 garlic cloves, peeled and thinly sliced
- 1 cup white wine or reduced-sodium chicken broth
- ¼ cup julienned soft sun-dried tomatoes (not packed in oil)
- 1 teaspoon dried basil
- 1 teaspoon Italian seasoning
- ½ teaspoon salt
- ¼ teaspoon crushed red pepper flakes
- ¼ teaspoon pepper
- 1 can (14½ ounces) reduced-sodium chicken broth
- 1 can (14 ounces) water-packed quartered artichoke hearts, drained
- 1 package (6 ounces) fresh baby spinach
- 1 cup (4 ounces) crumbled feta cheese
  Thinly sliced fresh basil leaves and shaved Parmesan cheese, optional

1. Cook the spiral pasta according to package directions. In a 6-qt. stockpot, heat 1 tablespoon oil over medium-high heat. Add the chicken; cook and stir 4-6 minutes or until no longer pink. Remove from pot.
2. In the same pot, heat remaining oil over medium heat. Add red pepper and onion; cook and stir 4-5 minutes or until onion is tender. Add garlic; cook 1 minute longer. Add wine, tomatoes and seasonings; bring to a boil. Reduce heat; simmer 5 minutes, stirring to loosen browned bits from pot.
3. Add chicken broth and artichoke hearts; return to a boil. Stir in spinach and chicken; cook just until spinach is wilted.
4. Drain pasta; stir into chicken mixture. Stir in feta cheese. If desired, top servings with basil and Parmesan cheese.
NOTE *This recipe was tested with sun-dried tomatoes that can be used without soaking. When using other sun-dried tomatoes that are not oil-packed, cover with boiling water and let stand until soft. Drain before using.*
PER SERVING *1½ cups (calculated without Parmesan cheese) equals 357 cal., 8 g fat (2 g sat. fat), 39 mg chol., 609 mg sodium, 42 g carb., 4 g fiber, 23 g pro.* **Diabetic Exchanges:** *2 starch, 2 lean meat, 1½ fat, 1 vegetable.*

Cheese & Pesto Biscuits

START TO FINISH: 25 MIN. • **MAKES:** 1 DOZEN

- 2 cups all-purpose flour
- 2 teaspoons baking powder
- ½ teaspoon salt
- ¼ teaspoon baking soda
- ⅓ cup cold butter, cubed
- 1 cup (4 ounces) shredded Italian cheese blend
- 1¼ cups buttermilk
- 1 tablespoon prepared pesto
- 1 tablespoon butter, melted
- 1 garlic clove, minced

1. Preheat oven to 450°. In a large bowl, whisk the flour, baking powder, salt and baking soda. Cut in butter until the mixture resembles coarse crumbs. Stir in cheese. In a small bowl, whisk buttermilk and pesto until blended; stir into the flour mixture just until moistened.
2. Drop dough by ¼ cupfuls 2 in. apart onto an ungreased baking sheet. Bake 10-12 minutes or until golden brown.
3. Mix butter and garlic; brush over biscuits. Serve warm.
PER SERVING *1 biscuit equals 175 cal., 9 g fat (5 g sat. fat), 24 mg chol., 357 mg sodium, 18 g carb., 1 g fiber, 5 g pro.*

Lemon Pepper Roasted Broccoli

START TO FINISH: 25 MIN. • **MAKES:** 8 SERVINGS

- 1½ pounds fresh broccoli florets (about 12 cups)
- 2 tablespoons olive oil
- ½ teaspoon lemon juice
- ¼ teaspoon salt
- ¼ teaspoon coarsely ground pepper, divided
- ¼ cup chopped almonds
- 2 teaspoons grated lemon peel

1. Preheat oven to 450°. Place the broccoli in a large bowl. Whisk oil, lemon juice, salt and ⅛ teaspoon pepper until blended; drizzle over broccoli and toss to coat. Transfer to a 15x10x1-in. baking pan.
2. Roast broccoli 10-15 minutes or until tender. Transfer to a serving dish. Sprinkle with the almonds, lemon peel and remaining pepper; toss to combine.
PER SERVING *1 cup equals 84 cal., 6 g fat (1 g sat. fat), 0 chol., 103 mg sodium, 7 g carb., 4 g fiber, 4 g pro.*
Diabetic Exchanges: 1 vegetable, 1 fat.

LEMON PEPPER ROASTED BROCCOLI

Lasagna to Love

Dinner with the whole gang is a treat. **Cooking it together** is even better. One Michigan daughter has built a lifetime of memories making **holiday dishes with Dad,** like her now legendary sauced-up lasagna.

RECIPES & STORY BY **DEBORAH LOOP** | CLINTON TOWNSHIP, MI

I have many wonderful holiday memories of the big meals my father would cook when my grandparents came to town. When I was in seventh-grade home economics, I learned that I loved being in the kitchen, too, and I started helping him.

Planning, preparing and serving our family's holiday feasts became our thing—our special time together, just me and my dad. Before Christmas, New Year's, Memorial Day—you name it—we pick a theme, then build a menu around it. We spend hours searching for just the right recipes, making tweaks and cooking, shoulder to shoulder.

After my folks visited Italy a few years ago, Dad and I chose an Italian theme for Christmas. My job was to prepare the trio of lasagnas. I always aim to please, but this time I wanted to impress Dad especially. I worked hard on all three but had the highest hopes for a lasagna based on an amazing cannelloni recipe.

You can imagine my relief when it was a huge success. Dad even went back for seconds—always my best compliment. I'm pretty proud of this dish. It's turned into a family favorite, the highlight of many Sunday dinners since, and another cherished holiday memory.

Pair Cannelloni-Style Lasagna with a refreshing side dish—Italian Salad with Lemon Vinaigrette. Your family will love it!

ITALIAN SALAD WITH LEMON VINAIGRETTE

EAT SMART **FAST FIX**
Italian Salad with Lemon Vinaigrette

START TO FINISH: 20 MIN.
MAKES: 8 SERVINGS (½ CUP VINAIGRETTE)

- 1 **package (5 ounces) spring mix salad greens**
- 1 **small red onion, thinly sliced**
- 1 **cup sliced fresh mushrooms**
- 1 **cup assorted olives, pitted and coarsely chopped**
- 8 **pepperoncini**
  Optional toppings: chopped tomatoes, shredded carrots and grated Parmesan cheese

VINAIGRETTE
- ⅓ **cup extra virgin olive oil**
- 3 **tablespoons lemon juice**
- 1 **teaspoon Italian seasoning**
- ¼ **teaspoon salt**
- ¼ **teaspoon pepper**

1. In a large bowl, combine the first five ingredients; toss lightly. If desired, add toppings.
2. In a small bowl, whisk vinaigrette ingredients until blended. Serve with salad.
PER SERVING *1¼ cups equals 109 cal., 11 g fat (1 g sat. fat), 0 chol., 343 mg sodium, 4 g carb., 1 g fiber, 1 g pro.* ***Diabetic Exchanges:** 2 fat, 1 vegetable.*

CANNELLONI-STYLE LASAGNA

Cannelloni-Style Lasagna

PREP: 1 HOUR • **BAKE:** 50 MIN. + STANDING
MAKES: 12 SERVINGS

- 1 tablespoon olive oil
- 1 small onion, finely chopped
- ⅓ cup finely chopped celery
- ¼ cup finely chopped carrot
- 2 garlic cloves, minced
- ¾ pound ground beef
- ¾ pound ground pork
- ⅓ cup white wine or beef stock
- ⅔ cup beef stock
- 1 bay leaf
- ¾ teaspoon Italian seasoning
- ½ teaspoon coarsely ground pepper
- ¼ teaspoon salt
- 2 jars (15 ounces each) Alfredo sauce, divided
- 2 large egg yolks
- 1 jar (24 ounces) marinara sauce
- 1 package (9 ounces) no-cook lasagna noodles

1. In a Dutch oven, heat the oil over medium-high heat. Add onion, celery and carrot; cook and stir 4-6 minutes or until tender. Add garlic; cook 1 minute longer.

2. Add the beef and pork; cook 4-6 minutes or until no longer pink, breaking meat into crumbles; drain. Stir in the wine. Bring to a boil; cook until liquid is almost evaporated, about 1 minute. Stir in stock and seasonings; bring to a boil. Reduce heat; simmer, covered, 15 minutes to allow flavors to blend. Cool slightly. Remove bay leaf; stir in 1 cup Alfredo sauce and yolks.

3. Preheat the oven to 350°. To assemble, spread ¾ cup marinara sauce into a greased 13x9-in. baking dish. Layer with four noodles, ¾ cup Alfredo sauce and 2 cups meat mixture. Top with four noodles and ¾ cup marinara sauce. Layer with four noodles, ¾ cup Alfredo sauce and the remaining meat mixture. Top with remaining noodles and marinara sauce. Drizzle remaining Alfredo sauce over top.

4. Bake, covered, 30 minutes. Uncover; bake 20-25 minutes longer or until bubbly. Let stand 15 minutes before serving.

PER SERVING *1 piece equals 347 cal., 18 g fat (8 g sat. fat), 88 mg chol., 632 mg sodium, 27 g carb., 3 g fiber, 18 g pro.*

MATTHEW HASS'
ULTIMATE GRILLED
PORK CHOP *PAGE 294*

Kitchen Techniques

Ready to cook? The ***Taste of Home*** **Test Kitchen pros** show you **their secrets** for making a mouthwatering pot roast, delectable brownies, lovely loaves of bread and more.

**NICK IVERSON'S
ULTIMATE POT ROAST**
PAGE 288

**SARAH THOMPSON'S
ULTIMATE FUDGY BROWNIES**
PAGE 296

**LAUREN KNOELKE'S
CHOCOLATE GINGERBREAD
YULE LOG** *PAGE 300*

Pot Roast Done Right

Take a **homey main dish** and make it a superstar. We've shared the secrets to your most **fork-friendly pot roast** ever, from the right cut to a perfect sear. The deliciousness is in the details!

Ultimate Pot Roast

While this juicy roast is braising in the oven, anyone who detects the aroma comes running in the kitchen to ask, "When can we eat?" The answer? Wait for it—it's worth it!

—NICK IVERSON

TASTE OF HOME LEAD TEST COOK

PREP: 55 MIN. • **BAKE:** 2 HOURS
MAKES: 8 SERVINGS

- 1 **boneless beef chuck-eye or other chuck roast (3 to 4 pounds)**
- 2 **teaspoons pepper**
- 2 **teaspoons salt, divided**
- 2 **tablespoons canola oil**
- 2 **medium onions, cut into 1-inch pieces**
- 2 **celery ribs, chopped**
- 3 **garlic cloves, minced**
- 1 **tablespoon tomato paste**
- 1 **tablespoon minced fresh thyme or 1 teaspoon dried thyme**
- 2 **bay leaves**
- 1 **cup dry red wine or reduced-sodium beef broth**
- 2 **cups reduced-sodium beef broth**
- 1 **pound small red potatoes, quartered**
- 4 **medium parsnips, peeled and cut into 2-inch pieces**
- 6 **medium carrots, cut into 2-inch pieces**
- 1 **tablespoon red wine vinegar**
- 2 **tablespoons minced fresh parsley Salt and pepper to taste**

1. Preheat oven to 325°. Pat roast dry with a paper towel; tie at 2-in. intervals with kitchen string. Sprinkle the roast with pepper and 1½ teaspoons salt. In a Dutch oven, heat the oil over medium-high heat. Brown the roast on all sides. Remove from pan.

2. Add onions, celery and ½ teaspoon salt to the same pan; cook and stir over medium heat 8-10 minutes or until the onions are browned. Add the garlic, tomato paste, thyme and bay leaves; cook and stir 1 minute longer.

3. Add the wine, stirring to loosen browned bits from pan; stir in broth. Return roast to pan. Arrange potatoes, parsnips and carrots around roast; bring to boil. Bake, covered, 2-2½

ULTIMATE POT ROAST

hours or until meat is fork-tender.

4. Remove the roast and vegetables; keep warm. Discard bay leaves; skim fat from cooking juices. Bring to a boil; cook 10-12 minutes or until the liquid is reduced by half (about 1½ cups). Stir in vinegar and parsley; season with salt and pepper to taste.

5. Remove the string from the roast. Serve with vegetables and sauce.

PER SERVING *3 ounces cooked beef with 1 cup vegetables and 3 tablespoons sauce equals 459 cal., 20 g fat (7 g sat. fat), 112 mg chol., 824 mg sodium, 32 g carb., 6 g fiber, 37 g pro.*

RULE THE ROAST

Keep these helpful hints from the *Taste of Home* Test Kitchen pros in mind to make your roast a succulent success:

- Look for a chuck-eye cut of beef. It's tender, flavorful and ideal for a long braise. Can't find chuck-eye? A standard chuck roast will do just fine.

- To see if your pot roast is done, remove it from the oven and give it a quick stab with a long-handled fork. If the fork pierces the meat and twists easily, you're good to go. If the pot roast is cooked until it falls apart, the meat is actually overcooked and will be stringy, tough and dry.

- Leftover roast (if there is such a thing) tastes pretty amazing the next day diced into a breakfast hash. Want more options for leftovers? Simmer shredded meat in beef broth for soup or stuff it into tortillas for enchiladas or burritos.

POT OF GOLD

1. TIE IT. Wrap kitchen string around your roast to give it a uniform shape. This helps it cook evenly.

2. SEAR IT. Pat your entire roast dry first so it browns nicely.

Divine Angel Food

Break out your tube pan and bake up a **pure, pillowy classic.** Then we'll show you how to ring the inside with a rich ribbon of delight and **finish it all off** with a tempting topping.

Turn to page 293.

EAT SMART
Vanilla Bean Angel Food Cake

I think angel food cake is the perfect blank slate for making awesome desserts. The recipe here produces a simple but scrumptious vanilla version. Want to get creative? Turn to page 293. You'll find more options for toppings as well as delectable cake fillings.

—LEAH REKAU

TASTE OF HOME FOOD STYLIST

PREP: 30 MIN. • **BAKE:** 45 MIN. + COOLING
MAKES: 16 SERVINGS

- 12 large egg whites (about 1⅓ cups)
- 1 cup cake flour
- 1½ cups sugar, divided
- 1 vanilla bean (see Note) or 1 teaspoon vanilla extract
- ½ teaspoon cream of tartar
- ¼ teaspoon salt

GLAZE
- 2 cups confectioners' sugar
- 1 vanilla bean or 1 teaspoon vanilla extract
- 3 to 4 tablespoons 2% milk

1. Place egg whites in a large bowl; let stand at room temperature for 30 minutes.

2. Preheat oven to 325°. In a small bowl, mix the flour and ¾ cup sugar until blended.

3. Add the seeds from the vanilla bean (or vanilla extract if using), cream of tartar and salt to the egg whites. Beat on medium speed until soft peaks form. Gradually add the remaining ¾ cup sugar, 1 tablespoon at a time, beating on high after each addition until the sugar is dissolved. Continue beating until soft glossy peaks form. Gradually fold in the flour mixture, about ½ cup at a time.

4. Gently transfer the cake batter to an ungreased 10-in. tube pan. Cut through the cake batter with a knife to remove air pockets. Bake on the lowest oven rack 45-55 minutes or until the top springs back when lightly touched. Immediately invert the pan; cool cake completely in the pan, about 1½ hours.

5. Run a knife around the sides and center tube of the pan. Remove cake to a serving plate.

6. For the glaze, in a small bowl, mix the confectioners' sugar, seeds from the vanilla bean (or vanilla extract if using) and enough milk to reach the desired consistency. Spread the glaze over cake, allowing some glaze to drip down the sides.

NOTE *To remove the seeds from a vanilla bean, cut bean lengthwise in half with a sharp knife; scrape out the dark, pulpy seeds.*

PER SERVING *1 slice equals 177 cal., trace fat (trace sat. fat), trace chol., 80 mg sodium, 41 g carb., trace fiber, 3 g pro.*

— **OUT OF THE OVEN**

Angel food cakes are done when the top springs back when touched with your finger and the cracks at the top of the cake look and feel dry. Always cool angel food cakes upside down in the pan; otherwise they will collapse and flatten. If your tube pan has legs, invert the pan onto its legs until the cake is completely cool.

If your tube pan does not have legs, place the pan over the neck of a sturdy narrow bottle or funnel until the cake is completely cool.

VANILLA BEAN ANGEL FOOD CAKE

CHOCOLATE FILLING & CHOCOLATE GLAZE

LEMON FILLING & CITRUS GLAZE

SHERBET FILLING & CITRUS GLAZE

PICK A FILLING

A surprise center makes Vanilla Bean Angel Food Cake (p. 290) even more awesome. Choose one of the fabulous fillings below. To create a tunnel in the cake for the filling, see the how-to at the bottom of the page.

Chocolate-Filled Angel-Food Cake

Microwave 1 cup 60% cacao bittersweet chocolate baking chips, ¼ cup heavy whipping cream and 1 tablespoon amaretto on high 60-90 seconds or until chocolate is melted, stirring every 30 seconds. Stir until smooth. Cool to lukewarm (90°), about 25 minutes. Beat ¾ cup heavy whipping cream with 1 tablespoon sugar until soft peaks form. Fold into lukewarm chocolate; fill tunnel. Replace the cake top. Glaze and refrigerate at least 4 hours. Cover once glaze sets.

Lemon-Filled Angel Food Cake

Beat ½ cup heavy whipping cream until it begins to thicken. Add ½ cup mascarpone cheese and 2 tablespoons confectioners' sugar; beat until soft peaks form. Fold in one-third of a 10-oz. jar of lemon curd. Line tunnel bottom with 1 cup sliced fresh strawberries (patted dry); top with mascarpone mixture, then remaining lemon curd. Replace cake top; glaze and refrigerate at least 4 hours. Cover once glaze sets.

Sherbet-Filled Angel Food Cake

Spoon 2½ to 3 cups raspberry sherbet (or any other sherbet or ice cream) into tunnel, mounding slightly. Replace cake top. Wrap securely in plastic wrap; freeze overnight. Glaze before serving.

TEMPTING TOPPINGS

From fresh fruit to a drizzle of chocolate sauce, the possibilities for topping angel food cakes are endless. Try any of these yummy options for finishing your dessert:

CITRUS GLAZE. Mix 2 cups confectioners' sugar, 1 teaspoon grated lemon or lime peel and 3-4 tablespoons lemon or lime juice; spread over the cake.

CHOCOLATE GLAZE. In a saucepan, heat ½ cup heavy whipping cream and 1 tablespoon sugar just to a boil, stirring to dissolve the sugar. Remove from the heat; add 1 cup 60% cacao bittersweet chocolate baking chips. Whisk until smooth; stir in 2 tablespoons amaretto. Cool 15 minutes. Pour over the cake; sprinkle with ¼ cup toasted sliced almonds.

LIGHT FROSTING. Thaw a large container of light frozen whipped topping and fold in one package of any flavor sugar-free gelatin powder. Spread over the top and sides of cake.

FRUIT SAUCE. Spoon canned cranberry sauce (melted in a saucepan) or canned pie filling over slices of cake.

TUCK A SECRET INSIDE

Fill your cake with a tunnel of love! Start by preparing the recipe for Vanilla Bean Angel Food Cake (p. 290). When the cake has cooled completely, remove it from the tube pan and follow these simple steps for filling the cake.

1. Insert toothpicks an inch from the top of the cake on all sides as a guide for your knife. Slice the top off the cake with a serrated knife.

2. Cut the outline of the tunnel with a small paring knife, leaving a 1-in. shell on each side. Use your fingers to pull out the cake. (Better go ahead and sample it, too.)

3. Fill the hollow with chocolate, lemon or sherbet filling (recipes above). Replace the top of the cake, then finish with your favorite glaze or other topping.

Sizzlin' Up Top Chops

Clear room on the grill for your new backyard cookout favorite. Our Test Kitchen tips for buying, prepping and sizzling make these pork chops **stand out from the rest.**

Ultimate Grilled Pork Chop

A brine bath and special dry rub go a long way toward producing the perfect chops. You'll be enjoying them all summer and beyond.

—**MATTHEW HASS**

TASTE OF HOME TEST COOK

PREP: 20 MIN. + BRINING • **GRILL:** 10 MIN.
MAKES: 4 SERVINGS

¼ cup kosher salt
¼ cup sugar
2 cups water
2 cups ice water
4 bone-in pork center-cut rib chops (1 inch thick and 8 ounces each)
2 tablespoons canola oil

BASIC RUB

3 tablespoons paprika
1 teaspoon each garlic powder, onion powder, ground cumin and ground mustard
1 teaspoon coarsely ground pepper
½ teaspoon ground chipotle pepper

1. In a large saucepan, combine salt, sugar and 2 cups water; cook and stir over medium heat until salt and sugar are dissolved. Remove from heat. Add 2 cups ice water to cool brine to room temperature.

2. Place the pork chops in a large resealable plastic bag; add the cooled brine. Seal the bag, pressing out as much air as possible; turn to coat the chops. Place in a 13x9-in. baking dish. Refrigerate 8-12 hours.

3. Remove chops from brine; rinse and pat dry. Discard brine. Brush both sides of chops with oil. In a small bowl, mix the rub ingredients; rub over the chops. Let stand at room temperature 30 minutes.

4. Moisten a paper towel with cooking oil; using long-handled tongs, rub on the grill rack to coat lightly. Grill the chops, covered, over medium heat 4-6 minutes on each side or until a thermometer reads 145°. Let stand 5 minutes before serving.

PER SERVING *1 pork chop equals 300 cal., 18 g fat (4 g sat. fat), 72 mg chol., 130 mg sodium, 5 g carb., 2 g fiber, 30 g pro.*

CROSSHATCH 101

Mmm...nothing makes mouths start watering at cookouts like those gorgeous crosshatch grill marks on meat. Want to create them on your pork chops? Place the chops on the grill to sear, then rotate them a quarter turn and cook 2-3 minutes longer before flipping to cook on the other side.

ULTIMATE GRILLED PORK CHOP

We grilled our *Taste of Home* Test Kitchen expert on the best cut, rub, temperature, cook time and more to produce the juiciest pork chop this side of summer. Here's what you need to know!

CHOOSE IT
Look for 1-inch bone-in rib chops. Why? A thicker chop can handle direct heat for a nice sear without overcooking. Rib chops have more fat than other chops, and fat means flavor. Go with bone-in because it insulates the chop to keep it moist and gives it a richer pork flavor.

BRINE IT
A saltwater bath adds moisture and tenderizes. We tested the pork chop at 2 hours, 12 hours and 24 hours in the brine. The verdict? Go for 8 to 12 hours for optimal juiciness and texture. It gets too salty (and actually toughens up) if brined longer than 12 hours.

RUB IT
Oil the chop first so the rub sticks well. Let the meat stand for 30 minutes at room temperature to warm up for more even grilling.

GRILL IT
Use tongs or a spatula to turn, being careful not to pierce the meat during cooking. You'll lose those precious juices.

TEMP IT
Pork dries out easily, so use a meat thermometer and pull your chops from the grill at 145° for the perfect doneness.

EAT IT
Faintly pink inside is A-OK! It's the preferred color for a truly moist, tender chop.

A rub is a blend of dry seasonings, such as fresh or dried herbs and spices, that coats the surface of uncooked meats. While rubs don't tenderize the meat, they add a lot of flavor.

The rub for the Ultimate Grilled Pork Chop recipe combines onion powder, ground chipotle, paprika and more for plenty of zip. Want more options? Try these simple ideas:

SMOKY PORK RUB
Prepare the basic rub as directed in the Ultimate Grilled Pork Chop recipe, using smoked paprika in place of regular paprika.

SWEET PORK RUB
Add 3 tablespoons brown sugar to the basic rub mixture.

SPICY PORK RUB
Add ½ teaspoon cayenne pepper to the basic rub mixture.

Best-Ever Brownies

Taste of Home's Test Kitchen manager prepared 19 batches of brownies on her **quest for perfection.** When this version came out of her oven, the search was over. Say hello to the **richest, fudgiest, chocolate-chippiest** brownie ever!

ULTIMATE FUDGY BROWNIES

Ultimate Fudgy Brownies

In these ultra-fudgy brownies, a little bit of coffee boosts the chocolate flavor. Add chocolate chips to the batter, and you've got goodies no one will be able to resist.

—SARAH THOMPSON

TASTE OF HOME TEST KITCHEN & FOOD STYLING MANAGER

PREP: 20 MIN. • **BAKE:** 45 MIN. + COOLING
MAKES: 16 SERVINGS

- 1 **cup sugar**
- ½ **cup packed brown sugar**
- ⅔ **cup butter, cubed**
- ¼ **cup water**
- 2 **teaspoons instant coffee granules, optional**
- 2¾ **cups bittersweet chocolate chips, divided**
- 4 **large eggs**
- 2 **teaspoons vanilla extract**
- 1½ **cups all-purpose flour**
- ½ **teaspoon baking soda**
- ½ **teaspoon salt**

1. Preheat oven to 325°. Line a 9-in.-square baking pan with parchment paper, letting the ends extend up the sides. In a large heavy saucepan, combine sugars, butter, water and, if desired, coffee granules; bring to a boil, stirring constantly. Remove from the heat; add 1¾ cup chocolate chips and stir until melted. Cool slightly.

2. In a large bowl, whisk eggs until foamy, about 3 minutes. Add vanilla; gradually whisk in chocolate mixture. In another bowl, whisk flour, baking soda and salt; stir into the chocolate mixture. Fold in the remaining chocolate chips.

3. Pour into the prepared pan. Bake on a lower oven rack 45-55 minutes or until a toothpick inserted in center comes out clean (do not overbake). Cool completely in pan on a wire rack.

4. Lifting with the parchment paper, remove the brownies from the pan. Cut into squares.

PER SERVING *1 brownie equals 344 cal., 18 g fat (10 g sat. fat), 67 mg chol., 197 mg sodium, 47 g carb., 2 g fiber, 4 g pro.*

Baking brownies in a 9-in.-square pan makes them thicker and fudgier. Before you pour in the brownie batter, line the pan with parchment paper, letting a couple of inches extend over each side.

When the brownies have cooled, grab the parchment-paper "handles" and tug. Out comes dessert! Then start cutting. A bench scraper (find one in the kitchenware aisle) is a handy tool for clean cutting or working with dough.

Cut four rows of four to make 16 brownies—or cut larger pieces for jumbo treats! When cutting with a bench scraper, get nice slices by pressing it into the brownies and lifting up; don't drag through.

After cutting, store any extras in an airtight container. To freeze individual brownies, wrap them in plastic wrap and stack them in an airtight container. Thaw at room temperature before serving.

A Loaf to Love

Baking **homemade bread** is easier to do than you might think. And once you break into that **crackling crust** and slather butter on a slice, you'll want to make sandwiches for the world.

⑤ INGREDIENTS

Crusty Homemade Bread

Enjoy this beautiful loaf as is, or follow the easy tips we've shared on this page to stir in cheddar cheese or cranberries with orange peel.

—**MEGUMI GARCIA**

TASTE OF HOME PREP COOK

PREP: 20 MIN. + RISING
BAKE: 50 MIN. + COOLING
MAKES: 1 LOAF (16 SLICES)

- 1½ teaspoons active dry yeast
- 1¾ cups water (70° to 75°)
- 3½ cups plus 1 tablespoon all-purpose flour, divided
- 2 teaspoons salt
- 1 tablespoon cornmeal or additional flour

1. In a small bowl, dissolve yeast in water. In a large bowl, mix 3½ cups flour and salt. Using a rubber spatula, stir in yeast mixture to form a soft, sticky dough. Do not knead. Cover with plastic wrap; let rise at room temperature 1 hour.

2. Punch down dough. Turn onto a lightly floured surface; pat into a 9-in. square. Fold into thirds, forming a 9x3-in. rectangle. Fold into thirds, forming a 3-in. square. Turn over; place in a greased bowl. Cover with plastic wrap; let rise at room temperature until almost doubled, about 1 hour.

3. Punch down dough and repeat the folding process. Return dough to bowl; refrigerate, covered, overnight.

4. Dust bottom of a disposable foil roasting pan with cornmeal. Turn dough onto a floured surface. Knead gently 6-8 times; shape into a 6-in.

round loaf. Place in the prepared pan; dust top with remaining 1 tablespoon flour. Cover the pan with plastic wrap; let rise at room temperature until the dough expands to a 7½-in. loaf, about 1¼ hours.

5. Preheat oven to 500°. Using a sharp knife, make a slash (¼ inch deep) across top of loaf. Cover pan tightly with foil. Bake on lowest oven rack 25 minutes.

6. Reduce the oven setting to 450°. Remove foil; bake 25-30 minutes longer or until deep golden brown. Remove loaf to a wire rack to cool.

PER SERVING *1 slice (calculated without add-ins) equals 105 cal., trace fat (trace sat. fat), 0 chol., 296 mg sodium, 22 g carb., 1 g fiber, 3 g pro.*

TASTY VARIATIONS

CHEDDAR CHEESE BREAD
Prepare the dough as directed. Before kneading dough in Step 4, sprinkle with 4 ounces diced sharp cheddar cheese.

RUSTIC CRANBERRY & ORANGE BREAD
Prepare dough as directed. Before kneading dough in Step 4, sprinkle with 1 cup dried cranberries and 4 teaspoons grated orange peel.

THE KNEAD TO KNOW

1. STIR. It's a wet dough, and that's the goal. Use a rubber spatula to make cleanup extra easy.

2. FOLD. Folding the dough sends fresh air to the yeast and creates gluten structure. Trust us, both are good things.

3. SHAPE (AND SLASH). Dust the top with flour for that beautiful artisan look. Hold the knife blade at a slight angle and make a single confident cut.

4. COVER. A heavy-duty foil cover keeps steam around the baking loaf, the key to that springy center and crispy crust.

RUSTIC CRANBERRY & ORANGE BREAD

CRUSTY HOMEMADE BREAD

CHEDDAR CHEESE BREAD

Yuletide Treat

Rich in tradition (and fluffy frosting), a yule log brings good fortune to all who share it. Follow our simple steps to serve your family this **cheery spiced version.** You can even make it ahead!

CHOCOLATE GINGERBREAD YULE LOG

Chocolate Gingerbread Yule Log

If you like yule logs, you'll love this one with fresh ginger and spices.
—**LAUREN KNOELKE**
TASTE OF HOME
TEST COOK

PREP: 1¼ HOURS • **BAKE:** 10 MIN. + COOLING
MAKES: 16 SERVINGS

- 5 **large eggs, separated**
- ¾ **cup cake flour**
- 1 **to 1½ teaspoons each ground ginger and cinnamon**
- ¼ **teaspoon each ground nutmeg and pepper**
- ¼ **teaspoon salt**
- ⅓ **cup packed dark brown sugar**
- ¼ **cup molasses**
- 2 **tablespoons canola oil**
- 1 **tablespoon grated fresh gingerroot**
- ⅛ **teaspoon cream of tartar**
- ¼ **cup sugar**
  Baking cocoa

FILLING
- 1 **carton (8 ounces) mascarpone cheese**
- ⅓ **cup confectioners' sugar**
- 2 **tablespoons heavy whipping cream**
- ⅛ **teaspoon salt**
- ⅓ **cup crystallized ginger, dried cranberries or miniature semisweet chocolate chips**

CHOCOLATE BARK
- 4 **to 6 ounces high-quality bittersweet chocolate, melted**

BUTTERCREAM
- 2 **egg whites**
- ½ **cup sugar**
- ⅛ **teaspoon salt**
- ¾ **cup unsalted butter, softened**
- 4 **ounces high-quality milk chocolate, melted and cooled**

1. Place the egg whites in a large bowl; let stand at room temperature 30 minutes. Preheat the oven to 350°. Line bottom of a greased 15x10x1-in. baking pan with parchment paper; grease paper. Sift flour, spices and salt together twice.

2. In a large bowl, beat the egg yolks until slightly thickened. Gradually add brown sugar, beating on high speed until thick. Beat in molasses, oil and fresh ginger. Fold in the flour mixture (batter will be thick).

3. Add cream of tartar to egg whites; with clean beaters, beat on medium until soft peaks form. Gradually add sugar, 1 tablespoon at a time, beating after each addition until the sugar is dissolved. Beat on high until stiff, glossy peaks form. Using a large whisk, fold a fourth of the whites into batter; fold in remaining whites. Transfer to prepared pan, spreading evenly.

4. Bake 10-12 minutes or until top springs back when lightly touched. Cool 5 minutes. Invert onto a tea towel dusted with cocoa. Gently peel off the paper. Roll up cake in towel jelly-roll style. Cool completely on a wire rack.

5. For the filling, in a small bowl, mix cheese, confectioners' sugar, cream and salt just until blended; stir in the ginger. Refrigerate, covered, while preparing bark and buttercream.

6. For the bark, line the underside of a 15x10x1-in. baking pan with parchment paper. Using an offset spatula, spread the melted chocolate in a thin, even layer on parchment. Refrigerate until set, about 30 minutes.

7. For buttercream, place egg whites, sugar and salt in a heatproof bowl; whisk until blended. Place bowl over simmering water in a large saucepan over medium heat. Whisking constantly, heat mixture until a thermometer reads 160°, about 1-2 minutes.

8. Remove from the heat. With the whisk attachment of a hand mixer, beat on high speed until stiff glossy peaks form and mixture has cooled, about 5 minutes. Gradually beat in the butter, a few tablespoons at a time, on medium speed until smooth. Beat in the cooled chocolate.

9. To assemble, unroll cake; spread the filling over cake to within ¼ in. of edges. Roll up again, without towel; trim ends. Transfer to a platter. Spread the buttercream over the cake.

10. To decorate cake, lift the chilled chocolate with your fingers and break carefully into shards; arrange over the buttercream, overlapping slightly. If chocolate becomes too soft, return to refrigerator as necessary.

11. Refrigerate cake, loosely covered, until serving. Using a serrated knife, cut cake into slices.

FREEZER OPTION *Entire cake can be made up to 1 week before serving. Prepare and decorate cake as directed; freeze 2 hours or until firm. Wrap in several layers of plastic wrap. Return to the freezer; freeze for up to 1 week. To serve, partially thaw wrapped cake in refrigerator overnight. Carefully remove plastic wrap; let cake stand at room temperature 15-30 minutes before serving.*

PER SERVING *1 slice equals 373 cal., 24 g fat (13 g sat. fat), 103 mg chol., 121 mg sodium, 38 g carb., 1 g fiber, 5 g pro.*

HOW YULE ROLL

1. WHIP. Fluffy egg whites are the key to making this cake light and airy. Add the sugar slowly to avoid weighing down your whites.

2. ROLL. While the cake is still warm, roll it into a log. (The towel keeps the cake from sticking to itself.) Keep it rolled until cool. This trains the cake to hold its final shape.

3. SPREAD. For bark, use an offset spatula to thinly spread 4 to 6 oz. melted bittersweet chocolate on a parchment paper-lined baking pan. The thinner your chocolate layer, the easier it is to break into shards. Refrigerate until set.

4. SNAP. This is the fun part! Get cracking. Uneven pieces add lots of barklike character. If the chocolate softens, just pop it back in the fridge.

Substitutions & Equivalents

EQUIVALENT MEASURES

3 teaspoons	=	1 tablespoon	16 tablespoons	=	1 cup
4 tablespoons	=	1/4 cup	2 cups	=	1 pint
5-1/3 tablespoons	=	1/3 cup	4 cups	=	1 quart
8 tablespoons	=	1/2 cup	4 quarts	=	1 gallon

FOOD EQUIVALENTS

GRAINS

Macaroni	1 cup (3-1/2 ounces) uncooked	=	2-1/2 cups cooked
Noodles, Medium	3 cups (4 ounces) uncooked	=	4 cups cooked
Popcorn	1/3 to 1/2 cup unpopped	=	8 cups popped
Rice, Long Grain	1 cup uncooked	=	3 cups cooked
Rice, Quick-Cooking	1 cup uncooked	=	2 cups cooked
Spaghetti	8 ounces uncooked	=	4 cups cooked

CRUMBS

Bread	1 slice	=	3/4 cup soft crumbs, 1/4 cup fine dry crumbs
Graham Crackers	7 squares	=	1/2 cup finely crushed
Buttery Round Crackers	12 crackers	=	1/2 cup finely crushed
Saltine Crackers	14 crackers	=	1/2 cup finely crushed

FRUITS

Bananas	1 medium	=	1/3 cup mashed
Lemons	1 medium	=	3 tablespoons juice, 2 teaspoons grated peel
Limes	1 medium	=	2 tablespoons juice, 1-1/2 teaspoons grated peel
Oranges	1 medium	=	1/4 to 1/3 cup juice, 4 teaspoons grated peel

VEGETABLES

Cabbage	1 head	= 5 cups shredded		Green Pepper	1 large	=	1 cup chopped
Carrots	1 pound	= 3 cups shredded		Mushrooms	1/2 pound	=	3 cups sliced
Celery	1 rib	= 1/2 cup chopped		Onions	1 medium	=	1/2 cup chopped
Corn	1 ear fresh	= 2/3 cup kernels		Potatoes	3 medium	=	2 cups cubed

NUTS

Almonds	1 pound	= 3 cups chopped		Pecan Halves	1 pound	=	4-1/2 cups chopped
Ground Nuts	3-3/4 ounces	= 1 cup		Walnuts	1 pound	=	3-3/4 cups chopped

EASY SUBSTITUTIONS

When you need...		Use...
Baking Powder	1 teaspoon	1/2 teaspoon cream of tartar + 1/4 teaspoon baking soda
Buttermilk	1 cup	1 tablespoon lemon juice or vinegar + enough milk to measure 1 cup (let stand 5 minutes before using)
Cornstarch	1 tablespoon	2 tablespoons all-purpose flour
Honey	1 cup	1-1/4 cups sugar + 1/4 cup water
Half-and-Half Cream	1 cup	1 tablespoon melted butter + enough whole milk to measure 1 cup
Onion	1 small, chopped (1/3 cup)	1 teaspoon onion powder or 1 tablespoon dried minced onion
Tomato Juice	1 cup	1/2 cup tomato sauce + 1/2 cup water
Tomato Sauce	2 cups	3/4 cup tomato paste + 1 cup water
Unsweetened Chocolate	1 square (1 ounce)	3 tablespoons baking cocoa + 1 tablespoon shortening or oil
Whole Milk	1 cup	1/2 cup evaporated milk + 1/2 cup water

Cooking Terms

Here's a quick reference for some of the cooking terms used in *Taste of Home* recipes:

BASTE To moisten food with melted butter, pan drippings, marinades or other liquid to add more flavor and juiciness.

BEAT To combine ingredients with a rapid movement using a fork, spoon, wire whisk or electric mixer.

BLEND To combine ingredients until *just* mixed.

BOIL To heat liquids until bubbles form that cannot be "stirred down." In the case of water, the temperature will reach 212°.

BONE To remove all meat from the bone before cooking.

CREAM To beat ingredients together to a smooth consistency, usually in the case of butter and sugar for baking.

DASH A small amount of seasoning, less than 1/8 teaspoon. If using a shaker, a dash would be a quick flip of the container.

DREDGE To coat foods with flour or other dry ingredients. Most often done with pot roasts and stew meat before browning.

FOLD To incorporate several ingredients by careful and gentle turning with a spatula. Used generally with beaten egg whites or whipped cream when mixing into the rest of the ingredients to keep the batter light.

JULIENNE To cut foods into long thin strips much like matchsticks. Used most often for salads and stir-fry dishes.

MARINATE To tenderize and/or flavor foods, usually meat or raw vegetables, by placing in a liquid mixture of oil, vinegar, wine, lime or lemon juice, herbs and spices.

MINCE To cut into very fine pieces. Used often for garlic or fresh herbs.

PARBOIL To cook partially, usually in the case of chicken, sausages and vegetables.

PARTIALLY SET Describes the consistency of gelatin after it has been chilled for a short amount of time. Mixture should resemble the consistency of egg whites.

PUREE To process foods to a smooth mixture. Can be prepared in an electric blender, food processor, food mill or sieve.

SAUTE To fry quickly in a small amount of fat, stirring almost constantly. Most often done with onions, mushrooms and other chopped vegetables.

SCORE To cut slits partway through the outer surface of foods. Often used with ham or flank steak.

STIR-FRY To cook meats and/or vegetables with a constant stirring motion in a small amount of oil in a wok or skillet over high heat.

General Index

This handy index lists every recipe by food category, major ingredient and/or cooking method, so you can easily locate recipes that suit your needs.

✓Indicates an **EAT SMART** recipe

Alphabetical Index

This convenient index lists every recipe in alphabetical order, so you can easily find your favorite dishes.

✓ Indicates an EAT SMART recipe

If you want to hear that song again,
go back to the beginning.

up with the clouds and the speedy planes,

all about Evie, who flew her kite

her father came and sang to her—

When she wanted a song,

her sister wrapped it around her.

When she wanted her blanket,

her grandma had it ready.

When she wanted to go home for supper,

her mother **ran to look.**

When she shouted, "Look how high!"

and the wind took it.

She wanted to fly her kite.

and her legs carried her.

She wanted to run up a steep hill,

and the door flew open.

She wanted to go out,

and her grandpa made it for her.

She wanted something new to play with,

and on the hook she found it.

She wanted something new to wear,

so she got ready.

Now this little Evie wanted to do something,

Lucky Song

Vera B. Williams

To Cassie

Good Luck

Vera B. Williams

Watercolor paints were used for the full-color art. The text type is Gorilla. Copyright © 1997 by Vera B. Williams.

Greenwillow Books ⬚ New York

Manufactured in China. First Edition 10 9 8 7 6

Library of Congress Cataloging-in-Publication Data: Williams, Vera B. Lucky song / by Vera B. Williams.
p. cm. ISBN 0-688-14459-4 (trade). ISBN 0-688-14460-8 (lib. bdg.)
[1. Day—Fiction. 2. Kites—Fiction. 3. Singing—Fiction.]
I. Title. PZ7.W66685Lu 1997 [E]—dc20 96-7151 CIP AC